SCIENCE FOR CAMP AND COUNSELOR

117 PROJECTS
FOR THE OUTDOORS

Science for

Camp and Counselor

WILLIAM T. HARTY

Illustrations by the Author

ASSOCIATION PRESS   NEW YORK

SCIENCE FOR CAMP AND COUNSELOR

Copyright © 1964 by

NATIONAL BOARD OF YOUNG MEN'S CHRISTIAN ASSOCIATIONS

Association Press   291 Broadway   New York   N. Y.   10007

Publisher's title stock number: 1545
Library of Congress catalog card number: 64-11418

Printed in the United States of America

To *the memory of*

ABRAHAM KRASKER

Late Professor of Education, Boston University

and

Director of Camp Indian Acres

Preface

THE PURPOSE OF THIS BOOK is to provide in one volume both pertinent subject matter and practical projects suited to the summer camp program and environment. It is hoped that providing such a basic reference will enable prospective science counselors to better prepare for their jobs and that the place of science will be raised from the side show category to an important place in camp program. Chapter 1 describes science in the camp perspective and offers suggestions for starting the expansion process from nature study to a full science program.

As complete as we have tried to make this book, it must be noted that it is not meant to be the exclusive source for the science counselor. It will best serve its purpose if used with the suggested references given at the opening of each chapter. Most of these references are paper-bound and their cost will be minimal. Anticipating the use of these books, we have avoided including here any of the material which they cover. Subject-matter material contained herein is included because it is particularly useful in the camp teaching situation or because it represents a relevant scientific development too recent to appear in the references listed. In addition to the chapter references, a bibliography is included in the appendix containing carefully selected books that will make worth-while additions to the library of camp or counselor.

Several years spent developing one camp science program and observing numerous other types of programs have served in developing the underlying plan for this book. As a result of this work, it is the author's firm belief that there is a real place for real science at camp. Our function here is to provide the first-year counselor with a ready storehouse of facts, information and ideas so he can carry out a vigorous program with inexpensive materials that are commonly available. Another purpose is to provide an outline for annual growth of the program by suggesting new equipment that may be added as conditions permit. It is expected that many years will pass before a total program as suggested by the total book is reached at most camps.

Although primarily designed for and addressed to summer camps, the usefulness of this book does not stop there. Being a collection of things to do in science, of ways to explore science, of outdoor projects in science and practical science information, it should be useful to teachers for field work and to many groups including various clubs, organizations and community houses. We should point out that girls as well as boys have enjoyed doing many of the projects contained in these pages. It is hoped that many counselors and science leaders using this material will be prospective science teachers, for the experience gained in this informal science teaching will be invaluable after leaving college and entering the teaching profession.

A word about suppliers and prices. There are numerous companies throughout the country that can supply materials for the projects. As a convenience, we have listed a few companies that are well-established mail-order houses which seek national distribution as indicated by regular advertising in the science periodicals. Some companies have been listed because they are unusually ready to assist with information and help on questions relating to their fields of work. Most of the listed companies make well-prepared catalogs available at no cost. Sources of a more local nature may be found in the telephone book.

As a further convenience, present prices of hard-cover books listed have been given when known. Since prices of paper-bound books are in a state of flux, they have been omitted but are generally less than one dollar.

Every effort has been made to anticipate campers' questions relating to the various projects and to provide answers. The index has been made as comprehensive as possible to help in locating specific material and answers quickly. Hopefully, this will reduce the load of science reference books which the counselor must bring with him to camp.

All projects have been designed to use the simplest possible materials. Oaktag has been selected as the basic building material because of its moderate strength, easy workability, and low cost. It could easily be replaced with wood or sheet metal where a more permanent construction is desired. Many projects are original. Some have come from the traditional standbys collected and passed on by science teachers, for which we are grateful. All projects have been tested and revised until made relatively foolproof.

The author wishes to express his gratitude to the following persons: For comments on various portions of the manuscript: John T. Ghiorse, science chairman of Weymouth, Massachusetts, Public Schools; Gilbert Merrill of the Boston Museum of Science; and Dr. Pearl Nelson of Boston University. David K. Sylvester, of Camp Becket and science teacher with the Weymouth Public Schools, has been of great assistance on the many field excursions that have been made. My colleagues at the Edmund W. Thurston Junior High School have been of continuing assistance. Special thanks are due to Thomas Del Signore for doing three of the more artistic illustrations. Professor John Read of Boston University offered many helpful suggestions when the work was in its earliest stages. The support of my science staff at camp helped to facilitate much of the work: Alan

Sirkin of Miami, Florida, Steve Leonard of Poultney, Vermont, and Joe Upchurch of Greenville, North Carolina. My thanks also to the many campers and students who have helped in developing the various projects. The manuscript was deciphered and typed in final form by Mrs. Eleanor Patterson, secretary at the Thurston Junior High School.

Finally, I wish to thank the many workers in scientific industries, institutions and societies who have responded to my letters and telephone calls to check on fine, obscure points of science about which youngsters delight in asking questions. Many of these people have gone out of their way to locate information that was not readily available.

In the years ahead, the writer will be making a further study of summer science programs and will be seeking new projects appropriate to the camp setting. I will consider it a favor to hear of experiences encountered in setting up science programs. Comments, suggestions or inquiries that may be helpful in planning future editions will be most welcome.

WILLIAM T. HARTY
West Medway, Massachusetts

Table of Contents

Indented numerals are project numbers.

Chapter

1: Planning the Camp Science Program

"What the classical Renaissance was to men of the fifteenth and sixteenth centuries, the scientific movement is to us. It has given a new trend to education. It has changed the outlook of the mind. It has given a new intellectual background to life."
— Sadler

THE LAST CENTURY has seen more progress and development in science than all previous centuries put together. Consider the advances that have been made during this brief portion of human existence. Sound is sent through space by radio, pictures are sent by television, automobiles have become commonplace, airplanes are a standard means of travel. The recently invented vacuum tube is being replaced by the more recently invented transistor, the moon has been illuminated by light from a laser on earth which can also vaporize steel girders at close range. Weather is being watched around the world and reported on by satellites. Man has traveled in space around our planet. He has sent his robot space ship to explore the planet Venus 36,000,000 miles away and report back to earth. Giant transistorized computers now do routine tasks in minutes that would take men years to finish. Satellites have brought us live transoceanic television.

Amazing as they are, these developments mark only the beginning because each new development breeds more of its own kind. Each discovery opens a new field of exploration. Even now scientists have accelerated plans to probe every portion of earth and space. There are now permanent expeditions in Antarctica. Rockets are collecting samples of the upper atmosphere, while Nansen bottles are doing the same in the lower ocean waters. Project Mohole will bring up specimens from the lower crust of the earth. Optical and radio telescopes are searching out into the most remote regions of space. Giant cyclotrons and accelerators are helping to explore the deepest secrets of the atom, that fundamental unit of all creation.

Science continues to make enormous advances as our present century moves on. But at camp, science often stands in the traditional status of a relatively static program consisting of isolated nature topics. Subject matter concentrates on plants and animals and falls off at a rapid rate as we move into the more dynamic areas of modern science. It is difficult to say why this should be the case. It is not the fault of the youngsters. Most of them have the interest, the curiosity, and the questions to be answered. It may be due to the unusually rapid development of science as an important force in our daily lives, and to the lack of printed material available for introducing science into camp program. It may be due to a shortage of well-prepared science counselors with a collection of camp-oriented scientific facts and projects. Whatever the reason, it is the purpose of this book to provide the foundation material so that true science can become a reality in camp programs.

Nature alone is not enough. All sciences are interrelated. The findings of atomic physics have shown us how closely all things are related under the unifying laws of the atom. No one science can rightly be singled out and studied as a separate unit isolated from all other sciences. The camp can play a unique and important part in clarifying the science of our modern world. It can aid the camper in finding his own place in this system of things and ideas. He who does not find that place is at a serious personal disadvantage. Camp has the unique opportunity to relate the science of school to the science of the natural world in an outdoor setting. It can help the camper to understand and enjoy his natural and man-made surroundings. With understanding comes enjoyment and appreciation, and only one step beyond that lies wisdom. Wisdom is that extra step which too few people take. It is the active mastery of knowledge, the creative use of knowledge. Taking that extra step is made just a little easier in the outdoor laboratory available at camp, with the guidance of a knowledgeable counselor, working with the actual materials of science, not words about science.

Most camps already have the beginnings of a science program in the form of nature study. Start with this, expand it, revitalize it and update it, and the development of a full science program comes into sight: a program with more subjects in which campers can find an interest, a program including the findings of modern science as well as the traditional material of nature, a program with appeal as being modern, timely and important.

Along with having wider interest appeal, the science program at camp has two more inherent virtues. It offers an opportunity for interesting the nonathlete in other camp activities and, with its indoor as well as outdoor projects, the science program is a blessing on a rainy day.

How does camp science differ from school science? Schools have steadily increased the amount of time devoted to science education, but they must work within certain limitations not imposed on the camp.

Camp science is primarily field science, a study of its materials them-selves, not of the books about it. It is a science of outdoor exploration and personal discovery; a pursuit that can be carried on at any time of day or night, not only during school hours. It is a science governed by in-dividual interest rather than by syllabus and outline. It is a science of mobility, freedom, feeling, crawling, climbing, hiking, testing, not a science of applying the seat of the pants to the seat of a school chair. It is the type of science which the schools strive to have more of, but which is very difficult to fit into the academic framework and large classroom structure.

Science is one of the fields in which the youngster can get out of what has been called the "junior rat race" of competing and performing in numerous organizations and activities. It offers him one of the few times when he can fulfill one of the basic purposes of childhood, that of discovery. He will get no medals, bronze statues, engraved paddles or applause, just satisfaction.

Below are ten goals or objectives of the many that could be listed for the camp science program. It will be noted that they attempt to tie the camp science program with school science experiences as well as with the growth and personal welfare of the individual.

The camp science program should be so constructed that it will:

1. Provide young people with an opportunity to develop an interest in some phase of science.

2. Lead young people to a better understanding and appreciation of the dynamics and the unity of the earth, the life it supports, the atmos-phere it holds down and the space through which it takes us.

3. Help the individual develop his mechanical skills and manual dexterity.

4. Provide young people with an opportunity to gain an understanding of the many mechanical and electronic devices, developed through science, which we use every day.

5. Lead young people to an understanding of the true meaning of conservation and develop the desire to use natural resources, both public and private, intelligently.

6. Provide young people with an over-all view of the scientific approach to understanding the universe, so they can see how the various branches of science are interrelated and are all parts of a whole.

7. Teach young people scientific facts and principles by using the materials of science rather than books about science.

8. Add meaning and enrichment to the school science program with the unique opportunity which camp affords to live with and work with the materials of science.

9. Provide for the different personal needs, interests and talents of each individual.

10. Encourage young people to develop functional use of the scien-tific method and observation skills through the presentation of real, physi-cal problem situations.

INITIATING THE PROGRAM

A complete science program as outlined in these pages cannot be established in a single year. A beginning can be made by enlarging existing nature study facilities into additional science fields. Once a trained science leader is chosen, he may be left to select science activities and plan a science program in keeping with stated objectives, camper interests and budget. Carefully prepared outlines should be kept so the program can be progressive from year to year.

In many ways, the science counselor is the science program. Fortunately, it is usually easier to find a counselor for science than to find one who specializes in nature. There is probably no better-qualified group of potential science counselors than students with two or three years of college who are planning to be general science teachers. These people have two important points in their favor: they are interested in young people, and they are interested in many fields of science. A position as science counselor is an excellent opportunity for them to gain experience in the type of work which they will be doing when teaching school. If an individual is weak in one of the areas of science, it will be to his lasting benefit to gain additional knowledge of that subject now. He will be acquiring valuable experience, which many science teachers lack, in teaching small groups of individuals in the field, with the materials of science, not the books about science.

The full-time science counselor will need some other counselors with scientific interests who will be available to assist with the program through the day as their schedules permit. This extra help is necessary because many science projects require that campers receive individual attention, and it is impossible for one person to handle this responsibility. Older campers of high school age are often anxious to assist in this way and help out with other jobs in the science program as needed. At least two other counselors should have part-time science responsibilities. Activity counselors in hiking, waterfront, climbing, etc., should be attuned to the science possibilities in their subjects.

FACILITIES

The need for facilities will grow as the science program grows. Because science is a major rainy-day activity, the building used should be large enough to hold a good number of active campers. FIG. 1-1 illustrates how one building has been arranged as a science building. Some of the rooms already existed; others were partitioned off as new activities, requiring separate work areas, were added to the program.

Focal point of the program is the combination work area and display area or museum. The only other room that must be specially provided is the darkroom needed for photography. An adequate darkroom is important because photography is one of the most popular science activities. If an amateur radio station is added, it should be in a separate room to prevent operation of the transmitter by unlicensed individuals. The elec-

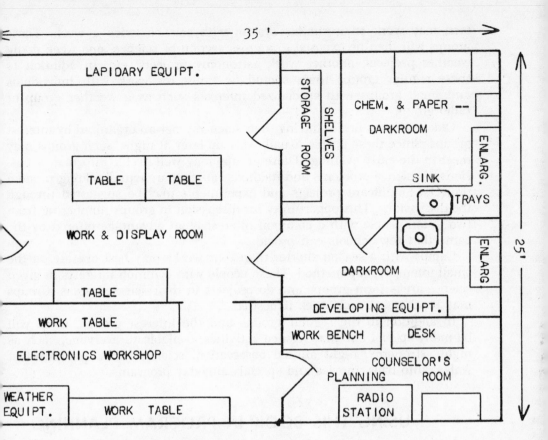

Fig. 1-1. Floor plan showing how one building has been converted to science by gradually partitioning off areas for various science activities. Most partitions are made of wallboard and serve as excellent bulletin boards for maps, charts, posters and projects. Not shown are weather instruments in outdoor shelter and radio and weather equipment on roof.

tronics area shown is lined with benches and many electrical outlets. It is in this area that radio kits are built and experiments conducted.

A library of science books should be available at camp and will be most conveniently located in the science building. A collection of books from the SUGGESTED REFERENCES and BIBLIOGRAPHY of this volume would make an excellent selection. These will then be available for reference and reading on rainy days and evenings.

ORGANIZING THE SCIENCE PROGRAM

Planning the actual organization and content of material in the science program will depend upon many factors: camper ages and interests, length of camp season, facilities.

At four- and eight-week camps, younger campers (up to age ten) may have science as a regularly scheduled activity three times a week with each week devoted to a different science subject. Campers eleven to fourteen may work on a similar system with science twice a week. These groups will then be exposed to a cross section of science, one week doing weather projects, another week astronomy projects, etc. In addition to these regular groups there should be times for work with individuals and small groups with specialized interests such as a weather group or radio group.

Older campers prefer having their science program organized by interest groups. Since these people usually stay up later at night, such groups may meet in the early evening. These groups may well prefer informal discussions of science problems and methods rather than actually doing random projects. Significant projects and experiments may be suggested through the discussions. This opportunity for discussion in groups numbering from two to ten people with a common interest is an advantage offered by the camp that few schools can provide.

Camps with a season shorter than four weeks may best operate on the small interest group method. Those people with common interests in given science areas form groups and do projects in their selected areas. Groups may be changed each week if desired.

In addition to the regular groups and the interest groups, there will be many special optional science activities available to everyone, such as night astronomy, night animal observation, science hikes, pre-breakfast walks, auto trips, movies and special rainy-day programs.

USING THIS BOOK IN PROGRAM PLANNING

This book has been prepared to give every possible assistance to the beginning science counselor. Long before the camp season starts, it is suggested that the following steps be carried out:

1. List the suggested references from each chapter and obtain or have the camp obtain as many of these books as possible. Most of them are paperbound and cost less than one dollar.

2. Go through the RESOURCES MATERIALS section of each chapter and send away for catalogs and free or inexpensive charts which are listed. When writing for free materials and science supply catalogs, it is sometimes necessary to use camp, school or college stationery, or to mention your work as science counselor at camp. The only problem usually encountered here is with the large science supply houses that do not generally send their complete catalogs to private addresses. They have advised that science counselors either use official stationery or have catalogs sent to their college addresses.

3. Learn what age groups you will be teaching at camp. Know what equipment is already available. Decide what subjects you will include in your program and go through this book selecting projects for each age group for the summer. Projects have been included for indoors and outdoors and for all age groups. You should have a separate list of rainy-day projects that can be done at a moment's notice. The projects have been consecutively numbered to facilitate listing.

4. Along with the list of projects, prepare a list of materials needed for the projects. Estimate quantities with the help of camp administration and have the materials ordered so they will be at camp when you arrive.

5. If the camp has a sixteen-millimeter sound movie projector, you will want to select some of the free films that may be borrowed. Two to three months in advance is not too early to book such films. Use films promptly when they arrive. Fill in the audience report card that is usually enclosed and mail it back to the sender. Your only expense is return postage (and postal insurance if requested by the film library).

6. Finally, this book should find constant use through the summer in carrying out the projects and as a reference for additional information in answering those obscure questions that are habitually asked by young people.

The INFORMATION OF IMPORTANCE section of each chapter contains much material, not readily available elsewhere, that is particularly practical in the camp situation. These sections should be read once before the season begins. It will be very helpful to read each section again just as you begin to take it up in your program.

METHODS OF TEACHING AT CAMP: STIMULATE AND CHALLENGE

The main purposes of science at camp are to stimulate interest, to permit discovery, to sharpen the powers of observation and to find pleasure in the world around us through scientific understanding of its mysteries. Nobody wants to see the camp become school-like. It has too many virtues in its present informal structure. The science to be included is the science of exploration and of the universe, not the science of books. The prime job of the science counselor is to stimulate interest in science as a method of exploration of the universe by having a personal enthusiasm for his subject and spreading that enthusiasm by contagion to every camper he meets. For young people, the summer can properly be only a time of fun and relaxation from school work. First comes stimulation, interest and motivation in science; then come facts.

Education comes from the Latin *educo*, "to draw out." Whenever possible, young people should learn facts by observing and studying an object and drawing their own conclusions through their powers of observation and reasoning. It does the youngster much more good if the counselor asks questions leading to the answer rather than simply handing out the answer without providing any challenge.

When starting any project suggested in this book, first challenge the group by asking them to tell what they already know about the topic at hand. Ask specific questions. They will give you clues about major areas of interest for further development and also indicate the present status of knowledge on the topic already possessed by the group so that known facts will not be needlessly repeated. The key thoughts to remember throughout the summer are: *stimulate* and *challenge*.

Science may be defined as a method of obtaining knowledge about our surroundings through observation and experimentation. The actual steps of the *scientific method* may be needed at camp from time to time to help solve problems, so they are included here for reference: 1. Statement of the problem; 2. Gathering all possible facts about the problem; 3. Forming a hypothesis or possible solution; 4. Testing the hypothesis with some sort of experiment or observation; 5. Evaluating the results of experiment to see if they prove or disprove the hypothesis. If the hypothesis is proven false, the scientist returns to the second step and goes through the method again using a different hypothesis. Youngsters age twelve and up enjoy knowing about the scientific method and applying it to simple problems that may be found in their environment.

DEVELOPING A LIVELY PROGRAM

It will help greatly if the science counselor, along with being a rare worm identifier, thunderstorm forecaster, and star pointer, can also be a one-man public relations force. There are many ways to keep campers aware of the science program and of the ever-present possibilities for exploring science. The announcement of the camp weather forecast at breakfast is a good way to start the day and special astronomy sessions for small groups at night is a good way to end the day.

Unusual happenings or findings during the day should be announced and explained at meal times. Science movies may be shown for all interested campers during evenings and rainy days. Announcements of science trips always create a wave of renewed interest.

The most effective advertising may be done through the other counselors. Make every effort to acquaint them with activities of the science program. This may be done informally through the day and in a more formal atmosphere at counselor meetings. When the counselors become interested, their interest will spread to the campers. If the counselors are apathetic, this too may spread. Such apathy is usually easily avoided by explaining the purpose and activities of the science program.

Keep your program varied. Change the topics that are covered and the type of projects that are done. Have trips as frequently as possible. Plan one or two overnight trips. Dramatize whenever possible and don't hide your own enthusiasm for scientific exploration. Take advantage of every opportunity to pass it along to the campers.

SCIENCE TRIPS AND OTHER PROJECTS

Auto trips should form an important part of the science program. Such trips serve to broaden the range of experiences of young people and these experiences form the basis for new learning both at camp and at school.

Since the trips will depend upon the camp location, no definite suggestions can be offered here. Some ideas may come from the following list of places visited by small groups from our camp in Maine: sawmill, hydroelectric dams, Telstar earth station, shoe plant, paper mill, quarries and mines, seacoast, historic forts, radio stations, dairy plant, fish hatcheries, marine laboratory, farms, and museums.

Before camping season opens, obtain tourist information concerning the state in which camp is located, and neighboring states. Plan trips carefully so a number of interesting sites may be visited on each trip. Most trips will probably be one-day journeys with a box lunch. Longer trips may develop into overnight excursions with a suitable camping area selected or reserved in advance.

Most industries are pleased to have groups of young people visit to see the processes carried on in the plant. Make arrangements in advance by telephone. Get names of people at the plant who should be contacted when you arrive. Save all information (names, addresses, phone numbers, special details and cautions) for future years. Prepare campers in advance by explaining the purpose of the plant. Remind them that people are taking time out of their daily work to show them through the plant and the best way to show their thanks and interest is to ask intelligent questions. Knowing that these youngsters are truly interested in his line of work by the questions they ask will repay your guide many times over.

There are many other science projects not described in this book that may be included in a camp program. One of the most interesting may be provided by obtaining a junked automobile engine, mounting it in the science building and allowing older campers to take it apart, clean various sections and perhaps color-code the parts with paint for a permanent display. Chemistry may be provided for older campers with the help of a large chemistry set. Keep it locked when not in use.

BASIC MATERIALS FOR PROJECTS

Wherever possible, the projects included in this book have been designed to use the same basic materials. Following this plan will greatly simplify the purchasing, maintenance and inventory procedures. Most of these items are available from any art- or school-supply house. Although many projects require one or more special items, a large percentage of the projects may be done if the following materials are kept on hand in needed quantities:

Oaktag, 18″ × 24″ (also called "Tagboard" and "Manila Tag")
White drawing paper
Colored construction paper (red, green, blue, brown, assorted)
Scissors
Duco cement
Rulers marked in inches and centimeters
Nonsterile cotton batting

Mimeographed sheets (See Projects 1, 12, 18, 19, 112.)
Brass fasteners
Length of ¾″ × ¾″ soft pine wood
Pencils
Black plastic electrical tape
Scotch tape
Masking tape
Assorted paint brushes
Crayons
Stapling machine
Plaster of Paris
Plastic pails
Compass
Magnifying glass (ten-power)
Paper clips
Modeling knives and pocket knife
Poster board
Wide-mouth jars
Thumbtacks
Drawing compasses
Protractors

Chapter

2: Meteorology

SUGGESTED REFERENCES

Burnett, Lehr and Zim, *Weather*. New York: Golden Press, 1957, OR Fisher, Robert, *How About the Weather?* New York: Harper & Bros., 1958. $3.75. An excellent hard-cover book on the subject with emphasis on local forecasting.

WEATHER, the supreme program director, is certainly the most important subject at camp. With the common use of central heating systems, food preservation and means of transportation, people have become increasingly indifferent to the capricious changes of weather. Of course, there are many people to whom the weather is of vital importance: fishermen and other boatmen, farmers, flyers, forest rangers, operators of hydroelectric dams and others who work with or in the out-of-doors. These people who are conscious of the weather realize that each year hurricanes, tornadoes, floods and lightning take thousands of lives and cause millions of dollars' worth of damage. They also realize that each year rain and snow provide the needed moisture for plant life to feed millions of people and every other form of animal life on earth as well as providing pure drinking water for all these creatures. The remainder of us normally go about our own air-conditioned shells until we want to do something outside. Then the weather becomes suddenly important to us and we realize that, having ignored it for so long, we know very little about its mysteries.

It is at camp, where the weather does matter to us, that it is not only possible to learn about its mysteries, but is also important to be weather-wise. It is no exaggeration to say that there are many outdoor situations in which an understanding of the weather can be a lifesaver. Each year, people are needlessly lost in storms on the water and in the mountains, and from lightning in fields, golf courses and beaches when some weather knowledge could have saved them.

The study of meteorology at camp may accomplish many objectives. It should develop an awareness of the nature of our atmosphere, that it is a material substance at the bottom of which we live, that it is constantly changing and moving up and down as well as horizontally, that these changes happen, not instantaneously, but gradually, always offering a number of signs which tell those who can read them what the weather is going to be. The person interested in weather should also be aware of the merits and limitations of Weather Bureau forecasts compared with his own. Neither is a perfect system. The Weather Bureau must make twenty-four- to thirty-six-hour forecasts for large areas and necessarily conditions its forecasts with such precautionary phrases as "Possible . . . chance of . . . scattered. . . ." The local forecaster is not concerned with a large area. He makes his forecast for the space above his head. But without the use of maps and charts, he must limit himself to twelve-hour forecasts. Obviously the best system is to get the general picture from the Weather Bureau and then decide on your own weather from the signs around you.

Finally, campers should realize that they can learn something about the weather from books, pictures and maps. But if they are really going to understand it, time must be taken each day to observe its changes. It is important to practice and test our skill with the weather every day, for it is only by living with it that we can get to know it.

INFORMATION OF IMPORTANCE

The science of meteorology includes much more than the forecasting of weather. Meteorology is the study of the atmosphere, its composition and the changes that take place in it. Although in camp we will be primarily concerned with the weather phase of meteorology, we should always be aware of the over-all scope of the subject. To assist in developing this over-all view, a look at the composition and mechanics of the atmosphere is in order.

Our atmosphere is a mixture of many things. Some are part of it, others are floating in it. It contains earth dust and meteor dust, salt crystals and gases. The atmosphere is 78 per cent nitrogen, 21 per cent oxygen, 0.9 per cent argon, 0.03 per cent carbon dioxide. The remaining fraction of a per cent is divided up among other rare gases. The amount of water vapor in the air varies from 1 per cent to 4 per cent.

Gravity holds our atmosphere down to earth. Thus it is thickest here at the bottom and becomes thinner as we move out from the surface of the earth. The atmosphere thins out in such a short distance that 75 per cent of it is beneath an altitude of seven miles. Above that it continues getting thinner, and the last traces of terrestrial atmosphere seem to be over 100,000 miles away. There, the atmosphere of the earth probably merges with the outer fringes of the sun's atmosphere which becomes thinner as the distance from the sun increases, until the solar atmosphere merges with interstellar gas at some point half way between earth and Mars.

All of this air being pulled in toward the earth naturally exerts a pressure at the bottom, just as many fathoms of sea water exert a pressure at the bottom of the ocean. Like sea water, this pressure does not just push down, but pushes equally in all directions. The average pressure of the atmosphere at earth's surface is 14.7 pounds on each square inch of surface area. If you have a book on your desk which is one foot square the atmosphere is pressing on it with a force of over 2,000 pounds, or one ton! This is one of the facts of meteorology about which young people really become excited.

The atmosphere may be divided into four important layers. From the bottom up to an altitude of seven miles is the *troposphere*. This is the layer in which we live. It is in this layer that there is life, atmospheric turbulence, storms, weather changes, clouds. There is a drop in temperature of 3.3° F. for every 1,000 feet of altitude. Above the troposphere is the *stratosphere*, a layer of constantly cloudless cold air with temperatures as low as −70° F. At an altitude of about twenty miles is a warm layer known as the *ozonosphere*. The existence of this layer is vital to life itself, for it is here that most of the ultraviolet (sunburn) rays of the sun are used and made powerless before they reach earth. At this height, the ultraviolet rays split the O_2 oxygen molecules and reform them into O_3 ozone molecules. During this process, the ultraviolet rays spend their deadly energy and produce the heat that remains in the ozone layer.

The next important layer is the *ionosphere*, starting at a height of fifty miles. Most of the dust in the atmosphere which scatters sunlight in the daytime, makes the sky light up, and gives it its blue color, is below the ionosphere. The ionosphere, therefore, is dark, with the sun appearing as a huge ball of brilliant light in a dark sky in which many of the bright stars are visible all day. The ionosphere is made up of various layers of ions or electrified atoms. These layers are designated by letters: D at 50 miles, E at 70 miles, F_1 at 140 miles and F_2 at 200 miles. Each layer, if it is present, is able to reflect radio waves back to earth like a mirror. The D layer is only present when the sun is shining on it and is strongest about midday. The others are more dependable but also exist at the mercy of solar activity, sunspots, flares, etc.

The ionosphere is the layer in which we see meteors glowing as they streak earthward and it is the layer in which we may observe the *Aurora Borealis*. The aurora seem to be caused by an interaction between the sun and another feature of the earth's atmosphere, the two Van Allen radiation belts which are located 3,000 and 10,000 miles above the equator. The present theory of the auroras is as follows. During a period of high sunspot activity, the sun releases a stream of charged atomic particles toward the earth in the form of a *solar flare*. These particles enter the Van Allen belts, disturb their equilibrium and cause them to shower charged atomic particles down toward the ionosphere. Being electrically charged, the Van Allen particles are deflected by the earth's magnetic field so that they enter the ionosphere only in the polar regions. Entering the ionosphere, they collide with the gas atoms found there. Upon collision, the electrons of the gas atoms are disturbed and jump from one shell to another on their atoms. Light is given off each time an electron changes position. The collective light from all the atoms involved is what we see as the beautiful aurora.

The aurora works much like a neon tube. Of all the "neon" signs we see, only the red ones contain neon gas. Pink ones contain helium, blue ones are argon, deep blue is krypton and other colors are made by mixing these gases and mercury. The atoms in a "neon" bulb are excited by high voltage instead of solar particles. With the aurora, nitrogen produces a blue glow, high-altitude oxygen a red glow and low-altitude oxygen a green glow. The aurora is one of nature's most beautiful shows and usually offers some good performances when the sun is in the active phase of its eleven-year sunspot cycle.

You may have noticed that it is much darker on a cloudy moonless night than it is on a clear moonless night. The ionosphere produces another type of light besides the aurora. This is called *airglow*. Unlike the aurora, airglow is produced constantly, day and night. Night airglow may also be called nightglow. It is produced by chemical reactions of hydroxyl and sodium ions. Using sensitive instruments, scientists have detected red, green, yellow and infrared colors in it. Although we cannot see airglow, we can find our way around using its light. (Compare the overcast with the clear night.) It is very rich in infrared light. Our eyes are not sensitive to infrared; but it is thought that those of many animals are and that it is with this infrared light that they see at night. If they do use it, it would never get darker than dusk for them except on cloudy nights. Airglow and the possible use of it by nocturnal animals is still not completely understood and the nature of airglow is being actively explored at this time with the use of rockets.

Before we go into actual forecasting, let us return briefly to the troposphere and become familiar with the mechanics of air flow and other changes that take place within this important layer.

First we have *high-* and *low-pressure areas*. In a high-pressure area the air is gently falling. This produces clear skies and fair weather. By contrast, the air in a low-pressure area is gently rising. As it rises, it cools, the water vapor condenses onto tiny crystals and particles floating in the air, and produces clouds. As the cooling continues, water vapor is squeezed out of the clouds and falls as rain or snow, thus producing the stormy weather which is characteristic of low-pressure areas. Winds in a high blow clockwise around the center and winds in a low blow counterclockwise around the center. Since highs and lows develop near the ground, they are rarely found above four to five miles and at these levels the prevailing westerly winds persist blowing constantly from the west, northwest or southwest. It is, in fact, the prevailing westerlies which help move and steer the giant highs and lows across the country from west to east.

Next we have *warm* and *cold air masses*. An air mass is a large body of air with a uniform temperature and humidity. The temperature-humidity characteristics of an air mass are the same as the characteristics of the place where it originated. If it formed over warm water, the air will be warm and humid; if it formed over cold land, the air will be cold and dry. FIG. 2-1 shows the principal places of origin for air masses which break free and move across the United States. The map also shows warm and cold ocean currents which have an effect on the air temperature.

The leading edge of a moving air mass is known as a *front* and is accompanied by some type of stormy weather. FIGS. 2-2 and 2-3 show the characteristics for warm and cold fronts and the resulting weather. A high-pressure area is usually found in the center of an air mass; but low-pressure areas often form along the fronts as warm air is forced to rise over cooler air.

Another factor in tropospheric mechanics is *wind*. Wind is a movement

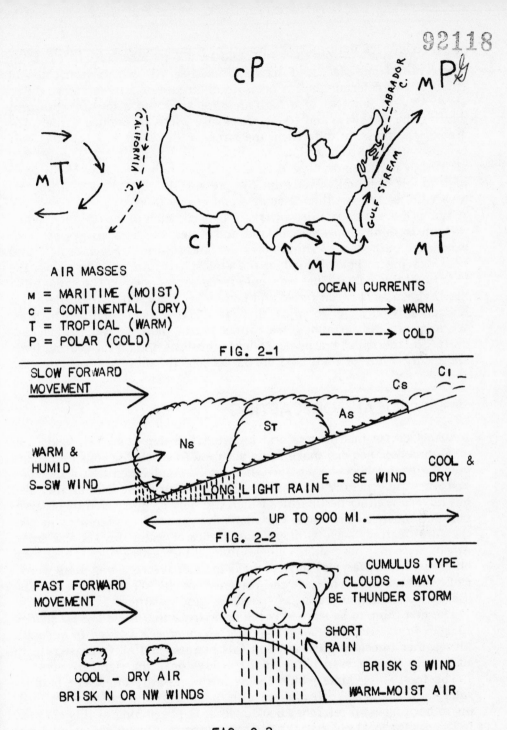

AIR MASSES

M = MARITIME (MOIST)
c = CONTINENTAL (DRY)
T = TROPICAL (WARM)
P = POLAR (COLD)

OCEAN CURRENTS
———————→ WARM
– – – – –→ COLD

FIG. 2-1

SLOW FORWARD MOVEMENT

Ci
Cs
As
ST
Ns

WARM & HUMID S-SW WIND

LONG LIGHT RAIN   E - SE WIND   COOL & DRY

←——————— UP TO 900 MI. ———————→

FIG. 2-2

FAST FORWARD MOVEMENT

CUMULUS TYPE CLOUDS – MAY BE THUNDER STORM

SHORT RAIN

BRISK S WIND

COOL - DRY AIR
BRISK N OR NW WINDS

WARM-MOIST AIR

FIG. 2-3

FIG. 2-1.   Climate controlling ocean currents and source areas of various air-mass types

FIG. 2-2.   Characteristic weather along a warm front

FIG. 2-3.   Characteristic weather at a cold front

of air horizontally across the earth; and air doesn't move unless it is being forced out of one place and drawn to another. Air will move because of either of two determinants: a pressure difference or a temperature difference. Air will flow out of a high-pressure area into a low-pressure area causing the clockwise and counterclockwise winds mentioned earlier. The greater the pressure difference, the stronger the wind will be. It is only because of the extremely low pressure in the center of a hurricane that air rushes in with great speed causing high winds. The flow of air from high to low eventually evens out the pressure in both areas and the low area with its foul weather dissipates and ceases to exist.

Winds due to temperature differences are common in the summer. When the sun is shining on areas of land and water, the land always becomes warmer than the water. The air over the land is heated, becomes light and rises, leaving a "hole" behind in the atmosphere. Air rushing across the land to fill this hole is what we would recognize as a wind. The same thing may happen as between forest and field areas. Very often when there is a horizontal wind for us to enjoy, there is also a vertical wind of which we are unaware. As earthlings, we cannot detect these vertical winds (updrafts and thermals) but pilots, glider enthusiasts and all the soaring birds are keenly aware of them and on the lookout for these upward currents.

LOCAL FORECASTING

Using simple instruments and knowing the signs told by clouds and wind direction, you can make fairly accurate forecasts for your immediate area for twelve hours in advance. It must be emphasized that some forecast rules are generally true throughout the country; but each locality also has its own weather peculiarities which can only be discovered by observation and practice. Such local variations are caused by differences in geographical features such as mountains, bodies of water, forests and cities. Any of these may necessitate changes in local forecasting rules. These local differences, however, also serve to make individual forecasting more worthwhile and exciting. They are the reasons that the Weather Bureau must use such conditional words as "possible," and "scattered."

The first thing to be learned is the basic truth that *there are no sudden changes in the weather. Signs of a change can always be seen in advance.* All weather forecasting is based on this premise and all forecasters gain confidence from it even if they don't always have the right answers.

The forecasting hints which follow are necessarily brief. For best results, they should be applied along with the background gained from reading either suggested reference book cited at the beginning of this chapter. In forecasting local weather, the two most important factors are wind direction and clouds. The person who becomes sensitive to changes in these is well on his way to becoming weather-wise. The barometer may be used along with these for additional assistance.

1. Weather changes usually come with the wind. If there is no wind and no cloud movement, changes in the weather will be slow in coming.
2. Weather patterns generally move across the country from west to

east (driven at upper levels by the prevailing westerly winds) at a rate of 500 to 700 miles per day (20 to 30 miles per hour).

3. The coldest time of the twenty-four-hour day is just before sunrise after the earth has been losing heat all night. But clouds act as a blanket holding heat near the earth, so expect warm evenings when it is overcast and cool evenings when the sky is clear.

4. Expect a cold front when cumulus clouds thicken and become lower with increasing winds. Cold front weather passes quickly (one to six hours) and is often characterized by thunder, lightning, heavy rain, hail, strong winds and occasionally tornadoes. The following cold-air mass is characterized by cool, dry air and fair weather. (See FIG. 2-3.)

5. Expect a warm front when high thin cirrus clouds are gradually followed by thicker, lower stratus-type clouds. Warm fronts pass slowly (one to three days) and are often characterized by cloudy skies, light or intermittent rain and drizzle often accompanied by mist and fog. The warm air mass which follows is characterized by warm, humid air, generally fair weather; but there is a good chance of afternoon or evening thunderstorms following a hot, sunny day (FIG. 2-2).

6. A rising barometer indicates the approach of a high-pressure area and fair weather. A falling barometer indicates a change in the weather and a possible storm.

7. If you stand with your back to the wind, a high-pressure area will be on your right and a low-pressure area on your left.

8. Air circulates counterclockwise in toward the center around a low. Thus winds on the east side of the low are from the southeast. The air circulates clockwise out from the center around a high, causing winds on the east side to blow from the northwest.

9. Often, but not always, the duration of a storm is inversely proportional to its intensity, which means that the harder it rains, the shorter the storm will last.

10. Southerly winds bring warm temperatures, northerly winds bring cooler temperatures.

11. If you see lightning but hear no thunder, there is a very distant (but very real) thunderstorm. If the lightning is to the east of you, it probably will not come your way; but lightning to the west is very likely headed in your direction.

12. An east, northeast or southeast wind indicates stormy weather. A northwest or west wind indicates fair weather. A southwest wind indicates generally fair weather but may bring heat and humidity and the possibility of thundershowers. Winds from the north or south indicate unsettled weather, scattered clouds and possible light showers. Chances of showers for a given locality with these winds can be better estimated after a period of learning by observation. (See WEATHER WHEEL project.)

Following are some "folk rules" of weather forecasting which have a scientific basis and are generally true.

13. When dew is on the grass, Rain will not come to pass.

14. A morning fog indicates the coming of a clear day. Both 13 and 14 are conditions which require clear, cloudless nights during which the

WEATHER FORECASTS BASED ON WIND AND BAROMETER INDICATIONS

(Courtesy of U. S. Weather Bureau)

WIND DIRECTION	BAROMETER CORRECTED TO SEA LEVEL	CHARACTER OF WEATHER INDICATED
SW to NW	30.10 to 30.20 and steady	Fair, with slight temperature changes for one to two days.
SW to NW	30.10 to 30.20 rising rapidly	Fair, followed within two days by rain.
SW to NW	30.20 and above and stationary	Continued fair, with no decided temperature change.
SW to NW	30.20 and above and falling slowly	Slowly rising temperatures and fair for two days.
S to SE	30.10 to 30.20 and falling slowly	Rain within 24 hours.
S to SE	30.10 to 30.20 and falling rapidly	Wind increasing in force, with rain within 12 to 24 hours.
SE to NE	30.10 to 30.20 and falling slowly	Rain in 12 to 18 hours.
SE to NE	30.10 to 30.20 and falling rapidly	Increasing wind and rain within 24 hours.
E to NE	30.10 and above and falling slowly	In summer with light winds, rain may not fall for several days. In winter, rain within 24 hours.
E to NE	30.10 and above and falling rapidly	In summer, rain probably within 12 to 24 hours. In winter, rain or snow, with increasing winds, will often set in when the barometer begins to fall and the wind sets in from the NE.
SE to NE	30.00 or below and falling slowly	Rain will continue one to two days.
SE to NE	30.00 or below and falling rapidly	Rain, with high wind, followed within 36 hours by clearing and in winter by colder.
S to SW	30.00 or below and rising slowly	Clearing within a few hours, and fair for several days.
S to E	29.80 or below and falling rapidly	Severe storm imminent, followed within 24 hours by clearing and in winter by colder weather.
E to N	29.80 or below and falling rapidly	Severe northeast gale and heavy precipitation. In winter heavy snow followed by a cold wave.
Going to W	29.80 or below and rising rapidly	Clearing and colder.

earth has cooled considerably. Thus it will be some time before a storm can set in.

15. A halo around the moon is a sign of rain. This halo is caused by the moonlight's being dispersed by ice crystals which compose cirrus clouds. Since cirrus clouds are often the first sign of an approaching warm front, the halo may be a true indication of future rain. But the front is still about eighteen hours distant. Although it may be cloudy in the morning, it may not rain for at least ten to twelve hours after the halo is first observed.

16. "Red sky at night, sailor's delight.
    Red sky at morning, sailors take warning."

This is an old one and one of the earliest references may be found in Matthew 16:2. Although it is not always correct, the first line is usually more dependable than the second. A red sky to the west as the sun sets indicates that the sunlight is shining through dry air containing dust but little moisture. This is the air that will reach your location during the evening and the following day. If the air were moist, the sun would set with a pale gray or yellow color.

These general forecasting hints apply equally throughout the country and are offered for your testing. You will probably adopt some of them for constant use and reject others as not being dependable for your particular area. Additional assistance in correlating wind direction with barometer readings will be found in the WEATHER FORECASTS table. This table has been compiled by the Weather Bureau from averages found to be generally true throughout the United States; but like all other general data there will be variations for certain localities.

The weather is dynamic, persistent in its changes and constantly introducing variety into our lives. It challenges us to exploration, discovery and understanding. These are some of the joys that campers may derive from a study of meteorology as they begin to understand the earth and seeing it in the context of space, realize that one of the main differences between earth and the other planets is that this one has an atmosphere and that one of the by-products of this atmosphere is weather, for without either one, man would not be here.

PROJECT 1

CONSTRUCTING AND OPERATING
A CAMP WEATHER BUREAU

A central activity to tie together all phases of weather study is the operation of a camp weather bureau issuing daily forecasts. Necessary equipment may be purchased or built by campers. Instructions for building many of the instruments are given later in this chapter.

MATERIALS

The following instruments would be desirable acquisitions for the weather bureau. A barometer for indicating atmospheric pressure. (In using a barometer, remember that more important than the reading for any given moment is whether the barometer is rising or falling. Serviceable barometers may be purchased for less than five dollars, making this one instrument that may be purchased.) Thermometers are also inexpensive and should be included among the purchased equipment. A wet- and dry-bulb hygrometer for measuring humidity may be made using two regular outdoor thermometers.

Someplace above the weather bureau should be a wind vane for wind direction and an anemometer for wind speed. These may be easily constructed or remote-reading electrical devices may be purchased at moderate expense. A nephoscope is often helpful in determining wind direction and construction data is given in this chapter.

There is little difference in price between buying and building a rain gauge. Both are inexpensive. It is good to have in camp one barometer and one rain gauge which have been purchased. Then the calibrations on these instruments may be used to check the instruments that campers will make. Other equipment that may be added includes dew-point apparatus, sunshine recorder and hail stick. Instructions for building these are found elsewhere in this chapter.

A final instrument to purchase is the maximum-minimum thermometer which is inexpensive and records the high and low temperatures for the day. When there are weather extremes, it is always of great interest to campers to know how hot or cold it has been.

One of the first building projects should be a shelter for the thermometers and hygrometer. These instruments are used to measure properties of the atmosphere, not sunlight. They must have a free flow of air, but they must be located out of the sunlight and be protected from the weather at all times. You have probably seen the weather bureau shelters, with four sides made of white shutter material, a roof, and legs to hold it three to four feet above the ground. A simpler shelter, suitable for most summer installations, may be constructed of three wooden sides with holes drilled through them to permit free air circulation and a large, overhanging roof. This shelter should be mounted on a post or tree with the open side facing north to prevent the entrance of direct sunlight. Paint the shelter white to further reduce the effects of direct sunlight.

34   Meteorology

Along with the equipment mentioned above, certain materials will be found helpful by the camp weathermen. A cloud chart including photographs of thirty-six different cloud types is available from the government for ten cents. There is no substitute for this chart in learning cloud identification. The *Daily Weather Maps* are available by mail on a monthly subscription basis. Although these arrive a day late, they do show the weather patterns across the entire country and are helpful in determining what type of weather is coming toward you. The actual records of the daily weather at camp are best kept on a mimeographed form. These records may be saved from year to year and used to build up a study of the camp climate. Shown in FIG. 2-4 are the headings of a sample form.

WEATHER DATA & FORECAST SHEET

TIME ____ AM ____ PM   YEAR_____

DAY	DATE	BAROM PRESS	TEMP	24 HR TEMP HI LO	HUM %	WIND DIR	CLOUDS TYPE-DIR	24 HOUR PRECIP.
PRESENT					FORECAST			
PRESENT					FORECAST			

FIG. 2-4. Sample headings for weather bureau records

PROCEDURE

There are many possible ways to operate the camp weather bureau. Remember that the type of forecasts being made are only good for a maximum of twelve hours. One forecast should be prepared in the morning in time for breakfast, another may be made later in the day. In order to keep all data relative, the forecasts should be made at the same time each day.

Who will make the forecasts and how will they be used? They may be made each morning by the same group of interested people, or each cabin may take its turn at supplying the forecasters. An important goal, remember, is to make everybody weather-conscious. The prepared forecast may be announced at some appropriate time during the morning. It may be posted in chart form or drawn onto a blackboard weather map. Campers might like to raise weather flags, in which case they should work out their own flag code and make it known to everybody in camp.

As director of the weather bureau, the science counselor will be the person consulted on weather problems. He should always be aware of the national weather picture from the weather maps and he should keep in touch with Weather Bureau forecasts for comparison with his own. Weather men do not work in a vacuum. They gather information from whatever sources are available. This example is one to be emulated.

WEATHER VANES

With wind direction being the most important single weather indicator, the weather vane, wind vane, or anemoscope is the most important single weather instrument. The temporary vanes illustrated in FIG. 2-5 are not designed to give campers long service, but to teach them how weather vanes work. Shown in FIG. 2-6 are vanes of more durable construction. Weather vanes come in many shapes, but whether they be cows, roosters or arrows, they all have one design feature in common. The surface area, which lies behind the pivot and is known as the tail is always larger than the surface area in front of the pivot (head). As the wind blows, it catches the tail and pulls it along with it, causing the head to point into the wind. A vital point to remember: Weather vanes tell the direction *from* which the wind is blowing. A vane pointing to the northwest indicates a wind blowing *from* the northwest to the southeast. Such a wind is called a north-west wind. Many people erroneously believe that the weather vane points with the wind, toward its destination.

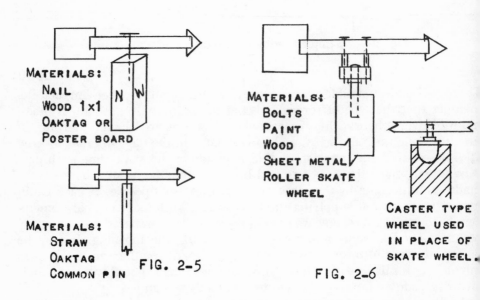

MATERIALS:
NAIL
WOOD 1x1
OAKTAG OR
POSTER BOARD

MATERIALS:
STRAW
OAKTAG
COMMON PIN

FIG. 2-5

MATERIALS:
BOLTS
PAINT
WOOD
SHEET METAL
ROLLER SKATE
WHEEL

CASTER TYPE
WHEEL USED
IN PLACE OF
SKATE WHEEL.

FIG. 2-6

FIG. 2-5.   Temporary hand wind vanes

FIG. 2-6.   Permanent wind vane. Place tin can weather shield over wheel for winter use.

VANE ANEMOMETER

An anemometer is a device to indicate wind speed. Its most common form is the cup anemometer, which has spinning cups attached to a small electric generator which is wired to a voltmeter inside the building. As the generator turns faster, it produces more voltage and the increase is shown on the voltmeter which is calibrated in miles per hour instead of volts.

MATERIALS AND PROCEDURE

Materials for an electric cup anemometer are costly and an adequate substitute may be found in a vane anemometer. On this device, the wind blows against a hinged vane. As the wind speed increases, the vane swings up farther. The unit is calibrated by holding it out the window of a moving car on a windless day. Marks are made on the scale as the car moves at five, ten, fifteen, twenty miles per hour. When in use, be sure the anemometer is headed directly into the wind as indicated by a weather vane.

Plans for a vane anemometer which may be adapted to any available building materials are shown in FIG. 2-7.

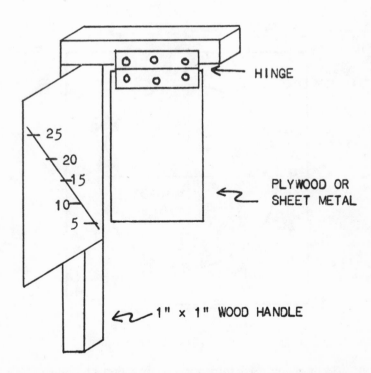

FIG. 2-7. Vane anemometer used to indicate wind speed

NEPHOSCOPE FOR THE WEATHER BUREAU

The importance of using wind direction in weather forecasting has already been mentioned many times. It has also been said that if the wind is very light, weather changes will be slow in coming. However, wind at ground level may be light and variable, while winds at higher altitudes may have considerable velocity and a definite direction. Under such conditions high-altitude winds are just as useful as ground winds in preparing a forecast of future weather. Barring the use of weather balloons, a simple method for determining the direction of upper winds is with the use of a nephoscope.

A nephoscope, in its simplest form, is a mirror with the points of the compass marked on it. It is placed in a horizontal position under the sky (See FIG. 2-8.) Once the mirror is properly oriented with the "north" marking pointing to true north on earth, it is an easy matter to trace the paths reflected by clouds as they are propelled by the upper winds. For greatest accuracy, a grease pencil may be used directly on the mirror to track the progress of clouds, thus determining their direction of travel and the direction from which the high-level winds are blowing.

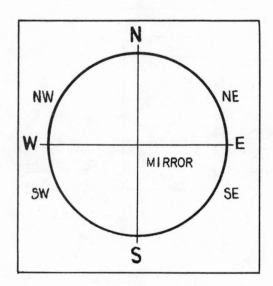

FIG. 2-8. Nephoscope used to determine direction of upper winds through cloud movements

Mirror, oaktag or wood, scissors or saw

PROCEDURE

The nephoscope which is illustrated is simply a large mirror which has been masked by a piece of oaktag with a large circular hole cut out. The hole represents the form of the sky as seen from horizon to horizon even though the whole of this sky is not visible. The compass points are marked on the paper around the hole. A nephoscope provides a much simpler and more accurate way of determining cloud direction than simply looking up into the sky. A comparison of the two methods will soon prove the value of adding this instrument to the camp weather bureau.

BAROMETERS

A barometer is an instrument used to detect changes in atmospheric pressure. Decreasing pressure often indicates a storm and rising pressure usually indicates fair weather. Barometers may use a fluid such as water or mercury, or they may be designed without fluid (aneroid). The standard barometer uses mercury. The atmosphere will support a column of mercury about thirty inches high and even aneroid barometers are marked in inches of mercury. Water barometers have also been built, but because water is lighter than mercury, the atmosphere can support a column of water thirty-four feet high, making water barometers large and immovable objects.

Various barometer designs are shown in FIG. 2-9. Some of these may be built at camp. A barometer should be located in a place where the temperature is fairly constant. Any barometer containing air is also likely to act as a thermometer; by keeping the temperature constant, you know that any changes are being caused by air pressure. If you build the milk bottle–rubber barometer, place it in the sunlight and watch what happens.

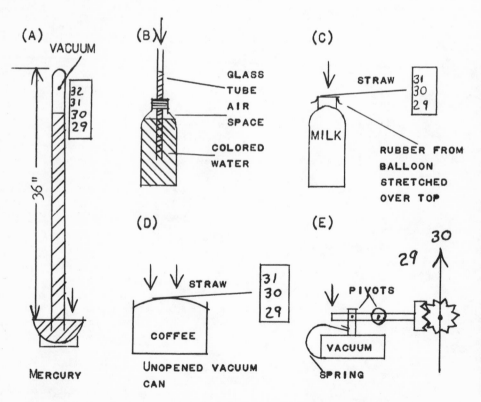

FIG. 2-9. Barometers. A and B are liquid types, others are aneroid. Arrows indicate application of air pressure.

AIR-PRESSURE DEVICES

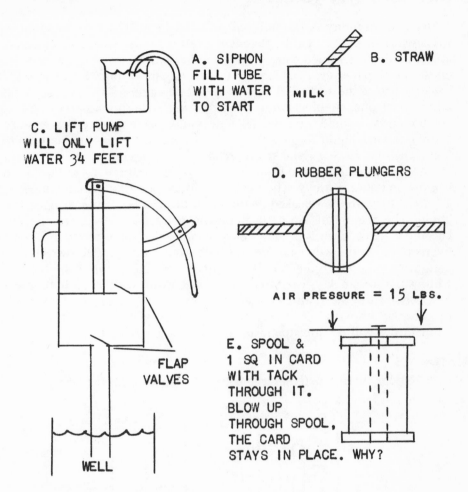

A. SIPHON FILL TUBE WITH WATER TO START

B. STRAW

MILK

C. LIFT PUMP WILL ONLY LIFT WATER 34 FEET

D. RUBBER PLUNGERS

FLAP VALVES

AIR PRESSURE = 15 LBS.

E. SPOOL & 1 SQ IN CARD WITH TACK THROUGH IT. BLOW UP THROUGH SPOOL, THE CARD STAYS IN PLACE. WHY?

WELL

FIG. 2-10. PROJECT 6. Illustrates some devices which work on air pressure. It is interesting to draw, find or make these and have campers explain how they work.

MEASURING HUMIDITY WITH WET- AND DRY-BULB HYGROMETER

Relative humidity is the amount of moisture in the air compared with the amount it *could* hold at that temperature. It is measured in percents and is easily determined using a wet- and dry-bulb hygrometer which works on the principle of evaporation. That is, the faster a liquid evaporates, the cooler it leaves the surface it was on. Good examples of this are seen when ether or alcohol is placed on the skin. Both of these liquids are very volatile and evaporate quickly. Like all liquids, they require heat energy to change from a liquid to gas. This heat is absorbed from the body and we feel a cooling effect. By the same process, we keep cool by the evaporation of perspiration; but on a humid day the perspiration doesn't evaporate, leaving us hot and sticky. The heat used in evaporation remains in the gas as *latent heat* and is released again when the gas is converted back into a liquid. The release of latent heat during condensation causes the air to become warmer during a snowstorm or any other precipitation. With the hygrometer, as the water on the wet bulb evaporates, it will lower the temperature of the thermometer. If the air is dry (low humidity) the water will evaporate quickly, carrying much heat away with it as it becomes a gas, cooling the thermometer and lowering the temperature considerably. By contrast, humid air will permit only slow evaporation and the wet-bulb temperature will remain up closer to that of the dry bulb.

MATERIALS

Two outdoor thermometers, large cotton shoelace, small jar of water

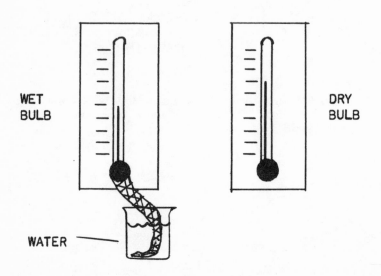

WET BULB

DRY BULB

WATER

Fig. 2-11.   Wet- and dry-bulb thermometers set up to indicate relative humidity

PROCEDURE

'it shoelace over bulb of one thermometer. Place end of lace in water so hermometer bulb will be wet at all times (FIG. 2-11). Hang both thermometers outdoors in instrument shelter.

Dry Bulb Temp	DIFFERENCE BETWEEN DRY-BULB AND WET-BULB THERMOMETERS															
	1	2	3	4	5	6	7	8	9	10	11	12	13	14	15	16
45	93	86	78	71	64	57	51	33	38	31	25	18	12	6		
46	93	86	79	73	66	58	52	45	39	32	26	20	14	8		
47	93	86	79	72	66	59	52	46	40	34	28	22	16	10	5	
48	93	86	79	73	66	60	54	47	41	35	29	23	18	12	7	1
49	93	86	80	73	67	61	54	48	42	36	31	25	19	14	9	3
50	93	87	80	74	67	61	55	49	43	38	32	27	21	16	10	5
51	94	87	81	75	68	63	56	50	45	39	34	28	23	17	12	7
52	94	87	81	75	69	63	57	51	46	40	35	29	24	19	14	9
53	94	87	81	75	69	63	58	52	47	41	36	31	26	20	16	10
54	94	88	82	76	70	64	59	53	48	42	37	32	27	22	17	12
55	94	88	82	76	70	65	59	54	49	43	39	34	29	24	19	15
56	94	88	82	77	71	65	60	55	50	44	40	35	30	25	21	16
57	94	88	83	77	71	66	61	55	50	45	40	36	32	27	22	18
58	94	89	83	78	72	67	61	56	51	46	42	37	33	28	24	19
59	94	89	83	78	72	67	62	57	52	47	43	38	34	29	25	21
60	94	89	84	78	73	68	63	58	53	48	44	39	34	30	26	22
61	94	89	84	78	73	68	63	58	54	49	44	40	35	32	27	23
62	95	89	84	79	74	69	64	59	54	50	45	41	37	32	28	24
63	95	89	84	79	74	69	64	60	55	51	46	42	38	33	29	26
64	95	90	85	79	74	70	65	60	56	51	47	43	38	34	30	27
65	95	90	85	80	75	70	65	61	56	52	48	44	39	35	31	28
66	95	90	90	85	75	71	66	61	57	53	49	45	40	36	32	29
67	95	90	85	80	76	71	66	62	58	53	49	45	41	37	33	30
68	95	90	85	81	76	71	67	63	58	54	50	46	42	38	34	31
69	95	90	86	81	76	72	67	63	59	55	51	47	43	39	35	32
70	95	90	86	81	77	72	68	64	60	55	52	48	44	40	36	33
72	95	91	86	82	77	73	69	65	61	57	53	49	45	42	38	35
74	95	91	86	82	78	74	70	66	62	58	54	50	47	43	40	36
76	95	91	87	82	78	74	70	66	63	59	55	52	48	45	41	38
78	96	91	87	83	79	75	71	67	63	60	56	53	49	46	42	39
80	96	91	87	83	79	75	72	68	64	61	57	54	50	47	44	41
82	96	92	87	84	80	76	72	69	65	61	58	55	51	48	45	42
84	96	92	88	84	81	76	73	69	65	62	58	56	52	49	46	43
86	96	92	88	84	81	77	73	70	66	63	59	57	53	50	47	44
88	96	92	88	85	81	77	74	70	67	64	60	57	54	51	48	46
90	96	92	89	85	81	78	74	71	68	65	61	58	55	52	49	47
92	96	92	89	85	81	78	74	72	68	65	62	59	56	53	51	48
94	96	93	89	85	82	79	75	72	69	66	63	60	57	54	52	49
96	96	93	89	86	82	79	76	73	69	66	63	61	58	55	52	50
98	96	93	89	86	83	79	77	73	70	67	64	61	59	55	53	50
100	96	93	89	86	83	80	77	73	70	68	65	62	59	59	56	54	51

FIG. 2-12. Relative humidity in per cent. If difference between dry bulb and wet bulb is zero, humidity is 100%.

USE

Fan air around wet bulb to obtain lowest temperature and read both ther-mometers. Subtract wet-bulb reading from dry-bulb and calculate humidity from table in FIG. 2-12. Example: D.B. = 70, W.B. = 65. Difference = 5. Follow 70° column from left and 5° column from top, R.H. = 77 per cent. W.B. will always be lower than D.B. If both have same reading, R.H. is 100 per cent.

Compare humidities found this way with those found using the dew-point apparatus.

Using the wet- and dry-bulb thermometers, you can also calculate the "comfort index" or temperature-humidity index (THI) using the following formula: Comfort index = 0.4 (D.B. + W.B.) + 15.

The comfort index is an attempt to combine temperature and humidity into a single index that will be meaningful in terms of personal comfort. The index may be interpreted as follows:

COMFORT INDEX	MEANING
70	People begin to feel discomfort.
75	50% of people are uncomfortable.
79	99% of people are uncomfortable.
80	Discomfort becomes serious.
86	Index used by many offices to close due to heat.

FOREST FIRE DANGER INDEX

An average of five million acres of trees are lost every year due to forest fires large and small. This figure has come down from the twenty-six-million-acre average in 1940. With the trees destroyed, land is open to the ravages of floods and soil erosion, wildlife of all description decreases or vanishes for lack of food and shelter, valuable timber and recreational facilities are lost. Unlike insects and disease which destroy more timber annually, fire is caused by human carelessness and can be prevented. A very few forest fires are caused by lightning and campfires. Most are caused by careless smokers and people burning trash. It would be hard to count all the times one sees lighted cigarettes thrown from car windows to fall where they may. Calculating and reporting the daily *fire danger rating* or *burning index* is an excellent way to make campers aware of the burning index in woods and to encourage good fire safety at all times, not only when camping.

The U. S. Department of Agriculture Forest Service, Division of Fire Control, reports that fire danger is influenced by both constant and variable factors. *Constant factors* for a given area of land would include its slope, drainage, elevation, exposure to prevailing winds, and the density, size, quantity, distribution and arrangement of fuels. The *variable factors* which cause the fire danger to change from day to day include wind velocity, visibility distance (humidity), flammability and stage of curing of green vegetation, and flammability and moisture content of dry fuels on the forest floor.

PROCEDURE

Based upon the above variable factors, we may use the following scale to estimate fire-danger from low to high.

	Low				High
Wind	1	2	3	4	5

	Wet				Dry
Relative humidity	1	2	3	4	5

	Wet				Dry
Ground dampness (dry fuels)	1	2	3	4	5

	Green-Moist				Dry-Browning
Plants	1	2	3	4	5

	(1 day)	(2)	(4)	(6)	(8)
Days since heavy rain	1	2	3	4	5

Add the ratings selected for each factor and divide by five to obtain aver-age fire-danger rating. The rating may be given with the daily weather forecast or shown on a dial scale reading: 1 low; 2, 3 medium; 4, 5 high. Fire-danger rating, in its entirety, is a complex process and this scale is open to revision as seen by local need. You may wish to substitute num-bers 2, 4, 6, 8, 10 for "Days since Heavy Rain" instead of the numbers shown. This is a factor which would depend upon your survey of the con-stant factors such as slope and drainage. Rapidly draining land would require greater emphasis placed upon the rain factor.

DEW-POINT APPARATUS

Relative humidity figures are not given on weather maps. This quantity, although fairly meaningful to the public, is not often used by weathermen in their own work. Instead they use a more meaningful and useful measurement called *dew-point temperature* or just dew point. We know that as air is cooled, it can hold less and less moisture. Imagine a glass tank measuring one cubic foot into which is sealed air at a certain temperature containing a fixed amount of water vapor. The air is now cooled and as the temperature decreases, the water vapor comes continually closer to saturating the air. When the temperature is low enough, the air will not be able to hold the water vapor any longer and drops of water will begin condensing out of the air onto the inside of the tank. If this air were outside and cooled in the same way, the result would be drops of water condensing onto blades of grass to form dew. As the air became still cooler, water would condense onto dust and salt crystals floating in the air thus forming a fog or cloud.

The temperature at which the air becomes saturated with moisture is known as the dew-point temperature. Of course, this is also the temperature at which the humidity becomes 100 per cent. The dew point can be easily determined with simple equipment and, once known, it may be used to calculate relative humidity, the possibility of dew or frost, and even the height at which clouds will form in the atmosphere.

MATERIALS

Shiny tin can from which the paper label has been removed, a thermometer that may be immersed in water (a darkroom thermometer is fine), a stirring rod, some water and possibly ice.

PROCEDURE

Nearly fill the can with water at about room temperature. Place the thermometer in the water and hold it against the side of the can. (You want the temperature of the can.) Now put some ice into the water and stir the mixture as you very carefully observe the outside surface of the can. As the can cools, drops of water will be seen forming on the shiny surface. Read the temperature of the thermometer at the first sign of moisture (condensation) on the can. The temperature at that instant will be the dew point. By cooling the can, you have also cooled a thin layer of air around the can and caused it to reach its saturation point or 100 per cent relative humidity. The dew-point temperature which you have found is the temperature to which the air around you would have to be cooled before fog or clouds would form. On a warm humid day, you may be able to omit the ice and use cool tap water.

USE

Compare the air temperature with the dew point. If they are close to-

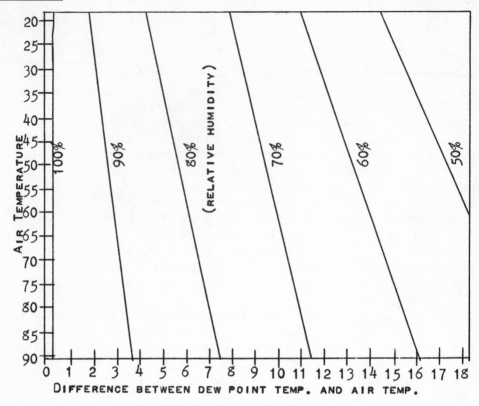

FIG. 2-13.   Chart for finding relative humidity from temperature and dew point, or for finding dew point from temperature and relative humidity

gether, the air is very humid and would only have to be cooled a few degrees to form dew and fog. Under these conditions, you could expect dew and fog to form if the night is cloudless, allowing the earth to lose its daytime heat rapidly. When dew point and air temperature are far apart, you know the air is dry and humidity low. You may calculate the relative humidity from the air temperature and dew point by using the chart in FIG. 2-13. Compare the relative humidity found this way with that found using the wet- and dry-bulb hygrometer.

Cumulus clouds are formed by a parcel of air breaking away from the surface and rising straight up. As such an enclosed parcel (*thermal*) rises through the atmosphere, it cools at a faster rate (4.5 F. per 1,000 feet) than we would if we made a vertical ascent in a balloon (3.3 F. per 1,000 feet). Knowing this rate and the dew point of the air, you may calculate the height at which *cumulus* clouds would begin to form on any given day (the base of the cloud) using this simple formula:

$$H = \frac{T - DP}{4.5} \times 1,000$$

H = height in feet.
T = air temperature F.
DP = dew-point temperature.

48   Meteorology

MINIATURE WATER CYCLE

Miniature water cycle (FIG. 2-14) happens on a large scale in nature as water evaporates from oceans, collects and condenses on dust particles to form clouds. These eventually become overburdened and the moisture falls back to earth·as some form of precipitation: rain, snow, sleet or hail.

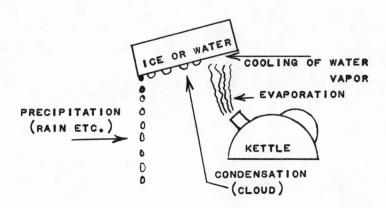

FIG. 2-14.   Miniature water cycle illustrates larger-scale cycle existing in nature.

DEMONSTRATION OF RELATIVE HUMIDITY

MATERIALS

Sponge, glass, water

PROCEDURE

Completely saturate a sponge with water and squeeze all this water into a glass (FIG. 2-15A). The sponge represents the atmosphere and the water the total amount of water it can hold. Draw up half the water into the sponge. Its relative humidity is now 50 per cent (FIG. 2-15B). Draw up three-fourths of the water. What is the relative humidity now? If all the water is drawn into the sponge, drops will begin falling from it. This is precipitation. You may illustrate that warmer air will hold more moisture by using a larger sponge representing air at a higher temperature.

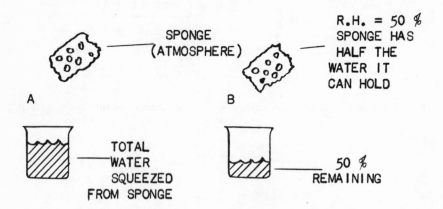

FIG. 2-15. A demonstration of relative humidity using a sponge to represent the atmosphere

COBALT CHLORIDE WEATHER INDICATOR

Cobalt chloride is a crystalline compound which has a blue color when it is dry and a red color when it is moist. This property makes it possible to use cobalt chloride as a humidity indicator and often as a weather forecaster. Two or three days before you plan to use this project, make the following preparations. Make a solution of cobalt chloride in warm water, soak some paper in the solution. Remove the paper and allow to dry thoroughly. Do the rest of this project on a day when this paper is blue in color.

PROCEDURE

Give a piece of the cobalt chloride paper to each camper. Have him breathe on it. What happens to the color? Why? Have him moisten it with his finger. What happens to the color? What would happen to this paper on a humid day? On a dry day? Is there any way that this paper may be used as a weather forecasting device? These are the questions that the campers should find answers to. As the topic is discussed, somebody will probably realize that as the moisture in the air increases, the chances of rain increase.

At the conclusion of the discussion, each person may make his own cobalt chloride forecaster. You may provide mimeographed pictures of flowers or local camp scenes which are colored with crayons except for some special section which is painted with cobalt chloride solution. (See FIG. 2-16.) More creative, or older campers, may make their own drawing to be colored and painted with the solution. Campers should observe the colors of these pictures in mid-day when it is warm. The cool temperatures of morning or evening may cause a temporarily high humidity which will turn the color red.

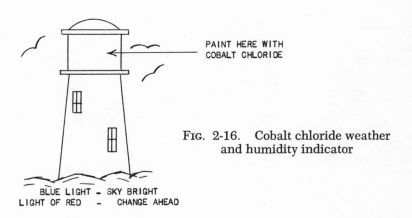

PAINT HERE WITH
COBALT CHLORIDE

FIG. 2-16.   Cobalt chloride weather and humidity indicator

BLUE LIGHT - SKY BRIGHT
LIGHT OF RED   -   CHANGE AHEAD

COTTON CLOUD PICTURES

MATERIALS

Non-sterile cotton, glue, crayons, blue paper.

PROCEDURE

This project may be worked in with your discussions of cloud formation, warm fronts and cold fronts. After one of these topics has been discussed, you can supply needed materials and set the campers to work making cotton models of the clouds talked about. When clouds are studied in this way, they seem more real and more is learned about them because a third sense, that of touch, is added to the usual sight and sound used in the learning process.

Warm and cold fronts are described and illustrated in the first part of the chapter. (See FIGS. 2-2 and 2-3.) As warm air moves in, it slides up forming a wedge of stratus-type clouds with the highest at the front being cirrus and cirrostratus. Cold air moving in stays close to the ground and plows the warm air up over it, forming the towering, billowing cumulonimbus clouds and short, heavy downpours. If these are done on blue paper, use crayons to make lines and labels.

Clouds, as such, are classified by height and form (shape). The three basic forms are cirrus, stratus and cumulus. *Alto* added to a name means higher, *strato* means sheet, *nimbo* means rain, *fracto* means broken or torn. Thus we have altocumulus, fractonimbus, nimbostratus, etc. The CLOUD CHART lists the common clouds by height and form. This list and the government cloud chart will prove very helpful in discussing clouds and making the cotton cloud reproductions.

For added interest, you may combine this project with the cobalt chloride weather indicator and pre-dip the cotton in cobalt chloride solution so it will be dry and may be glued when the campers use it.

CLOUD CHART

HEIGHT	FORM	SIGN	DESCRIPTION
High— above 20,000 ft.	Cirrus*	Ci	Detached, delicate white clouds (ice)
	Cirrostratus	Cs	Thin whitish veil or sheet, halos (ice)
	Cirrocumulus	Cc	Rippled cloud bands, "mackerel sky"
Middle— 7,000 to 20,000 ft.	Altostratus	As	Uniform broad bands, grayish, weak sun visible, no shadow on ground (rain)
	Altocumulus	Ac	Globular units, woolpack, gray shadows underneath, bands
Low— Below 7,000 (average 2,000 ft.)	Stratus*	St	Uniform gray cloud sheet over entire sky. Sun casts little or no shadow.
	Stratocumulus	Sc	Large heavy rolls in long, gray parallel bands
	Nimbostratus	Ns	Low dark-gray cloud sheets from which rain is falling
Vertically towering clouds (bases about 2,000 ft.)	Cumulus*	Cu	Flat base, individual white cloud masses, fluffy domes (fair weather)
	Cumulonimbus	Cb	Towering cumulus clouds two to five miles thick, thunderhead (thunderstorms with rain, hail)

* This cloud is one of the three basic cloud forms.

Meteorology   53

RAIN GAUGE

Constructing a rain gauge for the camp weather bureau is a simple matter. A rain gauge is designed with a larger area at the top of the funnel than the area of the measuring tube so the water height will be exaggerated and more precise measurements be possible. In the instrument shown in FIG. 2-17, for example, a one inch of rainfall will produce four inches of water in the tube. One-fourth inch of water in the tube will be produced by a rainfall of only .06 inch. Such a small amount of rain would be impossible to measure without the exaggeration produced by the large collecting funnel.

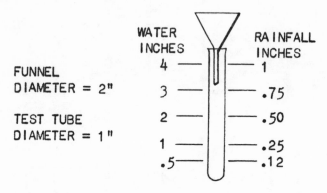

FUNNEL
DIAMETER = 2"

TEST TUBE
DIAMETER = 1"

WATER INCHES | RAINFALL INCHES
4 — 1
3 — .75
2 — .50
1 — .25
.5 — .12

FIG. 2-17.   One form of homemade rain gauge

MATERIALS

Funnel, test tube or olive jar, ruler

PROCEDURE

Any combination of tube and funnel may be used. The one shown uses a two-inch-diameter funnel and a one-inch-by-six-inch test tube (25 by 150 mm.). Test tubes may usually be purchased at a local drug store. The following formula should be used to calculate the height of water produced in the tube by one inch of rain.

$$\frac{\text{Diameter of funnel}^2}{\text{Diameter of tube}^2} = \text{Height of one inch of rain.}$$

This formula is based upon the difference between the collecting areas of the funnel and tube. The rainfall height is exaggerated just as many times as the funnel area is greater than the tube area. This may be calculated using the formula for the area of a circle: $A = 3.14R^2$.

Using the first formula, the side of the tube should be marked in inches and tenths of inches of rainfall. Whereas a six-inch tube will only contain a one-and-one-half-inch rainfall, you may find it a good idea to put the funnel on a milk bottle for rain collection and then pour this water into the test tube for measuring the actual depth. A good summer thunderstorm may deposit much more than one and one-half inches of rain.

USE

Place the rain gauge on a post where the rainfall will not be affected by strong winds and where falling water from buildings and trees will not enter it.

HAIL MEASURING STICK

Summer thunderstorms are often accompanied by hail which always proves of tremendous interest to those on hand to experience it. The cumulonimbus clouds (thunderheads) in which hail forms have many strong vertical air currents in them and may be as high as five miles from the bottom to the top of the cloud. Rain drops falling through these clouds are often caught in an updraft and shot up to the top of the cloud where the temperature may be as low as —60° F. At such temperatures, the rain drop is naturally frozen, flies out of the updraft and begins falling as a solid drop of ice. Descending through the cloud, the ice drop is coated with more moisture, caught again in the updraft and this second layer is frozen into ice. This process is repeated continuously, adding frozen layers to the hailstone each time, until the updraft weakens or the hailstone becomes too heavy to be carried aloft and is dropped from the cloud. A person cutting through the center of a hailstone may easily see the layers of ice that have been built up.

When hail starts beating down and dancing on the ground, most people are curious to find out how large the stones are. Holding a hailstone in your hand and measuring it with a ruler is difficult as the heat from your hand is constantly decreasing its size. Part of a science session may be devoted to discussing hail and each camper might make a stick (FIG. 2-18) for measuring hailstones quickly.

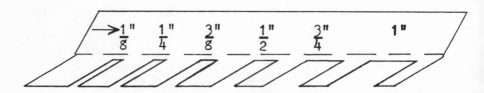

FIG. 2-18.　Hail measuring stick

MATERIALS

Oaktag, varnish, ruler, scissors

PROCEDURE

Fold oaktag on dotted line. A coat of clear dope or varnish will help protect it from moisture. In use, the hailstone is caught or placed on the small end and rolled down until it falls through a hole which indicates its size. Using a stick in this way minimizes handling and consequent melting of the hailstones.

CABIN WEATHER RECORDS

As the campers build and collect their own individual weather instruments, each cabin may want to keep its own weather records and forecasts. They may wish to devise their own record forms and might even like to keep their records in the form of graphs of temperature, rainfall, pressure, etc. Encouraging such activity will be in keeping with the goal of making everybody weather-conscious and a few weather-wise.

READING AND USING THE DAILY WEATHER MAP

Details on using the Daily Weather Map, available by mail from the Superintendent of Documents (See PAMPHLETS AND CHARTS) will be found in Fisher and other reference books listed. The following is an introduction to the five different maps included on each day's sheet and their use in understanding and forecasting your local weather. Remember that the government map may be supplemented with the less detailed but more timely newspaper weather maps which are also issued by the Weather Bureau.

There are five maps included on the weather-map sheet. The most use is made of the large map showing the surface weather at 1:00 A.M., EST, for the date of the sheet. Key weather stations are indicated by a circle with lines, symbols and numbers clustered around it. Each number has its own position around the circle and these positions are labeled in an explanatory illustration on the front of the map. A complete explanation of all symbols is printed on the back of every Sunday map. The readings of most interest are: temperature, dew point, cloud cover, wind speed, wind direction and barometric tendency. Campers should know how to find and read these symbols on the map. *Isobars* (lines of equal pressure) show the location of highs and lows. Pressure is given in *millibars* (thousandths of a bar, a unit of force), 33.86 millibars being equal to one inch of mercury pressure. There is a complete table for converting millibars to inches on the Sunday map.

One small map shows the weather at 1:00 P.M. yesterday: twelve hours previous to the large map. By comparing and measuring on these two maps, you can see how far, how fast and in what direction the weather has been moving. You can also tell if fronts have been forming or dissolving.

Another map is included which is of help in preparing your forecast: the 500-millibar map which shows wind direction and speed at upper levels (about 19,000 feet) as determined by balloon observations. The upper winds help to drive the weather systems over the country from west to east. Knowing their direction and speed will help you know what weather is coming and when to expect it.

The two remaining maps on the weather sheet show maximum-minimum temperatures, and areas and amounts of precipitation during the past twenty-four hours. These maps are of general interest. They offer an opportunity to compare your weather with that in other parts of the country and you may use them to compare the readings on your instruments with the readings of the Weather Bureau station located closest to you.

The weather map also includes a forecast for the Washington, D. C., area. Weather-minded campers will enjoy covering this up without reading it and making their own forecast for Washington, using the weather map. Then they can compare their forecast with the one printed on the map.

You may encourage this activity by posting the map with a flap of paper which may be lifted by the camper to reveal the Washington forecast. The paper might be labeled: "What is your forecast for Washington, D. C.? Lift paper and compare yours with Weather Bureau's."

WEATHER FORECAST WHEEL

Here is a weather device that can be made and used without difficulty by even the youngest camper. If you have the material mimeographed as shown on a single piece of paper, this project may be used as a stand-by if you discover at the last minute that some other plans cannot be carried out.

MATERIALS

Mimeo sheets (FIG. 2-19), brass fasteners, scissors, glue, oaktag.

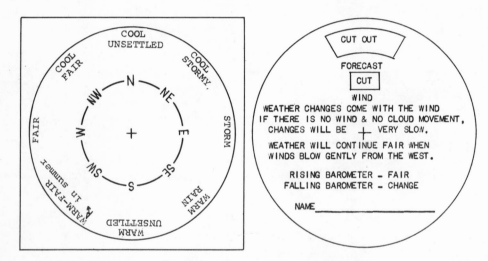

NOTE: ⚡ IS THE WEATHER MAP SYMBOL FOR THUNDERSTORMS.

FIG. 2-19. Weather forecast wheel. Wheel is attached to square base with brass fastener.

PROCEDURE

On the bottom plate are the wind directions and beside each is the weather which it usually brings. You may wish to change some of these to better suit your location. The top disk is held in place with a brass paper fastener. Both sheets may be pasted onto oaktag to make a sturdier instrument.

USE

The user first determines the wind direction. This is the direction *from* which the wind is blowing. He turns the wheel until that direction comes into view and then reads the probable weather from the window above. The forecasting hints printed on the disk may also be discussed while the guide is being made.

WEATHER FORECAST COMPUTER

A refined version of the weather wheel, this forecast computer is more accurate, more detailed and a better teaching aid. Like the weather wheel, the computer works on the theory that a given wind direction will bring a certain type of weather. The computer is unique in that it is programmed by you for the weather of your locality.

MATERIALS

Program Information Sheet (FIG. 2-20), mimeo computer (FIG. 2-21), scissors, glue, oaktag

		WIND	DIRECTION						
	CONDITIONS	W	NW	N	NE	E	SE	S	SW
TEMP.	WARM								
	COOL								
HUMIDITY	MOIST								
	DRY								
WEATHER	FAIR								
	UNSETTLED								
	RAIN								
△⟋	THUNDERSTORM								

FIG. 2-20.   Program information sheet for forecast computer

PROCEDURE

PHASE 1: Have each camper keep daily weather records on the FORECAST COMPUTER PROGRAM INFORMATION SHEET. (See FIG. 2-20.) At the same time each day, determine the wind direction and locate that direction on the top of the program sheet. Place a check mark in the wind-direction column for each of the four weather properties listed along the side. For

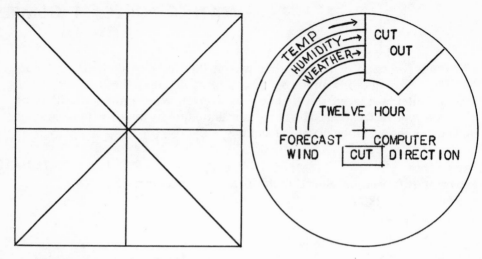

FIG. 2-21.   Forecast computer. Cut out, paste on oaktag and put brass fastener through center.

example, with a northwest wind, you may check cool, dry and fair. Continue this for at least two weeks, then go on to PHASE 2.

PHASE 2: Cut out the computer disk and base and paste them onto pieces of oaktag for support. Mount the disk on the base and, turning it an eighth of a turn each time, write the eight wind directions in the small square window. Now the computer is ready to be programmed. Do this in pencil so errors in the program can be changed as they are discovered through use. In this way you will be able to teach the computer. Turn the disk until a wind direction is visible in the window and do the following for each of the eight directions. Let us say that you have NW in the window. Look in the NW column of the program sheet and count the number of checks under warm and cool. Probably there are more under cool. You may temporarily assume, then, that a NW wind will bring cool temperatures. Write the word cool through the cutout in the disk beside the temperature arrow. Count checks in the same way for humidity, weather and thunderstorms. Do the same for the other seven directions.

In a two-week period, campers may not have enough time to record data for all wind directions. It will be helpful, therefore, if you have made a computer beforehand so that you can help out in places where the data is scarce. Since they are programming the computer in pencil, it can always be changed if errors are found. General weather for each direction is found on the weather wheel of the previous project. Much of the value of this project is in collecting data and organizing it into a meaningful pattern.

PHOTOGRAPHING LIGHTNING

It is an easy project to produce spectacular photographs of chain light-ning. First, observe these safety precautions. Take the photographs only through a *closed* window of clean glass. Take the photographs only while the storm is still at a distance and approaching you. Do not attempt these photographs when the storm is overhead. When the storm is overhead, lightning will come from all directions and you will waste film trying to point the camera at it.

MATERIALS

Tripod, camera with bulb or time setting

PROCEDURE

Lightning photographs must be made at night with the camera mounted in the window on a firm stand or tripod with the room in darkness. There should be no bright outdoor lights between the camera and the storm. Focus the lens on infinity and set the diaphragm at about F 11. As the storm approaches in the distance, notice where the majority of lightning flashes are located and point your camera in that direction. Set the shut-ter on time or bulb and leave it open until a lightning flash has appeared within the area covered by the camera.

You may close the shutter and turn the film after each flash, or you may get a number of flashes on the same picture. Usually chain lightning is the best type to get on film. If the storm is not producing this type, wait for another time. The negatives are developed in the standard manner and should produce very good enlargements.

LIGHTNING DISTANCE CALCULATOR

Lightning and the resulting thunder occur almost at the same instant. We hear the thunder after the lightning because light travels much faster (186,000 miles a second) than sound (1,100 feet per second). If you count the seconds between a flash of lightning and the thunder, you will find how long it took the thunder sound to reach you. Since sound travels about one mile in five seconds, dividing the number of seconds counted by five will tell you in miles how far away the lightning was. Notice that this gives you the distance of a single lightning flash, not necessarily the entire storm, which may be widely scattered.

MATERIALS

Oaktag, scissors, brass fasteners

PROCEDURE

The distance of lightning flashes may be instantly determined with the LIGHTNING DISTANCE CALCULATOR shown in FIG. 2-22. The calculator may be made from oaktag. It is provided with three pointers so a record may be kept of three successive lightning flashes, thus providing an average general distance and an approximate distance for the entire storm. Seconds may be counted by saying "one hippopotamus, two hippopotamus," etc. Remember, if you see lightning but hear no thunder, the storm is still very distant from you.

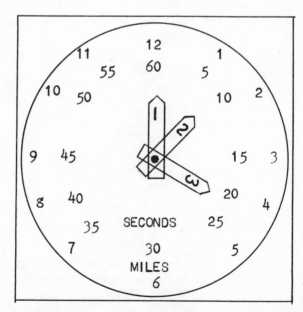

FIG. 2-22. Lightning distance calculator. Set one pointer for each bolt. Average of all three gives distance of storm.

LIGHTNING SAFETY

Although lightning is not completely understood, general information concerning its nature and causes will be found in the reference book cited at the beginning of this chapter. Lightning is static electricity and there are many simple demonstrations showing properties of this type of electricity, starting with charging a comb by running it through the hair and then using it to pick up pieces of paper, and to deflect a thin stream of water running from a faucet. Such demonstrations must be done on days which are not humid to prevent atmospheric moisture from drawing the charge away from the comb.

One science session should be devoted to a discussion of the nature of lightning and lightning safety. Children should learn not to be afraid of lightning; but they should also learn to respect it as they should respect all electricity. About 400 people are killed and 1,000 injured by lightning each year. These figures are not great; but too many of them are the result of carelessness. Most of these people were hit by lightning on beaches or in open fields and golf courses. Of all places, these are the places not to be during a thunderstorm. To give only one example, we have the story of people caught on the beach in a thunderstorm. To get out of the rain, they went under a sunroof on the beach which had a tall lamppost behind it. The lamppost was hit by lightning, which jumped to the roof. Some of the occupants were killed, others were injured. They would have been much safer lying on the beach. Of course, they would have got wet; but that is the reason most people go to the beach.

During a discussion of things to do and not to do during a thunderstorm, the following points should be brought out:

1. The most dangerous places to be are at the beach, in a boat, in an open field and on a golf course. If you are in these places, you should know the signs of an approaching thunderstorm and leave when you see them. In a boat, you are in danger of squall winds as well as lightning. Get to shore! If the storm takes you by surprise in a field or on a beach, lie down flat. Do not walk or seek shelter under trees.

2. Stay away from electrical appliances, especially television sets with outside antennas.

3. Stay away from open windows and doors, fireplaces and chimneys.

4. In a field, stay away from trees. In a forest, stay away from tall trees and seek shelter in a semi-clearing under bushes and brush.

5. Stay away from wire fences. Lightning will follow them for great distances.

6. Stay off hilltops and mountaintops. Move down along the side if a storm approaches.

7. There have been cases of people being bothered by lightning while using the telephone and tub. Avoid these during a storm.

8. You are safest in an automobile, in steel and cement buildings, and in wooden buildings with properly installed lightning rods.

9. If you have antennas or weather instruments on top of a building, be sure they are grounded by heavy cables to water pipes and stakes driven into the earth outside the building. Such protection is often as effective as a lightning-rod system for the building.

10. Like all electrical shock, lightning paralyzes the nervous system, including the nerves controlling breathing. Proper first aid includes artificial respiration and treatment for physical and emotional shock.

Finally, a discussion of lightning may lead to the topic of *ball lightning*. This is a highly controversial form of lightning which is said to take the form of a ball and roll around through windows, rooms, along wire fences, etc. Until recently most scientists classed ball lightning as an optical illusion. But as more evidence is gathered, this idea is losing strength. A recent summary of observation reports[1] reveals ball lightning as a luminous sphere about a foot across and as bright as a fluorescent lamp. It appears for about a minute following an ordinary lightning stroke. Present thoughts consider ball lightning to be a sphere of ionized air or *plasma*. Plasma is an ionized gas containing ions and free electrons. Cool plasma is in fluorescent and neon tubes; hot plasma is present in an electric arc and the solar atmosphere. The plasma of ball lightning is said to have sufficient heat to scorch wood.

---

[1] Harold Lewis, "Ball Lightning." *Scientific American*, March 1963, Vol. 208, No. 3, pp. 106-116.

RESOURCE MATERIALS FOR METEOROLOGY

Magazine

Weatherwise. Bimonthly, $5.00 per year. American Meteorological Society, 45 Beacon St., Boston, Mass.   02108.

Pamphlets and Charts

The following may be purchased from the Superintendent of Documents, U.S. Government Printing Office, Washington, D. C.   20025

Weather Forecasting. 25¢. Weather Bureau Bulletin.

Manual of Cloud Forms. 30¢.

Cloud Code Chart. 10¢.

Daily Weather Map. Subscription: $2.40 for three months; $9.60 per year.

Teacher's Weather Kit. Free upon request to American Meteorological Society, 45 Beacon St., Boston, Mass.   02108.

Manual of Lecture Demonstrations, Laboratory Experiments and Observational Equipment for Teaching Elementary Meteorology in Schools and Colleges, by Hans Neuberger and George Nicholas. A 183-page publication written under grant from N.S.F. and available free to teachers. Write Dr. Hans Neuberger, College of Mineral Industries, Department of Meteorology, Pennsylvania State University, University Park, Penna.

Films

The Unchained Goddess. This film is free, user paying only mail costs. Order through local Bell Telephone business office.

Hurricane Hunters. Free film, user paying mail costs. It may be ordered through the commandant of the naval district nearest you.

Weather Men of the Sea. This film is free, user paying return postage. It may be ordered from the U.S. Coast Guard, Commandant, Washington, D. C. 20025 or your local Coast Guard district.

Supplies

Taylor Instrument Co., Rochester, N. Y.   14601

F. W. Dwyer Manufacturing Co., Box 373, Michigan City, Ind.

Radio Shack Corp., 730 Commonwealth Ave., Boston, Mass.   02117

Lafayette Radio Corp., 111 Jericho Turnpike, Syosset, L. I., N. Y.

Wilfred O. White & Sons, Inc., 180 Anderson St., Portland, Maine.

Chapter

3: Photography

SUGGESTED REFERENCE   Zim and Burnett, *Photography*. New York: Golden Press, 1960.

PHOTOGRAPHY is perhaps the most diverse subject covered in these pages. It is both art and science. It is a tool of science and industry. It is one of the most popular hobbies in the country and it may easily become a source of income on a part-time or full-time basis.

At camp, photography may serve the dual purpose of teaching the subject to campers and being a source of photographs for camp booklets and publications. Older campers who become interested in this subject and have equipment at home should have little difficulty selling pictures to their school paper and local newspaper. They may have to donate a few pictures at first.

Use of cameras should be encouraged by allowing time for picture-taking around the camp and out on hikes and trips. Specific photographic trips for the purpose of doing a picture story in an area of historic, scenic, industrial, natural, or scientific interest are a good idea. Once beginners have been taught to use the darkroom, most darkroom work might best be done during free activity periods such as early evening.

A word about the suggested reference for this chapter. This is an excellent little book which covers every phase of the photographic process. Booklets giving details on each of these phases will be found in the Kodak Data Book Series, the Universal Photo Book Series and the Modern Camera Guide Series by Chilton Company. Most photographic stores have selections of these books or can order them for you. Further information is found at the end of the chapter.

INFORMATION OF IMPORTANCE

Most of the best opportunities for picture-taking are not specifically arranged at preset times. A basic task of the science counselor is to encourage campers to be on the alert for picture-taking opportunities at all times.

They must, of course, be notified in advance of the camp season of the photography program and encouraged to bring their cameras and a supply of film. A good way to encourage an awareness of picture-taking opportunities and a constant reminder to be ready for pictures is the posting of "Pictures of the Week" in a conspicuous camp spot, say the dining room. Such a display would exhibit the better pictures that have been processed in the darkroom during the week. They may be selected by a committee of campers.

The camp darkroom may be as simple or elaborate as desired. At the simple extreme would be a room with electricity which is dark at night. Water can be carried to such a room in jugs. However, most modern camps will probably be able to provide the more necessary facilities: a permanently dark room, no windows (or windows painted black), electricity, running water and sink, shelves and benches. Some type of ventilation, as a lightproof blower or hole in the wall inside a light trap box, should also be provided.

Following is a list of materials and equipment which may be used to outfit the darkroom. An asterisk indicates the minimum essentials to develop film and make contact prints. The chemicals and paper listed happen to be Eastman Kodak but other brands are available for the same purposes.

DARKROOM SUPPLIES

Chemicals
   *Dektol developer (for film and paper)
   D-76 or Microdol-X (for film in tank)
   *Acid fixer
   Tri-Chem Pack (Makes 8 oz. developer, stop and fixer.)
   *Indicator stop bath
   Photo-Flo (to dry films without water spots)
   Hypo clearing agent

Paper
   *Velox or Azo contact paper 2½" × 3½"
   Medalist or Kodabromide enlarging paper, F 3 SW
      (sizes 4" × 5", 5" × 7", 8" × 10", etc.)

Beginning Equipment
   *Four hard-rubber trays (5" × 7")
   *Printing Frame or
   Contact Printer
   Safelight (red or yellow)
   Ferrotype plate (to dry glossy prints)
   Thermometer
   Funnel

Other Equipment
     Enlarger (Federal 290, Dejur, Omega, etc.)
     Developing tank(s) for film
     Enlarging easel
     Four larger trays (8" × 10")
     Rubber print roller
     Electric print dryer
     Interval timer (G.E., Kodak)
     Exposure timer (FR, Time-O-Lite)
     Measuring graduate or cup
     Kodak stirring paddles
     Kodak projection print scale
     Kodak tray siphon (for washing)

Books
     The following inexpensive booklets should be in the darkroom for ready reference. They are available at photo stores.
     Processing and Formulas, Kodak data book
     Enlarging with Kodak Materials and Equipment, Kodak data book
     Developing, Printing and Enlarging with Kodak Materials, Kodak

From this point, the subject of photography goes off in all directions depending on individual interests. Entire separate courses are offered on the photographing of each possible subject and in the many applications of photography to other fields in and out of science. We will not attempt coverage of these subjects here. The three basic technical phases of photography are covered in the projects as specimen lessons in the construction and use of the camera, developing prints, and developing film. These are doubtless the phases of the subject which will be stressed and repeatedly practiced at camp.

There is one phase of photography which is only lightly touched on in the popular reference books and that is the chemistry of the photographic process. One reason for this is that the scientific experts who have devoted their lives to this study have yet to completely unravel its mysterious operation. They have come up with a considerable amount of interesting material which we include here for background and possible discussion at camp.

In simple terms, the photographic process consists of the following steps. The light from an illuminated scene is focused by a lens onto a piece of film in a camera, thus exposing various parts of the film to light. The film is placed in an alkali developer and the exposed areas turn black. When the film is developed to just the right point, it is placed in an acetic acid stop bath which neutralizes the developer and immediately stops any further developing action. Next the film is placed in acid fixer or hypo where is it further neutralized. Unexposed grains on the film are removed to clear those areas and the film emulsion is hardened. Finally the film is washed in water to remove all chemicals, and the wet negatives are hung up to dry, after which they will be used in a similar process to make the positive paper prints.

The above information is sufficient for a working knowledge of pho-

tography but the more advanced photographer begins to ask more fundamental questions such as: Why do only those parts of the film that are
struck by light turn black in the developer? What chemicals go into the
prepared photographic powders bought at the store? What is the purpose
of each of these chemicals?

The first question, why the film turns black, is the most fundamental in
all photography. Although the fact that it does is the basis for a multi-
million-dollar complex of industries, the reason is not known. There are
theoretical answers to this question and one of the most widely accepted
theories follows.

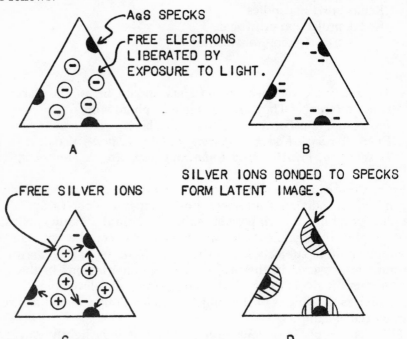

FIG. 3-1. Formation of photographic latent image (Courtesy of *Journal of
the Optical Society of America*)

The film consists of an acetate plastic base which is coated with an emulsion of silver bromide (AgBr) or silver chloride crystals suspended in gelatin. Exposure to light alters these crystals to form the mysterious invisible
latent image. It is thought that when AgBr is mixed with gelatin some of
the silver atoms combine with sulfur from the gelatin to form specks of
silver sulfide on the surface of each silver bromide crystal (FIG. 3-1A).
When the crystal is bombarded by packets of light waves (light quanta
called *photons*) electrons are released from the crystal and accumulate at
the AgS specks giving them a negative charge (FIG. 3-1B). Lacking electrons, some positively charged silver atoms also move to the specks where
they take on the free electrons thus becoming neutralized to silver atoms
and also being bound to the speck (FIG. 3-1C and D). This is the process
that occurs when the film is exposed to light and it is this rearrangement
of a few silver atoms onto the silver sulfide specks which forms the latent
image.

When placed in developer, only those crystals with some silver around their specks continue to be changed to metallic silver. The metallic clump acts as a nucleus for the development of the entire crystal. It appears that the AgBr crystal must have a minimum critical quantity of metallic silver created during exposure in order to reduce the entire crystal to metallic silver during development. If the black places on a negative or print are grains of silver, why aren't they shiny? Because of their very tiny size. If a piece of clear glass is pulverized, the resulting powder is white, not clear. In the same way we here get black silver.

No theory is needed to tell what chemicals are included in the various photographic preparations. (For details on this subject see "Processing and Formulas," an Eastman Kodak data book.) Three solutions are used: developer, stop bath and acid fixer. The *developer* consists of four agents: 1. developing agent which may be Metol (mono-methyl-para-aminophenol), hydroquinone or pyro (no longer in general use); 2. accelerator such as NaOH to activate the developer; 3. preservative (sodium sulfite) to preserve the developer and help prevent oxidation and discoloring; 4. restrainer (potassium bromide) to prevent developer from affecting the unexposed silver bromide crystals. The *stop bath* consists of acetic acid to neutralize the developer, stop development and keep excess developer from contaminating the acid fixer. The *fixer* (hypo) consists mainly of sodium thiosulfate which dissolves from the film or paper all unexposed silver salts, but does not affect the metallic silver image. Potassium alum is included to harden the gelatin emulsion. More acetic acid is included and sodium sulfite is added as in the developer to help preserve the solution and prevent oxidation. After processing, films and paper must be thoroughly washed to prevent any further chemical action which may result in fading or staining.

For practical application of photography to other fields of science, see the following projects:

Chapter 2: Photographing Lightning
Chapter 4: Photographic Moon Track
Photographing Artificial Satellites
Star Track Photographs
Telescopic Photography
Chapter 5: Field Geology
Chapter 6: Making Leaf Prints
Making Photomicrographs
Chapter 7: Field Trips to Observe and Photograph Animals

Table-top photography is a popular photo project which is not included here because the needed props are generally not available at camp. It involves creating little scenes with models and similar materials and then using them as subjects for the production of realistic photos. A model railroad would provide such a ready-made scene. Model dinosaurs set in some club mosses make another effective subject. Photos are made using lights and close-up lenses. The Revell pamphlet listed at the end of the chapter offers some ideas on this subject.

MOTION PICTURES ON THREE-BY-FIVE CARDS

A motion picture is a series of still pictures of figures with slightly chang
ing positions which are shown in rapid succession. Due to persistance o
vision any image we see is retained on the retina for about one-sixteentl
of a second. As long as the pictures of a movie are shown at a rate of one
or more every sixteenth of a second, the image is carried over from one
picture to the next. We do not notice the changeover and it appears as
one continuous moving picture. Sound films are shown at a rate of twenty
four frames per second and silent films at sixteen frames per second. Slow
a projector down below 16 f. p. s. and the picture changes will be noticec
as a flicker. A short "movie" illustrating these facts may be easily made
using three-by-five-inch file cards.

MATERIALS

Three-by-five-inch unlined file cards (about twelve per camper), pencil
or pens, staple machine

PROCEDURE

The procedure is very similar to that used by producers of cartoon films to
animate pictures. Decide on a simple subject: walking stick figure, cannor
shooting cannon ball, flying arrow, auto crash. We'll take the cannon bal
for example. On first card draw cannon to one side. Place card agains
window pane with another card over it so the first picture can be seen by
sunlight. Trace the cannon and add edge of ball leaving barrel. Place
third card over second on window, trace cannon but have ball come ou
further. Continue procedure until ball is all the way to opposite side o
last card. Put cards in order with first card on bottom, fasten with two
staples along one edge, place on table and flip cards so that pictures are
seen in rapid succession. You will see a moving picture of the cannon ball
Other productions may be more advanced with more than one object mov
ing at a time.

USE

This project and associated discussion should clarify the operation o
movies and how Donald Duck is made to go through his antics.

PHOTOGRAMS

This project is an excellent introduction to darkroom photography and first experience with the darkroom materials and equipment.

MATERIALS

Four trays, developer, stop bath, acid fixer, water, photographic paper (enlarging or contact), lamp or enlarger light, shadow materials as suggested below.

PROCEDURE

Under a red safelight in the darkroom, place a piece of photographic paper with emulsion (shiny) side up on table with a light bulb or enlarger lamp available directly overhead. Arrange various objects on the paper such as scissors, thread, sand, coins, pins, nails, jewelry, pencils, paper cutouts, paper clips and elastics. (A good first photogram uses only the maker's hands.) After materials are arranged as desired, turn on overhead light for about fifteen seconds to expose paper. Remove objects and develop in usual manner. Results will be a black paper with white figures where materials were placed.

Note: You can make photograms without a darkroom or developing equipment. Arrange materials on enlarging paper as above and place in bright sunlight for ten to twenty minutes. The exposed paper will gradually turn red or purple giving a red and white picture instead of black and white.

USE

Use this project as an introduction to the basic developing procedure and basic darkroom procedure (lights off, protecting paper, keeping stop bath and hypo out of developer, etc.). The next step is to do the same thing, placing negatives over the paper instead of objects. Prints produced by exposing paper while in contact with the negative are called *contact prints*.

REFLEX COPIES

   This is an easy way to copy any printed material without a camera even though both sides of the page are used. If only one side of the page has writing, it is a simple matter to place it over photographic paper, shine a light through it and develop a paper negative. However, with printing on both sides of the page this method would be far from satisfactory so we use the reflex method described below.

MATERIALS

   Four trays, developer (Dektol diluted one-to-one instead of the usual two parts water), stop bath, acid fixer, water, photographic paper (enlarging or contact. We prefer contact for this.), lamp or enlarger light, sheet of glass with tape around edges, copy material (black and white printing or drawing).

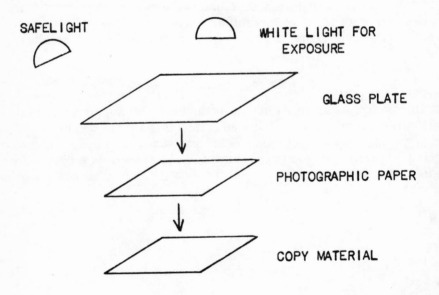

FIG. 3-2.   Arrangement of materials to make reflex copy from printed page

Under a red safelight in the darkroom, place a piece of photographic paper with emulsion (shiny) side down on the material to be copied. (See FIG. 3-2.) Press glass down on top of paper to hold it in close contact with copy material and expose to overhead light. Try a twenty-second exposure to start. Turn off light and develop paper in usual manner. Result will be a paper negative which should be dried.

A positive print may be made by using the dry paper negative as you would a normal negative to make a contact print. If a print box is not available, simply place photographic paper on table with emulsion side up, place negative on top with glass plate over both, and expose to light, developing positive print in normal manner.

USE

This is another good introduction to darkroom technique and an opportunity to learn the difference between positives and negatives. Campers will enjoy making copies of cartoon characters, I. D. cards, handwriting.

MOVING ATOMS TO FORM A PHOTOGRAPHIC IMAGE

The text accompanying FIG. 3-1 explains how a latent image is formed on film by light. It is possible to explore this process with some simple experiments in which the image formation is initiated by electrons rather than by light.

MATERIALS

Film or photographic paper, Dektol developer, source of direct-current electricity from three to twenty volts (batteries or transformer and rectifier).

PROCEDURE

The experiments may be done in a light or dark room. Try both and compare results. The idea is to soak the film or paper so it will conduct electricity, then pass an electric current along the paper. The flow of electrons will disturb the silver bromide crystals in a manner similar to that caused by the packets of light energy called photons.

1. Using film: In lighted room, agitate film in Dektol (mixed one ounce of Dektol to one quart of water) for fifteen seconds. Positive and negative electrodes are placed on wet film surface. See FIG. 3-3.

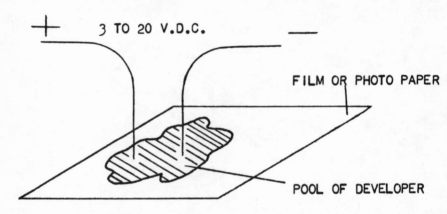

3 TO 20 V.D.C.

FILM OR PHOTO PAPER

POOL OF DEVELOPER

FIG. 3-3.   Electrodes placed on film or paper to form an image electrically

2. Using contact paper: Agitate paper in Dektol (mixed one part Dektol to two parts water) for ten seconds. Place positive and negative electrodes on wet paper surface.

3. Using enlarging paper: Agitate paper in Dektol (mixed same as for film) for one minute. Place positive and negative electrodes on wet paper surface.

Some activity will be obtained using batteries; but the higher current available with transformer and rectifier is more effective. If transformer is used, exercise caution. Do not touch wet table or floor or come in contact with water pipes.

In each of the above there will be a blackening (metallic silver) around the negative pole. The experiment will be most effective when done in a lighted room. Some of the blackening is due to the movement of positive silver ions toward the negative pole by electrolysis. When this blackening starts, remove the electrode. The black spot will continue to grow. This continued development of black metallic silver is evidence that the bombardment of electrons has disturbed the silver bromide molecules similar to the disturbance caused by photons to form the latent image.

Being in a lighted room, the entire paper will eventually go black, but the blackening (formation of free metallic silver atoms) will be fastest where started by the negative electrode.

USE

This simple demonstration shows the presence of metallic silver in photographic emulsions by the electrolysis of silver atoms to the negative pole. Continued growth of silver crystals after removal of electrodes shows that those silver bromide crystals that have the atomic structure disturbed by photons or electrons are the ones to attract free silver ions and become the black silver grains seen on negatives and prints.

An interesting variation is possible when using film for this project. While holding the positive electrode stationary on the wet film, move the negative wire slowly across the surface. With negative wire removed, the film will develop first along the track taken by that wire.

It is generally considered impossible to form any photographic image without using light. The technique herein described may be used to do just that "impossible" task: to create a photographic image, albeit somewhat obscure, with a source of energy other than light.

If time is available, this project may lead to a discussion of the nature of light. What is it? How does it travel? How is it generated? What is color? Many of these questions are within the realm of the atom and are still only answerable by theories; but if a few campers are stimulated by them, a useful purpose will be served.

LESSON OUTLINE: PARTS AND USE OF THE CAMERA

Have some unloaded cameras available for demonstration and inspection. Show parts and explain the purpose of each. Box cameras do not have adjustments for light, shutter speed and focus. These are set at the factory usually around F-12, 1/50 second, six feet to infinity, respectively.

Discuss the following steps in taking a picture:

1. Define the picture idea.
2. Limit the subject matter: decide what to include.
3. Pick a location for good lighting and background.
4. Decide on camera distance: long shot, medium shot or close-up.
5. Decide on camera elevation: near ground, eye level, ladder.
6. Decide best left-to-right position; look for natural frames—trees, branches, etc.
7. Take a number of shots of different poses or from different angles.

Discuss the following special tips for good pictures and what would happen if each were not observed:

1. Hold camera level, not tilted.
2. Hold camera steady. Squeeze shutter, do not jerk or punch.
3. If subject is moving or running, follow in viewfinder with a smooth turning of the camera, squeezing shutter as camera turns (pans).
4. Do not have subject face sun directly.
5. Keep lens clean.
6. Be sure you are not cutting part of subject off in viewfinder.
7. Watch focus. You must be more than six feet away with a box camera unless close-up attachment is used.
8. Handle camera so strap or fingers don't get in front of lens.
9. Avoid double exposures. Get in the habit of advancing the film immediately after taking a picture so you will be ready for next one.

Special topics may include use of exposure meters and Polaroid cameras. Any remaining time may be spent going around camp and having campers find picture-taking opportunities (action, buildings, scenes) and discuss best techniques for taking each picture: angle, camera setting and other details. Pictures may be viewed through frame made with hands held up at arm's length.

LESSON OUTLINE: DEVELOPING PRINTS

It is usually more convenient to introduce people to the darkroom and darkroom techniques through print developing rather than film developing. Prints can be made under the illumination of a safelight and if anything goes wrong with a print, it can always be made over again. Films must be processed in total darkness and there are no second chances with results. Most of the first lesson will doubtless be devoted to the darkroom equipment, procedure and contact printing (or hand photograms). Enlarging may be covered at a later time. The following topics should be covered:

1. Darkroom procedures and equipment. Introduction to the equipment, its uses, care, and approximate cost
   A. Purpose of safelights: paper ruined by white light, not sensitive to dull red, orange or yellow.
   B. Construction and purpose of print box
   C. Construction and purpose of enlarger
   D. Importance of cleanliness and absence of dust in darkroom. Keep everything labeled and in its proper place. Keep tables dry, especially where paper is kept and used.
2. Making contact prints
   A. Materials: paper, print box or frame, negatives, four trays and chemicals.
   B. Chemicals: purpose of each. Trays always arranged in same left-to-right order. Never get *any* stop bath or hypo into the developer, which will be ruined by them. Do not put fingers near eyes or mouth while working with chemicals. Wash and dry hands after making each print to avoid staining new pieces of paper.
   C. Photographic paper: Show a piece under white light and point out paper backing with light-sensitive coating or emulsion. Light causes changes in the coating so that when developed it turns black. Different sizes, surfaces and grades of paper. Contact paper not as sensitive as enlarging paper. Open paper box only under safelight and replace cover *immediately* after removing each piece. Do not leave cover off while making print.
   D. Making the print: Judge exposure needed by darkness (density) of negative: darker negatives need more exposure time. Negative on box emulsion side up, paper emulsion side down. Emulsion of film and paper always face each other when making any prints. Always develop for a full *two minutes*. If print is too dark, throw away and make again with shorter exposure. Exposures are always timed for a two-minute development. Shorter development does not process all silver grains and prints will have a muddy appearance. Stop bath for a few seconds; fixer for ten minutes. Running-water wash for thirty to sixty minutes.
   E. Practice in making prints

3. Making enlargements
   A. Enlarger: a projector built similar to camera but with light behind the film. Focusing; controlling light; importance of clean lens and negative carrier.
   B. Enlarging paper: different sizes, surfaces, grades. More costly than contact paper. Replace box cover immediately after removing each piece.
   C. Making the enlargement: negative in carrier, extra piece of paper in easel for focusing, lens wide open. Close lens down about half way after focusing to assure maximum sharpness of picture by compensating for tilted film or easel or focusing error. Judge exposure planning on two-minute development (68 F.). Put enlarging paper in easel, expose and process print.
   D. Chance to improve picture while enlarging: Pictures can be *cropped* by raising enlarger to eliminate unwanted material around edges and enlarge only the main subject. Parts of print may be *dodged*, either burned in or held back. Parts are burned in by exposing them longer than other sections of print using either hand or cardboard with hole to select material. Parts are held back by giving them less exposure than rest of print. Skies with clouds often require burning in. Other methods: vignet to eliminate backgrounds; texture screens; turning easel; tilting easel.

LESSON OUTLINE: DEVELOPING FILM

Film developing is more painstaking than printing. There is no second chance with film. If light enters the room, if the wrong chemical is used, if the film is scratched or greased by the hands the usual result is a roll of no pictures. When a tank is used we have the added possibility of not having the film wound properly on the reel, resulting in partially developed negatives, so it is usually best to *start* beginners developing in a tray. The old *orthochromatic* films were not sensitive to red light and could be developed under a safelight; but all of the present popular films are *panchromatic*—sensitive to all colors—and must be developed in *total darkness*. The method of developing film must be demonstrated in a normally lighted room so people can see. Because of all these factors it is not wasteful to use a new roll of unexposed film each time a group is taught the process. The cost is a small investment in insuring later success.

1. Darkroom procedures: same as for making prints *but* total darkness.
2. Chemicals used: same sequence as for prints—developer, stop bath, fixer, wash. Films dipped in Photo-Flo before being hung to dry. Must take temperature of developer and compensate developing time.
3. The film: Completely unroll a new roll of film. Show backing paper with rows of numbers, plastic base of film, gelatin and silver bromide emulsion of film. Note "feel" of backing and emulsion, compare. Note curve in toward emulsion. Note tape holding film to paper.
4. Darkroom steps in developing: Demonstrate with film and three empty trays in line. Film is unrolled and torn from paper. Paper, not film, is dropped to floor. Note the following improved developing method instead of "see-saw" method: Film is held in a roll, placed at one end of developing tray (emulsion side will be in) and one end is drawn along bottom of tray to opposite end where film is rolled up. Continue to roll film from one end of tray to other and back until time is up (about three minutes in Dektol 1:1). At proper time, let excess developer drain from film and roll same method in stop bath two or three times, then in fixer. This method of rolling film reduces chance of light's striking it, of unwanted oxygen reaching it from the air, and of the snapping and twisting that fresh film is prone to. Have campers practice this with film in dry tray. *Warning:* Film emulsion becomes soft in the developer. Take care not to scratch with fingernails.

A PICTURE LETTER

Planning a picture letter to send home is one way to plan a series of photos which will illustrate a single subject. The subject in this case is the camper and his camp.

MATERIALS

Photos taken at camp, a picture letter form with captions for photos.

PROCEDURE

The picture letter form may be an 8½″ × 11″ sheet of paper with six captions mimeographed in place, or campers may start with a blank paper and write in their own captions. Some sample captions might be: camp from entrance, my favorite activity, raising the flag, an afternoon activity, at the waterfront, by the campfire. Campers then take pictures appropriate to the selected captions, process them, paste them in place on the letter and mail it home.

The reverse procedure is also good. Campers select six pictures from those taken so far at camp and make up appropriate captions for them. A similar idea may be used for a camp bulletin board but with comic captions instead of the more sober titles.

UNDERWATER PHOTOGRAPHY

It would be unusual if the subject of underwater photography should not come up at camp. Here are some simple techniques for a start in this field, but due to the nature of water and the pressures that develop below five or six feet, special equipment will be needed to do serious work of this type.

MATERIALS

May be 1: a waterscope made of wood, putty, glass and aquarium cement; or 2: a waterscope using only a large clear plastic refrigerator dish; or 3: a flexible camera housing using a clear plastic bag.

PROCEDURE

Two waterscopes are illustrated in FIG. 3-4. One uses a mirror to shoot at a 45° angle. The boxes cannot be made too long or they will cut off viewing

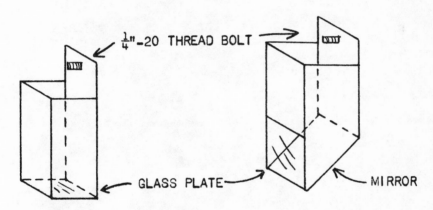

FIG. 3-4. Waterscopes for underwater viewing and photography

angle of the camera. A quarter-inch 20-thread bolt is installed to fit the standard tripod socket found on cameras. Corners may be waterproofed with putty, plastic tape or aquarium cement. Insides of box should be painted flat black to reduce reflections. To use, plunge glass end a couple of inches below the water surface, thus reducing ripple reflections and making vision and photography possible. Somewhat less convenient to use, a large plastic refrigerator dish will serve the same purpose as this waterscope. Exposure will have to be increased to compensate for reduction in sunlight under water.

The camera may be placed in a clear plastic bag which is tightly tied and used for one shot at a time. Some companies market flexible bags for this purpose. Do not attempt to turn the film knob through the bag under water. This method should only be used for inexpensive cameras and should not be used below five feet as there is a real danger of cracking the camera case from the water pressure at greater depths.

More serious work will require a rigid plastic case for the camera.[1] These may be purchased for most cameras and are designed to withstand underwater pressures.

---

[1] For details on underwater photography see Rebikoff and Cherney, *A Guide to Underwater Photography*. Philadelphia: Chilton Company. Modern Camera Guide Series.

PINHOLE CAMERA

The pinhole camera is an interesting project that can be done in many simple ways with different materials. Here are some suggestions.

MATERIALS

Any of these may be used for the camera body: cardboard box about 3″ deep, camera constructed from poster board, old roll-film camera with lens removed. A 1/16″ drill or No. 10 needle is used to make the pinhole in a piece of aluminum foil.

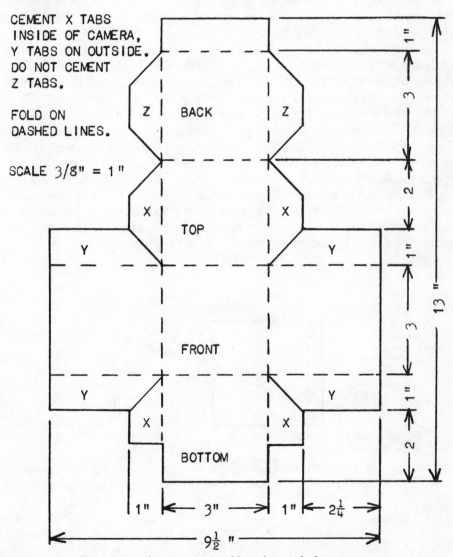

FIG. 3-5. Construction of box for pinhole camera

PROCEDURE

If a box is used, simply cut a hole in the cover, cement a patch of aluminum foil over the hole and carefully make the small, rounded hole in the foil. The box should have a dark interior to reduce reflections and the underside of the foil may be held over a candle flame to blacken that surface. The camera may also be fashioned from a tin can with one end removed and the pinhole drilled in the other end. A can with a pry-off lid, such as a coffee can, may be used and the film taped inside the lid.

The box may be constructed from poster board following FIG. 3-5. Cut board on all solid lines. Lightly score the board along the dotted lines and then fold the scores. Don't attempt to fold the board without first scoring. Tabs marked "X" are cemented inside the box, "Y" tabs are cemented outside the box and "Z" tabs are not cemented. Cut a hole in the front and make pinhole as described above.

For serious work, the most convenient equipment is an old box camera with the lens removed. This provides a shutter, light-tight box and film-rolling mechanism. You will probably want a camera capable of making time or "bulb" exposures. Use fast film (Tri-X).

The pinhole camera is able to focus an image of a lighted scene because light travels in straight lines. Point "A" in FIG. 3-6 is sending out light rays in straight lines in all directions. The tiny pinhole eliminates most of the rays from point "A" passing perhaps only one. By allowing only one ray to reach the film from each point on the object, the pinhole forms an image on the film. All extraneous light rays are kept out. As the pinhole size is increased more light rays are passed from each point on the object and the image becomes fuzzy and less distinct. The image may be seen and experimented with by focusing it onto a piece of paper.

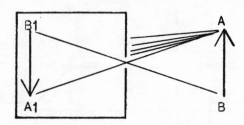

FIG. 3-6. Pinhole forms image by admitting only one light ray from each point on an object.

The simplest experience with pinhole equipment may be had by taping a piece of enlarging paper to the back of your box and taking a picture on that. Expose to a sunlit scene for about ten seconds and develop in the usual Dektol. Result will be a negative image on the paper.

By changing the focal length (distance between pinhole and film), you can change the camera from wide-angle to telephoto. As this distance is increased, the size of the image increases. Of course, the exposure should be increased as this distance becomes greater. There are no focusing problems with a pinhole. Everything will be in focus from a few inches away to infinity. This great depth of focus can be matched by no lens camera.

Note: For unusually great depth of focus *and* sharpness, you may use an aluminum foil pinhole in front of the regular lens on your camera. This will give the effect of a very small F-stop and will require longer exposures. The new F-stop will be about 75 per cent of the focal length of the lens in millimeters. (One inch equals 254 mm.). A 100-mm. lens would be F-75, a 50-mm. lens would be F-38. Perhaps your pinhole can be made in a tight-fitting lens cap. To use the camera, focus in the normal manner and have the diaphragm wide open.

SPECIAL EFFECTS: SOLARIZED PRINTS, TEXTURE SCREENS

Innumerable special effects may be created in photography both in and out of the darkroom. These two projects will offer variety to the darkroom work and add an artistic effect to some of the prints.

MATERIALS

Standard darkroom equipment and materials, cheesecloth.

SOLARIZED PRINTS

Expose and begin to develop a print in the normal manner, but remove it from the developer when only about three-fourths developed and expose it to a white room light at a distance of about three feet for five to ten seconds. After exposure return print to developer. Shining the white light on the paper exposes all the previously unexposed silver grains which will now turn black. The silver grains that had already formed an image are in a relatively stable condition and are not as easily changed by the new exposure. Some people prefer to use a more diluted developer after the exposure (ten parts water to one part developer). Continue development in the normal manner.

TEXTURE SCREENS

This technique adds a canvas oil painting appearance to enlarged prints. Set up film and paper in normal manner for enlarging. After the enlarging easel has the paper and has been set in place, stretch a piece of cheese-cloth across the paper surface, then expose paper with enlarger and negative. Increase exposure time somewhat. Develop paper in the normal manner. This technique may be varied by using the texture screen at different heights above the paper and by having the texture screen in place for only part of the exposure.

RADIOGRAPHY

The existence of radioactive rays and particles was first discovered by a photographic accident. Henri Becquerel in 1896 happened to place some uranium bisulfate in the same drawer containing some of the early photographic plates. Much later he used his plates to take some pictures, but upon developing discovered they had been fogged. Further experiments proved the films had been fogged by rays from the uranium. The rays were called Becquerel rays.

Today these rays are called alpha, beta and gamma and they are deliberately used to produce very important photographs in medicine and industry. (See Chapter 9, GEIGER COUNTER.) Such pictures, called radiographs, may be easily made at camp.

MATERIALS

Film (Fast film such as Tri-X or Royal Pan is best.), developing materials, radioactive source (luminous watch, clock or compass, highly radioactive mineral sample or Cenco isotope. See Chapter 9, GEIGER COUNTER), paper clip, lightproof box.

PROCEDURE

One of the most radioactive materials commonly available is the luminous watch or clock as described in the spinthariscope project mentioned above. In a completely dark room, tape a piece of film, emulsion side up, into bottom of box. Cover with a piece of black or dark paper. Put paper clip on top of paper and the watch (or other radioactive material) face down on the clip. Tape in position. Replace cover on box. If there is any doubt of its lightproof qualities, wrap box completely in aluminum foil. Now turn on lights and set box aside for a few days. When you develop the film there should be a dark area on the negative showing an image of the paper clip. This is in spite of the fact that visible light has never reached the film. This experiment is similar to one done by Becquerel, who used a key instead of the paper clip. The radioactive particles have split the silver bromide molecules on the film and caused the silver atoms to move around, forming an image in the same manner caused by light rays.

RESOURCE MATERIALS FOR PHOTOGRAPHY

Magazines

Popular Photography. Monthly, $5.00 per year. 434 South Wabash Ave., Chicago, Ill. 60605.

Modern Photography. Monthly, $5.00 per year. 33 West 60 St., New York, N. Y. 10023. Bookstore service at same address.

U. S. Camera. Monthly, $5.00 per year. 9 East 40 St., New York, N. Y. 10016.

Camera 35. Bimonthly, $2.50 per year. 9 East 40 St., New York, N. Y. 10016. Photo book service at same address.

Films and Pamphlets

Sales Service Division, Eastman Kodak Company, 343 State Street, Rochester, N. Y. 14604. Excellent selection of free films, many booklets and willingness to answer any question in photography. Write, telling of your camp science program and ask for the following free materials:

> Catalog of Free Films
> How to Run a Live Camera Club
> Photo Quiz Program
> Photomicrography with Simple Cameras
> Box Camera Photo Course
> Kodak Book Lists 1, 2 and 3.
> Booklets: B-9, C-11, C-21, C-27, J-3.

Customer Service Department, Polaroid Corporation, Cambridge 39, Mass. Many booklets on the Land camera and process. Following free materials of particular interest:

> How Polaroid Land Color Film Works
> Polaroid Pointers: C102F, C117C and C119D
> The Magic That Made Polaroid
> One-Step Photography

Series of Photo Books on Special Subjects

Kodak Data Books Series. Eastman Kodak Co., 343 State St., Rochester, N. Y. 14604.

Modern Camera Guide Series. Chilton Company, Book Division, 56 and Chestnut Sts., Philadelphia, Pa. 19139.

Universal Photo Books, New York, N. Y. 10010.

Supplies

Seahawk Products, Box 1157, Coral Gables, Fla. Catalog of underwater camera equipment.

A local photo store is usually the best source of information and advice on equipment, but the following national suppliers carry photo equipment:

> Sears, Roebuck and Co., Photographic Materials Division, 925 South Homan Avenue, Chicago, Ill.
> Montgomery Ward, Chicago, Ill. 60607.

Chapter

4: Astronomy

SUGGESTED
REFERENCE

Bernhard, Bennett and Rice, *New Handbook of the Heavens*. New York:
New American Library, 1958.

ASTRONOMY is ideally suited to the twenty-four-hour schedule which is available only at camp. Many astronomy activities can be carried out in the daytime but there is no substitute for night observation sessions which are so easily arranged there.

One of the most important objectives that the camp science program can strive for in astronomy is the building of concepts. Concepts of sizes, distances and motions of the gigantic masses that spin through the universe are very difficult for people of any age to comprehend, and particularly difficult for young people limited as to experience and powers of abstract thinking. Some understanding of the unimaginable vastness which is the universe is not gained in a short time. It must be built up over many years by repeated presentation of facts and exposure to many different experiences. Many of the activities described in this chapter are designed to help in this conceptual building in younger campers.

Most older campers have a fairly good idea of how and where things are located in space. As they do the experiments and observations described later, they will be reinforcing and adding to their present knowledge. Many of these activities can be enlarged upon to become science fair projects when campers return to school.

The construction and use of simple astronomical instruments is an excellent way to become familiar with methods of using scientific instruments to make personal "discoveries" about the sun, planets, moon, and stars. As to discoveries, the camp science leader should strive to be one who raises questions as well as one who answers them. You may want to get into the habit of answering a question with a question. There is no greater experience for a young person than to discover the answer to his own question, and he should be allowed this privilege provided it is within his power to reach some satisfactory conclusion. Such problem-solving as this is a true scientific method, and the opportunities for it usually come spontaneously from the children. The wise counselor must be alert to take advantage of them.

With the mention of astronomy, one of the first thoughts is the telescope. A telescope is not a necessary instrument to the study of the stars, but it certainly does help and after the science program has been going for some time, the camp will probably want to purchase one. There are two kinds of astronomical telescopes: *refractors* which have a series of lenses that the observer looks through, and *reflectors* which have a large open tube with a parabolic mirror at the bottom and magnifying lenses at the top, mounted at right angles to the large hollow tube. The major consideration in selecting a telescope is not magnification but light-gathering ability. This can be gauged by the diameter of the front lens on a refractor or the diameter of the mirror on a reflector. Given a certain diameter, the reflector is usually less expensive than the refractor, but both types have their merits.

Other considerations in buying a telescope are the stand, which should be sturdy to prevent vibration, and the mount, which should be of the equatorial type to permit following stars as they move across the sky. If much astrophotography is anticipated, a clock drive should be included in the equatorial mount.

Whether you have a telescope or not, don't overlook the use of binoculars in astronomy. The area seen through binoculars is much larger than that of the telescope, making it much easier to spot something quickly in the sky. Binoculars will often clarify the Milky Way, comets, and star clusters which appear as hazy patches of light to the naked eye. Many lunar features show nicely through binoculars. The moon is best observed at quarter phases when light is coming from the side and the longer shadows make features more prominent.

INFORMATION OF IMPORTANCE

Historically, the study of the heavens was one of man's first attempts to understand and use nature. Prehistoric man could not help but notice the longer days of summer and the shorter days of winter. He developed the ability to predict the seasons, and changes on earth associated with them. One of the best-known uses of early astronomy was the annual prediction of the flooding of the Nile River as a guide to the planting of crops. Advances in astronomy were closely related with advances in mathematics as the need arose for methods of measuring and keeping records, and as mathematical relationships were discovered in the motions of the heavenly bodies.

Progress in astronomy has been inversely proportional to man's feeling of self-importance. Prehistoric man considered himself as the center of the universe. The small patch of land over which he could walk was the limit to his world. As time went on, he became aware of the earth as a whole and this became the center of the universe with all the celestial bodies moving around it. Man began to feel even smaller when Copernicus announced that the earth was one of many planets traveling in space around the sun, which was the center. Since that time it has been discovered that the sun is only one of billions of stars forming a huge cluster called a galaxy, which is only one of millions of galaxies, each an island of stars in a sea of space. Man remains in this sea as a speck of dust. But possessing the human mind, he is able to comprehend all this vastness which surrounds him and has the power to accomplish many things.

The study of astronomy may be roughly divided into two sections. The first relates to bodies found inside the solar system, including the sun, planets, moons, comets, meteors, artificial satellites, and the motions and interaction of these bodies. The second part concerns things found outside the solar system including stars, double-star systems, star clusters, galaxies, nebulae and those mythical groupings called constellations.

It is important in studying astronomy that we have suitable systems of measurement for the vast distances involved. Computation by miles just doesn't work. The most familiar standard is the *light year,* the *distance* light will travel in a year going at the rate of 186,000 miles per second. One light year equals six trillion miles. The nearest star, *Proxima Centauri,* is 4.3 light years away. Our galaxy, the *Milky Way,* is about 80,000 light years across from edge to edge. Our nearest neighboring galaxy, the great spiral in *Andromeda* is more than one and one-half million light years away.

The light year is too large a measuring stick for use within the solar system, so we use two other devices. For measuring distances, we use the *Astronomical Unit.* One astronomical unit equals the distance from the earth to the sun, which is 93,000,000 miles. Thus the distance from the earth to the sun is 1 A.U.; from the sun to Jupiter is 5 A.U. *Earth Diameters* are used to measure diameters in the solar system. One E.D., the diameter of the earth, equals 8,000 miles. The diameter of the sun is 110 E.D., and the diameter of Jupiter is 11 E.D. A.U. and E.D. are much easier to use and remember than are larger figures.

The sun, the center of the solar system, is a medium-sized yellow star with a surface temperature of 11,000° F. and a temperature in the center of 40,000,000 degrees. It takes sunlight eight minutes to travel to earth. Spectroscopic examination indicates that the sun has all elements found on earth, but the most plentiful elements at the surface are hydrogen and helium. The energy of the sun comes from the process of *fusion* which is also the principle of the hydrogen bomb. In this process, two hydrogen atoms are fused together to form one helium atom. When the atoms are fused, there is energy left over in the nuclei (nuclear energy) which is released in the form of heat and light. Sunspots are an interesting and important feature of the sun. They are dark, cooler spots which can be seen moving with the sun's surface as it rotates on its axis once every twenty-five days.

A discussion of the solar system is likely to lead to the question of *Bode's Law,* formulated in the eighteenth century and included here for reference. According to this law, if we prepare a series of numbers based on three, doubling each one and adding four to it, we should arrive at the distances of planets from the sun. This is written as follows:

THE PLANETS

NAME	DISTANCE FROM SUN	DIAMETER	NUMBER OF MOONS	SPECIAL FEATURES
Mercury	.4	.37	0	Same time for rotation and revolution causes same side to always face sun. About 400 F. on light side and —400 F. on dark side. No atmosphere observed.
Venus	.7	1.0	0	Our sister planet. Closest planet. Bright CO_2 atmosphere. Water vapor discovered in 1960. Morning or evening star.
Earth	1.0	1.0	1	Oxygen in atmosphere. Water. Moderate and varying temperatures.
Mars	1.5	.5	2	Red planet, oxidized surface. "Canals." Polar ice caps. Tilted on axis and has seasons. Water and some oxygen.
Jupiter	5.0	11.0	12	—200 F. frozen methane and ammonia atmosphere. Colored bands. Red spot may be hole in atmosphere melted by volcano on surface, making surface visible.
Saturn	10.0	9.0	9	Three rings, each 10,000 miles wide and eight inches thick,[1] are composed of small rock or ice particles. Atmosphere of all outer planets is similar to Jupiter.
Uranus	20.0	4.0	5	Green color. Faintly visible to naked eye.
Neptune	30.0	4.0	2	Discovered by inconsistencies in orbit of Uranus.
Pluto	40.0	.5	0?	Temperature close to —400 F. 250 years to go around sun; six light hours from sun. From Pluto, sun would appear as a bright star.

Distances in the above chart are given in Astronomical Units.
Diameters are given in Earth Diameters.

[1] **Science News Letter,** March 16, 1963. Vol. 83, No. 11.

0	3	6	12	24	48	96	192	384	768
+4	4	4	4	4	4	4	4	4	4
.4	.7	1.0	1.6	2.8	5.2	10.0	19.6	38.8	77.2

The sums are shown here divided by ten to coincide with the earth distance as 1.0. The accuracy clearly falls off for Neptune and Pluto. But more important is the figure 2.8, at which location there is no planet. There are, however, thousands of planetoids or *asteroids*. These may be the remains of a planet once formed in that location and since shattered, perhaps by tidal forces from Jupiter or from its own internal pressures. As for Bode's Law, there is no real explanation for it and it may just be a mathematical coincidence.

Another body of the solar system which is of great interest is our natural satellite, the moon. The moon is 240,000 miles away and has a diameter greater than one-fourth the diameter of the earth. The size relationship between our moon and earth is unusually large compared with that of other planets. Like Mercury, the moon makes one rotation in the same time that it makes one revolution of its orbit. For this reason, the same side is always facing the earth although all sides have a turn facing the sun. The gravity of the moon is sufficient to attract the ocean waters when they are turned toward it, causing the daily tides. The surface of the moon is thought to be rugged rock and perhaps dust in places. Its topography is mountainous with straight and circular chains of mountains, some over 20,000 feet high. The circular mountain chains are often confused with craters. There are craters too, and their formation has yet to be explained. They have been attributed to both meteors and volcanic activity.

When the moon comes directly between the sun and earth, we have a *solar eclipse* with the sun being blacked out by the moon's disc. When the earth comes between the sun and moon, sunlight is cut off from the moon and we have a *lunar eclipse*. Although solar eclipses occur more frequently than lunar eclipses, they are only visible from a very narrow band on the earth, while lunar eclipses are visible to the entire dark half of the earth. So we are likely to see lunar eclipses more often than solar eclipses.

Every day, the earth is invaded by millions of space visitors leaving fiery trails behind them as they plunge down through the atmosphere. These visitors are *meteors*. Most of them originate in the solar system, but many are the remains of comets which have passed through our orbit in years past. Meteors are tiny bits of dust or stone which first become visible about eighty miles up in the ionosphere. There, the air is thick enough to heat them by friction as gravity pulls them downward at average speeds of twenty-five miles per second. Most are visible only for a second or two before they are vaporized into ashes. If a meteor is large enough to avoid being burned completely, it will become cool and dark at an altitude of forty miles because the thickness of the lower atmosphere acts as a bumper and slows it down. As the earth moves through its orbit, the rear half pulls meteors in by gravity; but the leading half captures meteors both by gravity and by colliding with them. Between midnight and 6:00 A.M., we are on the leading edge, making this the best time to watch for meteors provided there is no moon. It has been conservatively estimated that meteor ash adds 5,000,000 tons of material to the earth every year.[1] This is one fact which helps support the *dust-cloud hypothesis* of the origin of the solar system.

Other travelers in the solar system are the *comets*. Few sights are more inspiring than the streamlined shape of a comet apparently hanging motionless in the night sky, while in reality it is speeding at thousands of miles per hour in its path around the sun. The heads of comets are composed of loosely packed meteor material, and perhaps frozen gases. The tail exists only while the comet is close to the sun. During that time, the pressure of sunlight is strong enough to push the smaller particles back from the head and away from the sun. The tail does not stream out behind the comet, it pushes out into space in a direction directly opposite the sun. Comets seem to produce light both by reflected sunlight and by the action of solar rays which strike the atoms and cause them to glow as in a neon tube. To see a comet, it is not necessary to wait seventy-six years for Halley's Comet, which was last visible in 1910. There are many telescopic comets visible each year, and an average of two a year are visible to the naked eye. Comets are named after their discoverers, and amateur astronomers as well as professionals have many to their credit.

As we begin to study the space beyond the solar system, our attention is first called to the *constellations*. These groups of bright stars seemed to describe figures to the imaginative ancients and provided a basis for many myths and legends. The constellation groupings have no scientific significance and the average person today has considerable difficulty seeing the figures which they are supposed to represent. But they do form convenient groupings from which to learn about and identify various stars and other celestial bodies. These can be spotted by their position in relation to nearby constellations.

Looking closely at the stars which make up the constellations, we find they are of different brightnesses and different colors. Brightness is measured in *magnitudes*. The brightest stars such as Vega, Deneb and Betelgeuse are known as first-magnitude objects. Polaris is dimmer and is a second-magnitude star. The faintest stars that are visible to the naked eye are sixth magnitude. Sirius, the brightest star in the sky, is so bright that it has a minus magnitude of less than zero, which is −1.5.

Star colors are an indication of temperature. At the low end of the scale are the red stars at about 5,000° F., followed by orange, yellow, white, and blue, with temperatures over 50,000 degrees. Color is also related to the size, density and age of stars. Generally, as the temperature increases, the density increases and the size decreases. The relationship between color and age is still theoretical, but it is thought that a young star starts large, cool and red, condenses, becoming smaller and hotter, using its fuel at a faster pace, then becomes red again and finally becomes a dwarf, not much larger than some planets.

---

[1] Hans Pettersson, "Cosmic Spherules and Meteoric Dust." *Scientific American*, Feb. 1960, Vol. 202, No. 2.

There are many *double stars* to observe in the night sky. These are two stars, close to each other, which revolve around a common center of gravity, thus forming their own system. There are even multiple stars with three or more stars revolving about the same center in space. The members of these systems are rarely the same size and often have different colors, which should be watched for.

Also included among the stars of special interest are the *variable* stars which change their brightness regularly. The simplest of these are eclipsing variables which are double stars with a member that comes between the earth and the other star, thus reducing its magnitude. Still not completely understood are the true variables which actually change their temperature and brilliance as much as two magnitudes in a period of five days.

More numerous than the known facts about astronomy are the unknowns to which scientists are still seeking answers. Is the universe infinite or finite? If it is finite, what are the boundaries? Is time itself finite and, if so, when did it start? From whence did the material come to build universe? If it did come from some place, then there must be a place other than our known universe. These are disturbing questions but the search for answers is on: attempting to break down barriers to knowledge, not only in outer space but in the inner space of the human mind. Presenting these questions to young people today is one step toward finding the answers in the future.

DIMENSIONS OF THE SOLAR SYSTEM

It is almost impossible for the average person to imagine the true meaning of the enormous distances and sizes found in astronomy. With his very limited range of experience, it is most difficult for the young camper to begin to understand the meaning of 93,000,000 miles just by hearing the number. We must add to his limited range of experiences by involving him personally in a new experience. Have him become a planet in the solar system, holding a scale model of the planet he represents at a scale distance from the sun.

MATERIALS

Oaktag, cement, nails, scissors, pen and ink. Binoculars are optional.

PROCEDURE

Prepare materials before campers arrive. Cut planets from oaktag to dimensions given in chart. Push nails up through cardboard bases, cement nail to base, cement planet to point of nail. Write information about planet on base. Also write scale distance of planet from sun on base as given in chart. A model of a planet is illustrated, FIG. 4-1.

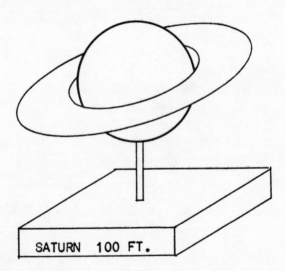

SATURN 100 FT.

FIG. 4-1. Simple model used to illustrate distances and sizes in the solar system

USE

Discuss solar system, what it is, what is in it, what is in the center, how many planets, names, and other facts about them. Outside in a large field distribute planets and sun to ten campers and have them stand at correct distances from sun. (The pace of a nine-year-old is about two feet.) With planets in position, call attention to proximity of the four small ones to the sun and the sizes and distances of giant planets. Note that sizes given will cause planets to appear much as they do in the night sky. Notice that Pluto cannot be seen from Earth. Binoculars may be used to see rings of Saturn, etc. Campers may want to take turns at Earth to observe system from that location. You will find that this activity will stimulate many comments and questions which will be of help in planning future activities in astronomy.

This chart gives scale distances and sizes for the planets. The sizes and distances are not both exactly to the same scale. If the sizes were to the same scale as the distances, a magnifying glass would be needed to see many of the planets. The scales provided do give the desired concept-developing effects.

PLANET	DISTANCE FROM SUN IN FEET	DIAMETER IN INCHES
Sun	0	2-3 feet (12 1/2′ actual scale)
Mercury	4	1/32
Venus	7	1/8
Earth	10	1/8
Mars	15	1/16
Jupiter	50	1 3/8
Saturn	100	1 1/8
Uranus	200	1/2
Neptune	300	1/2
Pluto	400	1/16

Note that on this scale one Astronomical Unit equals ten feet. In the solar system, one Astronomical Unit equals 93,000,000 miles. In doing this project with older campers, it should also be possible to teach the measuring systems of Astronomical Units and Earth Diameters.

A MODEL OF THE MILKY WAY GALAXY

Once again we deal with the conception of vast distances and immense numbers used to describe the universe. Our earth is a tiny planet going around a single star which is traveling around the edge of a galaxy of billions of stars. The galaxy itself is moving at enormous speed through the space of a universe dotted with millions of such galaxies. In all, they contain trillions of such suns which in all probability have countless tiny planets revolving around them. The stars in a galaxy and the galaxies in the universe are often compared to grains of sand on a beach. We can use this comparison to help us understand our place in space by making a sand-grain picture of the Milky Way.

MATERIALS

Dry sand (at hardware store if not naturally available), blue paper, glue, other paper of assorted colors, scissors, pencils.

PROCEDURE

FIG. 4-2 shows a finished model. There are three sections: the Milky Way, Star Temperatures, Detail of Stars around Sun. All three of these need not be included. Discuss the sections as work progresses.

Draw a light outline of our galaxy on blue paper. Paint enclosed area with glue and sprinkle handful of sand over glue, making it thick in the center and thinner toward edges and arms. One of the sand grains near the edge is our sun. (Planets are too close to it to be distinguished on this scale.) Sand grains around the sun are stars close to us which comprise most of the stars seen in the night sky. This technique also demonstrates that there are stars above and below us as well as to the sides. Mark this area of the galaxy with a dot of paint. You may wish to place an enlargement of that area in a corner of the paper as shown in the figure. Our nearest star (sand grain) is Proxima Centauri, 26,000,000,000,000 miles or 4.3 light years away. Since it is under the earth, it can only be seen from the Southern Hemisphere. Another "close" star is Sirius, the brightest star in the winter sky over the Northern Hemisphere. Sirius is eight light years away. (One light year equals 6,000,000,000,000 miles.)

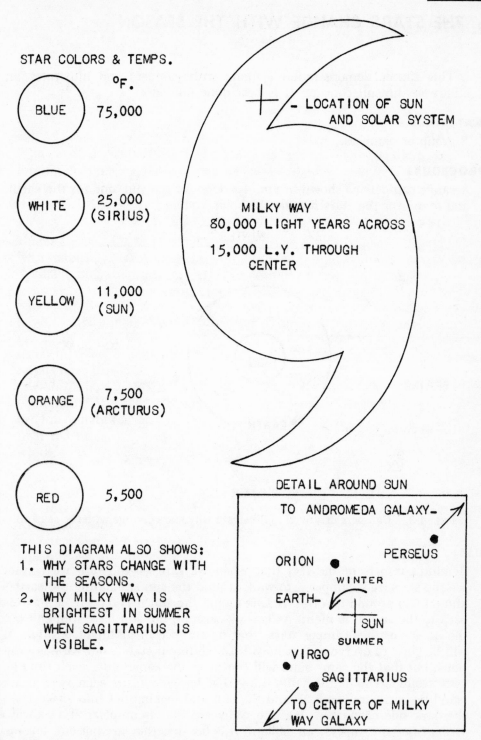

STAR COLORS & TEMPS.

°F.

BLUE   75,000

WHITE   25,000
        (SIRIUS)

YELLOW 11,000
        (SUN)

ORANGE 7,500
        (ARCTURUS)

RED   5,500

THIS DIAGRAM ALSO SHOWS:
1. WHY STARS CHANGE WITH
   THE SEASONS.
2. WHY MILKY WAY IS
   BRIGHTEST IN SUMMER
   WHEN SAGITTARIUS IS
   VISIBLE.

MILKY WAY
80,000 LIGHT YEARS ACROSS

15,000 L.Y. THROUGH
CENTER

- LOCATION OF SUN
  AND SOLAR SYSTEM

DETAIL AROUND SUN

TO ANDROMEDA GALAXY-

ORION   PERSEUS

WINTER

EARTH-

        SUN

SUMMER

VIRGO

SAGITTARIUS

TO CENTER OF MILKY
WAY GALAXY

Fig. 4-2.   Outline for sand model of Milky Way and other facts about the
stars

Astronomy   103

WHY THE STARS CHANGE WITH THE SEASON

This simple demonstration is done with campers and illustrates an otherwise difficult concept. It is best done outdoors.

MATERIALS
A group of campers.

PROCEDURE
Arrange campers as shown in FIG. 4-3. One for the sun, one for the earth, and many for the stars outside the solar system.

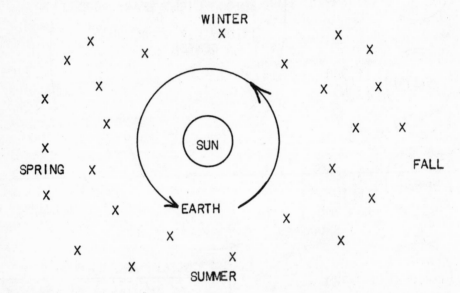

FIG. 4-3. Campers arranged to illustrate why stars change with the seasons

USE
Remind campers of the fact that when we can see the sun, we cannot see the stars. Ask camper E to walk around the sun simulating the earth's annual trip around its orbit. If E is facing the sun it is day; if he has his back to the sun, it is night. As E walks around the sun have him call out the names of the "camper stars" that he can see in his night position. It will be clear to everyone that he will see different stars from various locations; but that the same stars will repeat in the same order each time he goes around. This is the same thing that happens to us each year as we stand on earth traveling around the sun and looking out into space from the dark side of earth as we ride. Why are the circumpolar stars always visible? See if campers can explain. It is because they are not out, but up. Since "up" is always in the same direction no matter where the earth is in its orbit, we always see the same stars in that part of the sky.

PLANET WALL PLAQUE

This project produces something attractive to take home from camp and encourages research on the planets at the same time.

MATERIALS

Plaster of Paris, plastic pail, paper plates or aluminum foil pie plates, wire, assorted paints or dope, brushes and thinner, colored pictures of planets

PROCEDURE

Prepare a fairly thick mixture of plaster of Paris, add plaster to water. A plastic pail is recommended for mixing plaster. Pour plaster into paper dishes and put the ends of a wire loop into the plaster near the edge of dish. This wire loop will be used to hang plaque on wall. Allow plaster to harden completely (FIG. 4-4).

While plaster is setting, each person may look at pictures of planets and discuss features, deciding which one they would like to reproduce for the plaque. Using paper, they may draw a sketch plan of how they will do the plaster. Subjects with the most prominent features are: Earth, Jupiter, Mars, Saturn and the moon. The sun also has possibilities.

Remove hard plaster from dishes and sand down any unwanted markings. A thick mixture of plaster may be used to add relief features as mountains, craters, and ice caps.

When all is dry, the planets may be painted according to the colored pictures. When working on plaster be sure that it is turned so wire loop will be at top when you are finished.

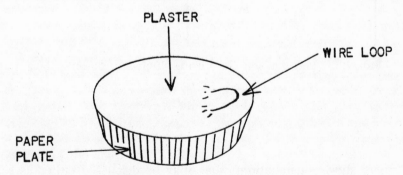

FIG. 4-4.   Molding plaster for planet wall plaque

MAKING A PERSONAL STAR CHART

MATERIALS

Small single-serving cereal boxes (Have each person save his box from breakfast. Large cereal boxes may be used but it will take longer to collect enough.); nails of different sizes.

PROCEDURE

Each person removes wax bag from box (if present) and selects a summer constellation from a star chart. Mark the stars on the box with a pencil then push a hole through the cardboard at each star. Punch larger holes for brighter stars. In a dark room, insert a flashlight in the open end of the box and all the stars will light up as the light is reflected from the inside through the holes (FIG. 4-5). Don't be concerned about the printing on the boxes. Since these are used in the dark, it is not visible. If large boxes are used, many constellations may be placed on each box.

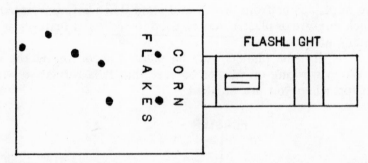

FIG. 4-5. Personal star chart using single-serving cereal box

USE

As campers show constellations, they may be discussed either as science or mythology. Campers should bring these star charts at night observation meetings and find their constellations in the sky.

MAKING A SUNDIAL

Making and using a sundial is a constant reminder of the location of the earth in the solar system and its motions in relation to the sun. The principle of the sundial is easily understood if we imagine a stick placed into the earth's axis at the North Pole. As the earth turns, the shadow of the stick will appear to go through a complete circle of 360 degrees. Since it will take twenty-four hours to make this circle, the shadow will go through fifteen degrees each hour. Thus we have a method of telling time at the North Pole. Notice that the stick is in line with the axis while the base on which the shadow will fall is parallel to the equator. If we design an instrument with these same characteristics, we will have a device to measure time any place on earth using the sun. The sundial described here fulfills these requirements in the simplest possible way.

MATERIALS

Oaktag, cement, pen and ink or pencils, scissors, protractor, rulers, your latitude in degrees.

PROCEDURE

Cut two pieces of oaktag as shown in FIG. 4-6. The hour lines, which are fifteen degrees apart, may be made with a protractor or you may supply each person with a wedge of cardboard cut to fifteen degrees. This is a good idea with young children unfamiliar with protractors. Calculate angle C (your angle of latitude) and draw dotted lines. Angle D should be ninety degrees minus your latitude. Fold on dotted lines. Cement base together and cement upright in place as shown in FIG. 4-7. The angle of tilt makes the base parallel with the plane of the equator.

USE

Position the sundial so N is pointing to North. If you know the time by a clock, the sundial may be used as a compass by setting it for the time and noting the direction of the N arrow. When using as a compass, remember that sundials tell standard time, not daylight saving time.

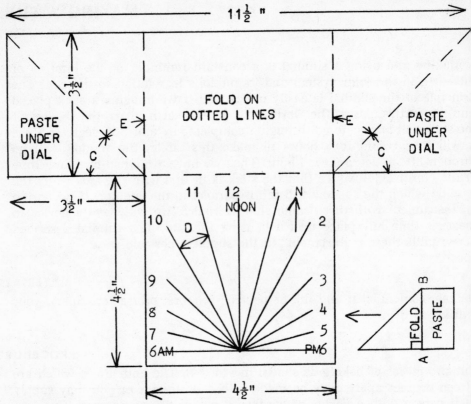

NOTES: CEMENT UPRIGHT IN POSITION WITH LINE AB ON 12 NOON.
C= YOUR ANGLE OF LATITUDE
D= 15 DEGREES BETWEEN HOUR LINES
E= 90° MINUS LATITUDE ANGLE

FIG. 4-6

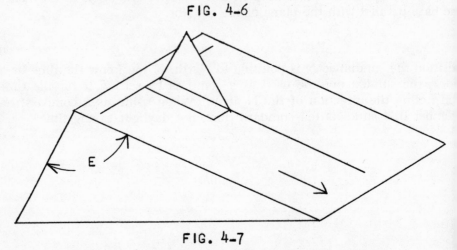

FIG. 4-7

FIG. 4-6.   Layout of sundial to be drawn on oaktag

FIG. 4-7.   Completed sundial. Arrow must point north.

WHAT ARE THE STARS MADE OF?

We can read in books that the sun is made of the same elements as the earth. Other sources will tell us what the other stars are made of. Astronomers learn this by using a *spectroscope*. The basis of spectroscope operation is the fact that when an element is heated to incandescence and the resulting light passed through a prism, it produces a series of bright or dark lines distributed along the color spectrum (red to violet) in positions which are characteristic of that particular element. Another element would produce lines in different locations. Lines of some elements are shown in FIG. 4-8. The lines of each element are known and have been charted (See in BIBLIOGRAPHY: *Handbook of Chemistry and Physics*) so that any glowing element may be identified from any distance by observing its light through a spectroscope. Spectral lines are to elements what fingerprints are to people: the set for each individual is different from any other.

Many spectroscopes use the familiar properties of prisms to divide the light and show the spectrum. (See FIG. 4-9.) Because different wave lengths of light have different velocities in glass, when white light enters a prism, the longer-wave-length red light travels fastest and is bent less than short-wave-length violet which is slower so the six major colors appear separated on the other side. The prism may be replaced by a *diffraction grating* which produces the same spectral effect by the different principle of wave interference.

The simple but effective spectroscope described here uses diffraction grating replica so inexpensive that most older campers will be able to make a personal instrument for experimentation and later use in school.

MATERIALS

Oaktag, ¾" × ¾" × 2" wood blocks, cement, black poster paint and brush, diffraction grating replica (Edmund Scientific, Transmission Type mounted in 35-mm slide mounts, about ten cents each in quantity), smooth black plastic electrical tape or aluminum foil, ruler, scissors, pencils, model knife.

PROCEDURE

Prepare oaktag as shown in FIG. 4-10. Paint inside flat black to reduce reflections. Crease on folds and cement wood blocks in place. While blocks are drying, prepare the front piece of oaktag containing slit. The slit is a critical part of the instrument. The edges of the slit must be smooth and even or the spectrum will show uneven and confusing vertical streaks. When completed, the slit should be about as wide as a knife blade. Cut a slit in the oaktag about one inch long. Cut two pieces of the smooth plastic electrical tape (not friction tape). Place them back to back so sticky sides are exposed, slide into slit, press top tape up to form top of slit and bottom tape down to form lower edge of slit. This will produce fairly smooth

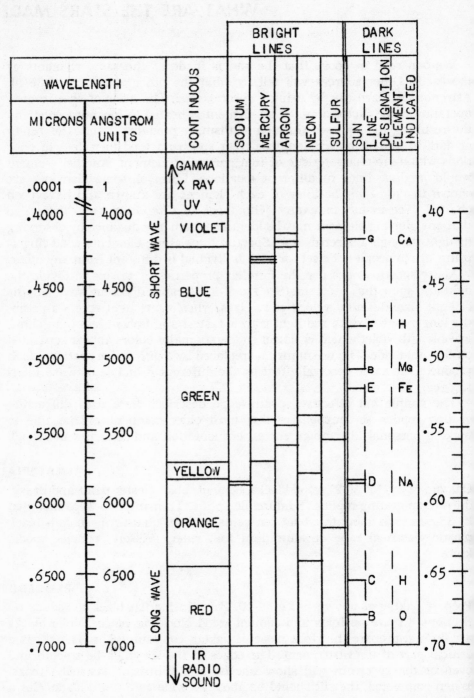

FIG. 4-8. Spectra of selected elements. Only the most prominent lines are shown.

edges. Another satisfactory slit is made by taping two razor blades to the oaktag, leaving a narrow slit between them. A less satisfactory method is to cement a piece of aluminum foil over a larger hole in the oaktag and cut the slit in the foil. Now cement the slit assembly onto its wooden block.

Cement the diffraction grating to its wooden block, making sure that the fine lines reproduced on the plastic are horizontal with the slit. The grating must be positioned to give a vertical spectrum when the slit is horizontal.

When all cement is dry, fold up sides to make a square tube, apply cement to one-inch tab marked "final cement" which holds the tube together and apply cement to sides and top of slit assembly and top of grating and press all cemented areas to adjoining parts until cement has set and tube will stay together. If you look through the grating (slightly down or up) with slit pointed to source of light, you will see a spectrum.

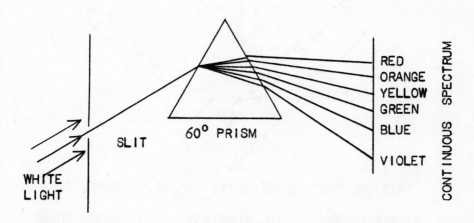

FIG. 4-9.　Refraction and dispersion of white light by a prism

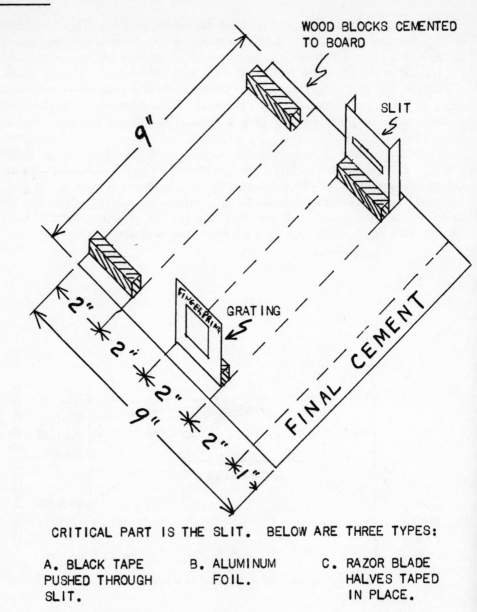

WOOD BLOCKS CEMENTED TO BOARD

SLIT

9"

2"

2"

2"

2"

9"

2"

1"

FINGER PRINT

GRATING

FINAL CEMENT

CRITICAL PART IS THE SLIT. BELOW ARE THREE TYPES:

A. BLACK TAPE PUSHED THROUGH SLIT.

B. ALUMINUM FOIL.

C. RAZOR BLADE HALVES TAPED IN PLACE.

2"

3"

SCHICK

FIG. 4-10. Plans for construction of simple spectroscope

USING YOUR SPECTROSCOPE

The spectroscope shows three types of spectra: 1. The *continuous* spectrum with all the colors of the rainbow is seen in incandescent lamps and other incandescent solids. 2. The *bright line* spectrum, with bright lines placed at positions in the spectrum for each element, is seen in incandescent vapors such as mercury vapor of fluorescent lights and the vapor of burning sodium. 3. The *absorption* spectrum shows dark lines for each element in place of the bright lines of the second spectrum. This happens when the continuous-spectrum light of an incandescent solid passes through a cooler incandescent gas. The gaseous element absorbs wave lengths which it would normally emit as bright lines.

Besides indicating the composition of the universe, the spectroscope has also told astronomers the direction in which distant galaxies are traveling through space. As they viewed the spectral lines of such galaxies, they observed that all lines were shifted toward the red end of the spectrum. Applying the *Doppler effect*, it was surmised that if the galaxies were speeding toward us, the light waves would be compressed, made shorter and shifted toward the violet end. Since they were being shifted in the other direction, it was theorized that the galaxies were speeding away from us, thus stretching or lengthening the light waves being emitted. This *red shift* phenomenon has led to the theory that the universe is expanding and every part is moving away from every other part.

EXPERIMENTS WITH SPECTROSCOPE

1. View sunlight reflected from a cloud or piece of paper. At first it will appear as a continuous spectrum; but look closely and you will see some of the dark lines produced as the gaseous elements of the solar atmosphere absorb their characteristic light waves. This is an absorption spectrum. Compare positions of your dark lines with those for solar spectrum in FIG. 4-8.

2. Spectra of mercury, argon and neon (bright line) may be observed in a fluorescent lamp, argon glow lamp and neon glow lamp respectively. The glow lamps may be purchased from the radio supply stores listed elsewhere.

3. Spectrum of sodium may be viewed by burning common salt (NaCl) in a gas or alcohol flame and observing the bright yellow 5890 Angstrom line in spectroscope.

The above experiments will probably lead to ideas for a number of other observations and uses for this simplified instrument. Spectral lines should be studied and plotted as outlined in FIG. 4-8 which shows only the very brightest lines of the dozens of specific lines plotted for each element but only visible to very sensitive instruments.

TEACHING TELESCOPE TECHNIQUE

If the camp is fortunate enough to have a good astronomical telescope it is important that the campers be familiar with its operation and use before they attempt to use it at night. Lack of knowledge and proper use of any scientific instrument will often lead to loss of interest due to the poor results obtained.

Use of the telescope is best taught in the daytime using distant objects on land and the sun. The technique for viewing the sun will be considered below, but it is important to remember NEVER *to look through a telescope at the sun!* The heat can permanently damage the eye! A session devoted to the following techniques will be well worth the time and an exciting introduction to proper telescope use.

1. Show a diagram of the optical system and show, or have the campers show, what happens to the light after it enters the telescope tube. Explain that the light comes in and is gathered by the mirror, which reflects the light back and focuses it on the diagonal mirror, whence it is reflected up to the adjustable eyepiece which magnifies the image.

2. Use the telescope to observe some distant object on land, such as a mountain top or fire tower. Explain that it is not necessary to hold onto the telescope as one views. The stand holds the instrument steady. If the viewer touches it he will cause the tube to move slightly. This movement is magnified by the lenses and the image flutters across the field of view.

3. Explain the equatorial mount. Aim it toward the location of the North Star and point the telescope at the sun in preparation for viewing sun spots. With the telescope aimed at the sun explain why we never look through the instrument in this position. Holding a sheet of paper, or a box with a white bottom, inside above the eyepiece, you will be able to project the image of the sun onto this "screen." It is perfectly safe to look at the sun's projected image in the box. A box, best of all a cigar box, is suggested because the sides will shade out unwanted sunlight from the sky. By the end of this session, everybody should be familiar with the operation and use of the telescope. They should be aware of the expense of purchasing such an instrument and of the need for great care in its handling. After this experience, most campers should be able to use the telescope in night viewing to its best advantage.

TRACKING SUNSPOTS

Sunspots, the whirling, tornado-like magnetic storms on the sun's surface, are under intense investigation by scientists. They seem to cause solar flares which shoot streams of high-energy electrically charged particles out of the sun deep into the solar system and past the earth. Many scientists feel that a trip to the moon is impossible or at least very dangerous until we are able to predict solar flares. Some things about sunspots are known. They are cooler than the sun's surface (8,000° F. compared with 11,000°). They have some effect on auroras, the location of the magnetic poles, radio communication, weather, plant growth, and other phenomena still under debate. For a discussion of auroras, see Chapter 2.

The number and size of sunspots fluctuate in cycles of about eleven years. There was a peak around 1961-62. Sunspots are larger than the earth and they go around with the sun as it rotates on its axis from left to right, making one turn every twenty-five days. It is when they are directly facing the earth that they are likely to cause disturbances here.

MATERIALS

Telescope or binoculars; small box, white paper, and pencil, or camera.

PROCEDURE

The method of observing sunspots in a box is explained in TEACHING TELE-SCOPE TECHNIQUE. With a piece of paper on your observing screen, you can draw the sun and its spots, following their progress as they move across the solar surface. Instead of drawing the sun each time, you may aim a camera into the observing box and photograph its image. This is an easy astronomical photo and makes good enlargements. Remembering that the diameter of the sun is 110 Earth Diameters, you can estimate the size of the sunspots observed. See if you can find any connection between sunspot occurrence and radio interference, auroras, or changes in compass readings. This field is under heavy experimentation at this time, and the observations described above are the same ones that top astronomers are now making as they explore the nature of sunspots.

IS THE MOON LARGER NEAR THE HORIZON?

We have all seen a "large" orange moon hanging just above the horizon and later on the same evening have observed a "smaller" white moon higher in the sky. This problem has puzzled thinking people for centuries. You can learn some things about the size of the moon as it rises by doing the PHOTOGRAPHIC MOON TRACK project described in this chapter. Recent experiments on the problem have been described by Kaufman and Rock,[1] who indicate that the effect of large moon or sun near the horizon is psychological and not optical.

Results in this field are still theoretical and simple experiments can be done with little or no equipment. The theory which appeared most acceptable to Kaufman and Rock is the *Apparent Distance Theory* which dates back to the second century. At that time, Ptolomy said that *a distant object viewed with other materials in the foreground appears more distant than when it is viewed in space with no other objects in view.* If both of these objects produce images in the eye of the same size, then in the process of perceiving, we automatically assume that the more distant-appearing one is larger.

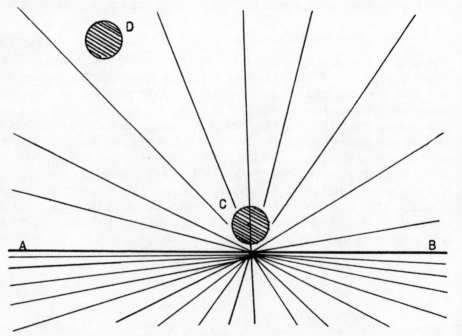

FIG. 4-11.   Draw perspective lines as shown for moon illusion experiments. Moons are not drawn on paper, see text. (Courtesy of *Scientific American*)

---

[1] "The Moon Illusion." *Scientific American*, July 1962, Vol. 207, No. 1.

Applying this to the moon, the horizon is seen in the same view with land, trees, or buildings, and appears farther away than the zenith moon which is seen in open space. Since both moons actually produce an image of the same size on the retina, but we think that one is more distant, then our powers of perception and reason tell us that the more distant moon must be larger.

You can do many experiments testing this and other theories on the moon illusion. Reference to the abovementioned article is highly recommended. A beginning in these experiments may be made with the drawing in FIG. 4-11.

MATERIALS

Large drawing paper, pencils, rulers, colored paper, scissors.

PROCEDURE

Have campers draw the above lines on paper. The moons will be cut out of colored paper and put in place later. Line AB represents the horizon and the lines below it give the impression of perspective which we see when we look across a surface to a distant point. Looking out into space, we seem to be looking from a single point and our view enlarges with distance. This effect is represented by the lines above the horizon. Have campers cut out moons of equal size and place them at various places in the "sky." Start with two blue moons. Go on to use different colors. (The moon does change color as it rises.) Cut out clouds and place them on the horizon. Judge the effect of each of these changes. Discuss other possible explanations and experiments for the moon illusion.

In the above drawing, both moons are the same size and the image in the eye is the same for both; but the perspective lines give the mind the impression that moon C (which is at the focus of the lines) is more distant. If it is more distant but both produce the same image in the eye, then the mind reasons that moon C must be larger and it deceives us by conveying that impression. If this is done as a project, the problem should be started with a discussion of the Apparent Distance Theory; but try to leave as many facts as possible to be found by the processes of discovery, discussion and experimentation, and imagination. See also PROJECT 84: OPTICAL ILLUSIONS.

PHOTOGRAPHIC MOON TRACK

MATERIALS

Camera, film, tripod.

PROCEDURE

Using a time exposure, a small lens opening and a steady camera mounted on a tripod, make a photo of the track of the full moon as it rises from the horizon high into the sky.

Instead of a continuous track you may prefer to make a series of instantaneous exposures every thirty minutes, all on the same piece of film. Once again, do not move the camera.

USE

There are at least two things to check on the print: 1. Is the track (or moon) the same width all the way? 2. Is the track (or moon) the same brightness all the way? Discuss and explain the results of the above observations.

MEASURING THE MOON'S DIAMETER

This is a problem in measurement, and like all such problems it should be done many times to reduce errors. Instead of one person's doing it many times, many people may do it once each. It is, therefore, an ideal group project. Take care to make *all* measurements with the greatest accuracy. (See MATHEMATICS: CALCULATING POSSIBLE ERROR.)

MATERIALS

Oaktag, stick, thumbtacks, ruler and yardstick.

PROCEDURE

Each person should prepare a piece of heavy paper or oaktag by cutting a slot exactly one inch wide down from the top of the paper (FIG. 4-12). Actually, this slot could be any width but the exact measurement must be known. Some people may try one and one-half or two inches to compare results.

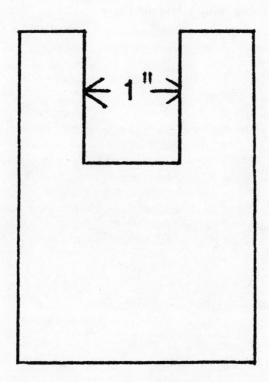

FIG. 4-12.   Cut one-inch opening in card to measure moon's diameter.

USE

At night, tack paper to the top of a stick driven into the ground so you can sight the full moon through the slot in the paper. This is best done in an open field with plenty of space behind you. Sight through the slot at the moon and move back slowly so that the moon's image just fills the space. Now measure the distance from the stick to the place you were standing when the moon just filled the slot. By working a direct proportion you may calculate the moon's diameter as follows:

Size of slot (inches) = A   (1″)
Diameter of moon (miles) = B
Distance from you to stick (inches) = C
Distance from stick to moon (miles) = D   (240,000)

A is to C as B is to D,   or $\dfrac{A}{C} = \dfrac{B}{D}$

You may like to test this system during the day on a building whose width is known to see how accurate it is. Once again, have many people try it and average the results.

If you had a helper 500 or more miles away, you could find the distance to the moon by using simple trigonometry.

PHOTOGRAPHING ARTIFICIAL SATELLITES

This project has three phases. The first two are photographic, the third is mathematical. You may do phase one alone, phases one and two, or all three.

MATERIALS

Camera, film, tripod.

PROCEDURE

PHASE 1: Artificial satellites may be easily photographed by setting the camera on "time," placing it on a tripod and aiming it at the portion of the sky to be crossed by the satellite. Take your picture when the satellite is at its highest point for the evening and use a large lens opening: 4.5, 5.6, or 6.3. The moving satellite will leave a continuous track of reflected light on the film.

PHASE 2: For added interest, set camera up as above, but interrupt light to lens every second (or two or five seconds) with hand or card in front of lens. This will produce a picture of the satellite track broken at known time intervals. Seconds may be called out by someone with a watch or by listening to WWV or Canadian Observatory time signals on a short-wave receiver.

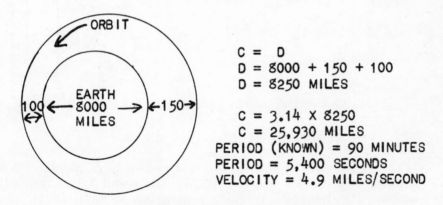

$$C = D$$
$$D = 8000 + 150 + 100$$
$$D = 8250 \text{ MILES}$$

$$C = 3.14 \times 8250$$
$$C = 25,930 \text{ MILES}$$
PERIOD (KNOWN) = 90 MINUTES
PERIOD = 5,400 SECONDS
VELOCITY = 4.9 MILES/SECOND

FIG. 4-13. Calculating approximate distance traveled by satellite in photograph when apogee, perigee and period are known

PHASE 3: Determine the distance traveled by the satellite in a single one of your time intervals. You must know the apogee and perigee and period of the satellite. (This information is published in papers and science magazines. Keep a chart of them.) First step is to find the total circumference

of the orbit. Since we incorrectly assume the orbit to be circular, the fina
results will not be truly correct. Satellites have elliptical orbits but man
are nearly circular and in such cases, these results will be a very close
approximation of the truth. The example given in FIG. 4-13 indicates a
satellite moving 4.9 miles for each one-second streak of light. Counting
the streaks all across your photo, you can see how many miles it traveled
during the photographing. This is a good chance to use your homemade
slide rules. (See MATHEMATICS.)

STAR-TRACK PHOTOGRAPHS

The earth, spinning on its axis, makes one complete turn every twenty-four hours, while the stars and sun remain relatively fixed in space. Fast though it is, people living on earth are not aware of this spinning. Instead it appears to us that the stars are turning around the earth at night and the sun is moving around us in the day. It is possible with any camera to photograph the apparent movement of the stars across the night sky.

MATERIALS

Camera, tripod, film.

PROCEDURE

Set the camera on time with a lens setting of about F-8 to 6.3. Place it on a tripod and aim it at the North Star. Make sure that no glare will reach the lens from cars, house lights, streetlight, or other source. Leave the camera to make an exposure from four to eight hours. Since the camera is located on earth, it is spinning with the earth under the stars. Aiming the camera at the North Star should cause the star tracks to make increasingly larger circles out from the center.

USE

Since the earth's axis, the center of our turntable, points at the North Star, we might expect the North Star to leave a dot in the center of the other star tracks. You will notice that this is not true. The North Star makes a very small circle of its own, indicating that our North Pole points not at the North Star but a little off to the side. True north would be in the center of this circle. Find this on your photograph, then see if you can estimate the location of true north in the night sky.

TELESCOPIC PHOTOGRAPHY

In the procedures previously described for photographing star and satellite trails, no telescope was needed. Good pictures may also be made of the moon and planets with the use of a telescope. Since each setup is different, this project will require a certain amount of individual experimentation.

MATERIALS

Camera, film, tripod. In choosing a camera for this, it is best to have a ground-glass viewer, either a single-lens reflex or a press-type camera which will show in the viewfinder exactly the same picture that will go on the film. A bracket may be purchased to mount the camera on the telescope or the camera may be mounted on an elevator tripod which permits exact control of the height.

PROCEDURE

To make the photographs, set your telescope up as usual with the desired object sighted and in focus. Place the camera in position over the telescope lens and refocus the telescope so the image is in focus on the ground glass of the camera. The camera may be used with or without its own lens in place. Both methods have merits to recommend them. If the lens is used, critical adjustment must be made to insure that the camera lens and telescope lens are directly in line so the image will fall on the film and not on the side of the lens barrel. Various exposures may be tried. As a start you may try F 3.5 for one second on Plus-X film. Exposure should be as brief as possible to reduce grain in the negative. It is also well to use a cable release on the camera to prevent vibration.

Develop the film in a fine-grain solution such as D-76 or Microdol-X. Whereas the image on the film will be very small, considerable enlargement will be desirable, and is best done by placing the enlarger in a horizontal position and projecting the image across a dark room onto paper held in a vertical easel. Because conditions vary with each individual setup, these instructions are necessarily sketchy. But with a little experimentation and careful work, the effort made should be well rewarded. (See also Chapter 6, MAKING PHOTOMICROGRAPHS.)

FINDING LATITUDE WITH THE NORTH STAR

Polaris, the North Star, is located in space almost directly above the North Pole of the earth and is visible from any point in the Northern Hemisphere. This fact makes it possible to use the North Star to find the latitude of any place in the Northern Hemisphere. For a person at the North Pole, the North Star appears directly overhead in the sky. Its altitude is 90° and the latitude there is 90°. At the equator, the North Star appears on the horizon, or zero degrees altitude. The latitude is also zero degrees. We can determine our latitude simply by determining the altitude of the North Star. (See FIG. 4-14.) Since this is a problem in mathematical measurement, each camper should do it individually to have all results averaged out to one answer. If you wish, you may calculate the probable error of the answer as described in Chapter 8. The correct exact latitude will be found on a topographic map of your area.

MATERIALS

The altitude of stars is found with a clinometer. Plans for a simple clinometer that each camper can make are found in Chapter 8.

PROCEDURE

Sight through the straw at the North Star and read its altitude (your latitude) directly from the protractor scale. It may be easier to sight along the top of the straw to get it into the general position, then sight through it and center the star.

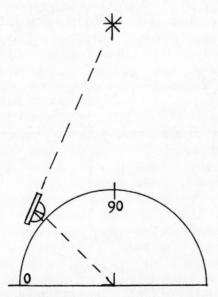

FIG. 4-14. Using straw clinometer to find latitude with the North Star

MAKING A CIRCUMPOLAR STAR CHART

The circumpolar stars are those stars which appear to travel in a circle around the North Star and never set below the horizon. The circumpolar stars are the only stars which are visible every clear night all through the year. In learning the circumpolar stars and constellations, it is helpful to draw a chart of them as they are observed in the night sky.

For most of the United States, there are four bright circumpolar constellations. They are the Big Dipper, Little Dipper, Cassiopeia, and Cephus.

MATERIALS

Paper, pencils, rulers, lapboards or equivalent.

PROCEDURE

During a night observing session start the drawing with a circle which has an "X" in the center. This "X" will mark the location of the North Star. (See FIG. 4-15.) The distance from X down to the bottom of the circle is the distance from Polaris down to the horizon. Use this distance as a radius to draw an imaginary circle in the sky around Polaris. All stars within this circle are circumpolar and never set. It may be helpful in drawing the charts if the circle is divided into quarters. The projects may be started with a circle as shown in the diagram. If a flashlight is used, place paper over the lens to reduce the light so the eyes will not continually have to readjust from the bright paper to the dark sky.

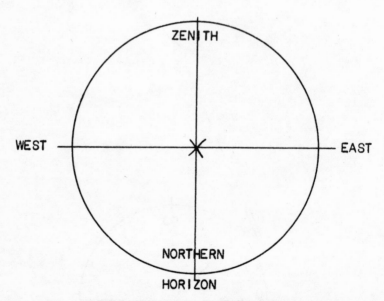

FIG. 4-15.   Paper prepared for drawing circumpolar star chart during night observation session

DEMONSTRATING ROCKET PROPULSION

Rocket propulsion is based upon Sir Isaac Newton's Third Law of Motion, which states that for every action there is an equal and opposite reaction. There are many simple demonstrations of this law. A person jumps from a boat (action) and boat moves in opposite direction (reaction). A bullet leaves a gun and gun is thrown backward. Air leaves a balloon and the balloon moves forward. In all these examples, a body moves because something is leaving it. From Newton's Second Law we find that the body's motion will increase if the material leaving increases in speed or mass (weight). Thus a large man will cause the boat to go farther than a small boy, and a person diving from the boat will send it farther than a person stepping from it gently. Rockets are pushed forward by internal gases that exert thrust against the front of the engine but not against the back, because there is a hole where the back would otherwise be. The rocket does not move because the gases are pushing against the atmosphere. Rocket propulsion and the increasing thrust with increasing mass is easily demonstrated with the following mousetrap rocket.

MATERIALS

Mousetrap, heavy-duty staple (Electrical staple will do), length of string, toy car or car large enough to support mousetrap (Build these with Erector set, or use roller skate), some weights (fishing weights or stones).

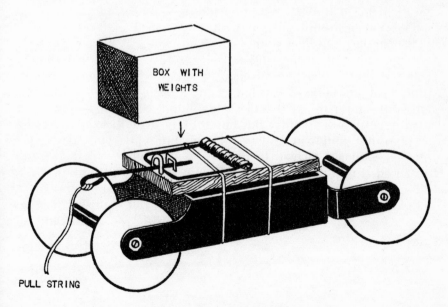

BOX WITH WEIGHTS

PULL STRING

Fig. 4-16. Mousetrap is tied to small cart to demonstrate rocket propulsion by action and reaction.

PROCEDURE

Prepare trap by removing bait holder and trip bar (but not staple). Insert another staple opposite the present one so the spring bar will fit between the two when pulled back. Tie string in loop of trip bar and cut off bent end. Fasten trap with string securely to the free-wheeling cart. To use, pull spring bar back and hold under trip bar which is placed under the two staples. Pulling the string should snap the trap. (See FIG. 4-16.)

USE

Set trap and release with a quick pull of string. Car will not move. Set trap again and place a small box containing a couple of stones on the spring bar, release again and as box is thrown off, car moves forward. Try again but with more stones. As the weight of stones increases, the thrust and forward motion of the car increases. This is the principle of the rocket ship but instead of throwing off a few boulders, it throws off billions of gas molecules at high speeds for forward thrust.

EVENING WITHOUT A TELESCOPE

The purpose of this evening activity is to see as many of the stars as possible without a telescope and become familiar with their locations in the sky. During the evening such concepts as *magnitude, altitude* and *azimuth* may be introduced. In finding and observing stars it is a good idea, whenever possible, to use pointer stars of a familiar constellation to locate a less familiar object, the best-known example being the pointers in the Big Dipper.

We can begin early in the evening with the bright circumpolar constellations. The Big Dipper is always easiest to find—most of its stars are second magnitude. There is a double star in the handle, Mizar, with magnitudes of two and four for the two components. The two stars on the front of the bowl point directly to Polaris, the North Star, which is the last and brightest star in the handle of the Little Dipper, magnitude of two. Polaris is also a double star but the other component, magnitude nine, is visible only with a telescope. Polaris is located directly above the North Pole of the earth and as the earth spins, all the stars seem to turn around Polaris counterclockwise. Across Polaris, directly opposite the Big Dipper, is Cassiopeia, looking like a sprawling "W" in the sky. Between the Little Dipper and Cassiopeia is a fourth circumpolar constellation, Cephus. Mythology called it a king. Actually it looks more like a very simple house. Cephus is not bright and you have to look carefully to see it. Delta Cephei (F-6.5) is a variable star with a period of five days, in which time its brightness changes from a magnitude of 3.5 to 4.5.

We can move out of the circumpolar region now to the stars that are seen only in summer. Our guide will be the handle of the Big Dipper. Follow the handle around in an arc a short distance to a first-magnitude star with a reddish-yellow color. This is Arcturus, twenty-five times the diameter of the sun, but cooler by 4,000 degrees (only 7,000° F). This star is thirty-six light years away. In the same region, notice the Corona Borealis or Northern Crown.

Go back to the Big Dipper's handle and swing that arc again but this time continue through Arcturus to the next brightest star, a little over first magnitude, Spica, a very hot blue star, 36,000° F.

Moving from the southern sky to the east, we turn to the summer triangle and the Northern Cross. Start from Cassiopeia, using the two stars on the end of the "W" as pointers. Follow a line through Cephus to the very bright white star Vega. Moving down slightly from Vega, you come to the Northern Cross (Cygnus) with the 1.5 magnitude star Deneb at its head. From those two stars look down to the southeast to the first-magnitude Altair. The summer triangle is seen by connecting these three stars together to form a triangle which is visible during the summer months. Deneb is actually as bright as the other two stars but because they are only twenty light years away and it is 465, it appears less brilliant.

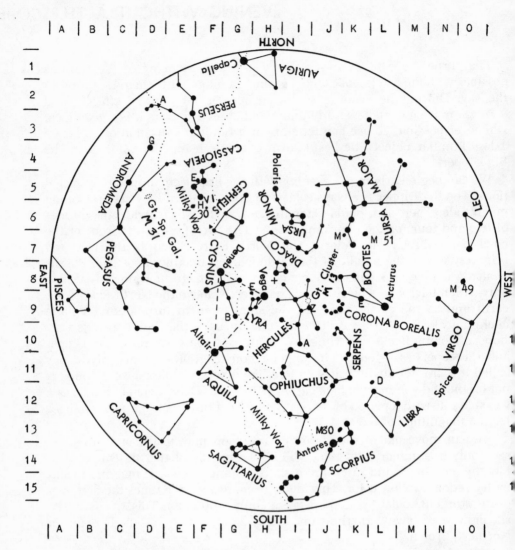

FIG. 4-17. Sky map showing principal stars visible during July and August. If held overhead, the + near the head of Draco marks the zenith, and the outer circle represents the horizon with compass directions as marked. (Courtesy of Hayden Planetarium, Boston Museum of Science)

While at the Northern Cross, follow a line through its length down to the southeastern horizon where you will find a group of bright stars forming the image of a giant teapot with its handle on the left, sitting on the horizon. This is the constellation of Sagittarius. Notice it is on the edge of the Milky Way. Pause here and follow the Milky Way across the sky. When you look at Sagittarius, you are looking into the center of our galaxy. Look carefully and see some hazy patches of light in this region. Binoculars or a telescope will reveal these patches to be clusters of thousands of stars. To the right of the teapot is the winding scorpion Scorpius with the supergiant red Antares near its head. Antares has a diameter 400 times that of the sun. It is only about 5,000° F. but 170 light years distant from us. Follow a line from Antares through the head of the Scorpion, past the diamond-shaped Libra with its faint stars and you arrive back at first-magnitude Spica. Go up to orange Arcturus, around to the handle of the Big Dipper to the pointers of the bowl and stop at the North Star. You have now made a fairly complete tour of the summer skies without instruments and should be able to feel on closer terms with the stars of summer, near and far.

There are some other special attractions during the summer months including two fairly dependable meteor showers when meteors should appear more often than on other nights. One shower should be reaching its peak around midnight on July 29 when most meteors will be seen in the eastern sky in Aquarius. Observers have counted up to twenty meteors per hour during this shower on moonless nights.

Perhaps the most celebrated shower of the year reaches its peak on August 11 and 12 when most meteors will appear in the northeast sky from the constellation Perseus. Up to fifty meteors per hour have been counted on this one. With all meteor showers, observation is best on nights when the moon is not in the sky and during the hours around and following midnight.

Another feature which is visible all winter begins to appear low in the eastern sky during August. It is the great spiral galaxy in Andromeda, our nearest galaxy in space, about 1,700,000 light years away, somewhat larger than the Milky Way but probably the same shape. Recent estimates of the number of stars in the Milky Way range from 40,000,000,000 to 200,000,-000,000. The great spiral galaxy is just barely visible to the naked eye as a hazy patch of light. Binoculars and telescopes will greatly improve the view.

AN EVENING WITH THE TELESCOPE

Before using the telescope for group observation at night, the counselor should become completely familiar with the use of the instrument through some private practice sessions. It is not a simple task to aim a five-foot tube directly at a single star millions of miles away, and a few hints are in order. First find the desired object in the sky without the telescope, then sight along the length of the telescope tube to place it in the approximate position. Next sight the object through small finder scope mounted on the large instrument and finally locate it in the main eyepiece. You should also know the width of the field visible in the telescope. Determine this by sighting stars in the Big Dipper and see how many stars are included in your viewing area. The distance between these stars may then be used as a measuring stick for the amount of space your instrument will include at one time.

The most often observed telescopic objects include double stars, nebula, variable stars and star clusters. The accompanying table lists these objects which are visible in July and/or August and which give the most rewarding views.

TELESCOPIC FEATURES VISIBLE IN JULY AND/OR AUGUST

CONSTELLATION	TYPE OF FEATURE(S)	IDENTIFICATION	LOCATION ON SKY MAP (Fig. 4-17)
Perseus	Eclipsing Variable—three-day period	Algol	D-2
Big Dipper	Double star	Mizar and Zeta	K-6.5
	Whirlpool Nebula	M 51	K-7
Little Dipper	Double and Variable—four-day period	Polaris	H-5
Cassiopeia	Star cluster	H. VI. 30	E-6
	Double star, yellow and purple	Eta	F-5
Cephus	Variable—six-day period	Delta Cephei	F-6
Andromedae	Spiral galaxy	M 31	D-5
	Double star, blue and gold	Gamma	D-4
Cygnus	Double star, yellow and blue	Beta (Albreo)	G-9
Bootes	Large orange star	Arcturus	L-9
	Double star, orange and green	Epsilon	K-9
Virgo	Nebula	M 49	O-8
Lyra	Double, double	Epsilon	G, H-8.5
Hercules	Double star, yellow and blue	Zeta	I-9
	Globular star cluster	M 13	I-9
	Variable four double, orange and green, two-day period	Alpha (Ras Algethi)	I-10
Libra	Variable—two-day period	Delta	L-11.5
Scorpius	Globular cluster	M 80	J-13
	Other clusters		

RESOURCE MATERIALS FOR ASTRONOMY

Magazines

Sky and Telescope. Monthly, $5 per year. Sky Publishing Co., Harvard College Observatory, Cambridge 38, Mass.

Sky Map. Monthly bulletin $2 per year. Hayden Planetarium, Museum of Science, Boston, Mass. Check local sources for similar service.

Spaceflight. Bimonthly, $3.50 per year. Sky Publishing Co., Harvard College Observatory, Cambridge 38, Mass. Also catalog of astronomy books and charts.

Missiles and Rockets. Weekly, $5 per year. American Aviation Publications, Inc., 1001 Vermont Ave., N.W., Washington, D. C.   20005.

Pamphlets and Charts

National Aviation Education Council, 1025 Connecticut Avenue, N.W., Washington, D. C. 20006. Request *Aviation Education Bibliography* and *Pictures, Pamphlets and Charts.* Both free booklets contain valuable lists of materials.

National Aeronautics and Space Administration, Washington, D. C. 20025. Many publications. Ask to be placed on mailing list for "NASA Facts." May help with specific questions on orbiting satellites.

Space Vehicles Kit, Educational Affairs Dept., Ford Motor Co., The American Road, Dearborn, Michigan. Also request catalog of films and teaching aids.

Films

The following films are free, the user pays return postage. They may be ordered through the local Bell Telephone business office.

> *Our Mr. Sun*
> *Strange Case of Cosmic Rays*
> *All About Time*

Association Films, Inc., Broad at Elm, Ridgefield, N. J. Free, four space specials:

> *The Mastery of Space*
> *The Path to Space*
> *Pioneers of Space*
> *Your Share in Space*

Supplies

Edmund Scientific Co., 101 East Gloucester Pike, Barrington, N. J.

Unitron Instrument Co., 66 Needham St., Newton Highlands 61, Mass. Ask for "Observer's Guide and Telescope Catalog."

Criterion Manufacturing Co., 331 Church Street, Hartford, Conn. 06101. Producers of reflecting telescopes.

Swift Instruments, Inc., 1190 North Fourth Street, San Jose, Calif., or 924 Dorchester Avenue, Dorchester, Mass.

Chapter
5: Geology

SUGGESTED REFERENCES

Pearl, Richard, *How to Know the Minerals and Rocks.* New York: New American Library, 1958.

Rapport and Wright, editors, *The Crust of the Earth.* New York: New American Library, 1959.

Carson, Rachel, *The Sea Around Us.* New York: New American Library, 1959. (This book deals with oceanography.)

GEOLOGY, by definition, is the study of the earth and the changes taking place within it. Many people are satisfied to know geology only as mineral collecting or as the cutting and polishing of semiprecious stones. These people who collect or cut are usually well aware of the real meaning of geology and of how their minerals have been formed. They prefer not to deal with geology as a whole, but to specialize in the particular activities at which they are happiest. Yet to many people who have never done anything in geology, mention of the word means only collecting rocks . . . and after all, what can be interesting about a hard, dirty rock? Those who have not been properly introduced to the field of geology are missing a whole world of excitement, mystery, and ancient history, not to mention exercise and fresh air.

Geology is well suited to the summer camp because it is primarily an outdoor activity and, at many times, a vigorous activity. It is the study of the earth and the geologist must follow the earth wherever this study takes him. A geological project may take campers out hiking for miles across country, climbing mountains, camping out over night. If the group is so inclined, it may even go under water. In its fullest sense, geology is a highly desirable combination of science, sport and exploration all tied together in a purposeful activity which is both physically and mentally stimulating.

Studying geology in the field is like trying to solve a mystery after all the clues have been methodically collected, identified and evaluated, as explained in the field projects. Of course, some campers will prefer to specialize in mineral collecting or lapidary work (cutting and polishing). These activities have their own exciting aspects and should certainly be encouraged.

Another goal of geology is to help children develop an understanding of the earth—to see it as an ever-changing, moving thing with forces, pressures and tensions constantly pulling at it and working on it. This brings up a major problem in teaching geology. The earth and the forces working on and in it are large beyond the imagination or experience of any child and many adults. The fact that these forces work slowly over periods of thousands of years makes them no easier to understand. Some of the facts seem so fantastic as to be unbelievable when first heard. The counselor should be aware of this problem and be prepared to meet it with patience and repetition of facts. He should also watch for opportunities to demonstrate these forces speeded up and the structures made smaller through the use of models and mock-ups. Such efforts will make the unimaginable more concrete and realistic. Many of the projects in this chapter have been designed with this problem in mind, to bring a geological fact from the world of the unreal to something which can be made, felt, seen, handled and thus understood.

INFORMATION OF IMPORTANCE

Geology is the study of the earth. A knowledge of the structure of the earth is part of the basic background information. (See FIG. 5-1.) The *crust* is the hard brittle rock on which we live, of which our mountains are made and about which we know the most. The crust varies in thickness, being thinnest under the oceans and thickest under the highest continental mountain ranges. The Mohorovicic discontinuity *(Moho)* is the dividing line between the crust and *mantle*. It is at this depth that tests are under way to drill the Mohole and learn more about the crust and mantle. The mantle is a mysterious and important layer of the earth. It is believed that a layer of rock in the mantle has a semi-fluid plastic nature.[1] Many of our mountain-building theories depend upon the existence of this plasticlike rock and it is even possible that the continental masses have moved (floated) across the surface of the earth on it. The *outer core* is liquid iron and nickel, melted due to the tremendous heat and pressure from the overlying rock. The *inner core* is also a liquid; but because of the pressure on it, is under sufficient compression to have the structure and nature of a solid. Pressure at the center is presumed to be about 25,000 tons per square inch with temperatures about 5,000° F.

The most common elements in the crust are: oxygen 50 per cent, silicon 25 per cent, aluminum 7.5 per cent, and iron 5 per cent. Most minerals contain these elements along with small amounts of some of the other eighty-eight natural elements.

Much of the remaining material of geology may be divided into three categories: 1. materials which make up the earth—minerals and rocks;

---

[1] The nature of this semi-fluid rock may be nicely demonstrated with a plastic putty such as "Silly Putty." Under slow, constant pressure, it will take any desired shape as would a liquid. Under sudden tension or a hammer blow, it will fracture and break apart as would a brittle rock.

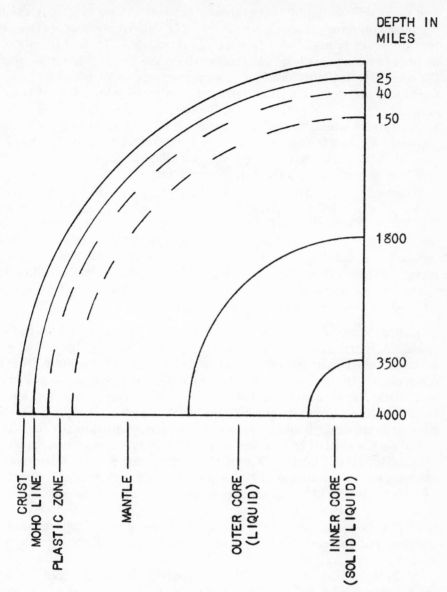

DEPTH IN
MILES

25
40

150

1800

3500

4000

CRUST
MOHO LINE
PLASTIC ZONE
MANTLE
OUTER CORE
(LIQUID)
INNER CORE
(SOLID LIQUID)

Fig. 5-1. Cross section diagram to center of earth

2. forces at work to level the earth—weathering and erosion; 3. forces at work to build up the earth—mountains and continents.

The theory that the present form of the earth's crust has been formed by alternation between forces of mountain building and forces of erosion was first proposed in the eighteenth century by James Hutton, a Scot, and advocated by his countryman Sir Charles Lyell. For this theory and the extensive substantiating field work which they did, both men are considered the founders of modern geology.

Information concerning types, formation and identification of minerals and rocks will be found in the various projects. As we look over the land, the most common substance usually seen is soil. Young people often forget that the earth is made of rock which is relatively solid. Soil is only a thin blanket covering this bedrock. Places where the bedrock is visible through the soil are called *outcrops*. In discussing igneous rocks, it should be known that there are two types: *extrusive* igneous rocks which flowed from volcanoes or cracks and cooled *above* the surface of the ground, and *intrusive* igneous rocks which flowed into openings underground and cooled *below* the surface. Granite and pegmatite are two igneous rocks which cool below ground. Note the three types of rocks described under IDENTIFYING ROCKS and that *all* rocks originally started as igneous.

Weathering and erosion are two distinct groups of forces at work to make the earth level by bringing down the high places and filling in the low places. *Weathering* is the process of breaking solid bedrock (originally the only material on the land) down into boulders, stones and smaller pieces and eventually to soil. *Soil* is a finely ground mixture of inorganic mineral matter and organic decaying plant and animal matter which forms a blanket over the bedrock of the earth. Following are the basic agents of weathering and their methods of operation:

1. *Ice*. Water reaches far down into cracks in rocks. When the water freezes, it expands and widens the crack. Upon melting, the water will go down into the newly deepened crack, refreeze and widen it more. This process is most active during seasons when day temperatures are above freezing and night temperatures are below. Under such conditions, the alternate freezing, thawing and deepening can break a rock in half in a very short time. It is true that boulders gradually move upward through the soil and a field that is cleared of boulders this year will have more on top next year. This is due to the heaving action of frost in the ground. When water in the soil freezes (ground frost), it expands in the only available direction— up. This upward heaving lifts boulders and leaves open spaces beneath them. Upon thawing, mud flows into these open spaces and the boulders have thus been raised a short distance. As this process repeats itself, the boulders rise increasingly higher through the soil until they arrive on the surface.

2. *Temperature extremes*. The sun beating down on a rock heats only the surface while the interior remains cool. Heating causes the surface to expand and alternate heating and cooling causes it to expand and contract, forming an outer layer on the rock which splits or *spalls* off. This type of weathering is known as *exfoliation*.

3. *Plants*. The tiny roots or stems of young plants including trees have little difficulty working their way into small cracks in rock. As soon as the plant has a footing, its root or stem widens out with sufficient force to enlarge the crack and often eventually splits the rock in two pieces. It is not difficult to find trees which appear to have grown through the middle of a large rock.

4. *Carbonic acid*. A solution of carbon dioxide in water forms weak carbonic acid. The same acid is found in carbonated beverages. This acid, working constantly in nature, slowly dissolves away various rocks, espe-

cially limestones. The carbon dioxide may be picked up in the atmosphere by rain water or be produced by plants, especially rock *lichens* wet with rain water.

5. *Oxidation and Hydration*. Two other methods of weathering are the addition of oxygen molecules (similar to rusting) and the addition of water molecules to the composition of the rock. The addition of each molecule of these substances weakens the molecular structure of the rock, increases its volume and makes it more vulnerable to other forms of more active weathering.

After the bedrock has been broken into smaller pieces by weathering, it is time for the activity of erosion to begin. *Erosion* is the process of actually carrying away or transporting the products of weathering. Nature carries this out by means of the following forces:

1. *Running water*. If any single erosional force had to be selected as most important in carving out the present surface of the land, it would be running water. Rivers and river beds are formed by running water. They first develop at the mouth (at ocean or another river) as gulleys or gorges and carve their valleys back into the higher land by a process of *headward erosion*. All rivers eventually reach the sea and as they flow, carry the continental rocks, products of weathering, into the oceans. Government geologists have estimated that rivers of the United States carry nearly 800,000,000 tons of earth material into the oceans every year. All the sand in the ocean consists of grains of rock (much granite) which have been carried from the continents by rivers. Likewise, the salts of the ocean consist mainly of sodium, magnesium and calcium carried out from the land. The sodium becomes sodium chloride (table salt) and remains in solution with the magnesium salts. Calcium salts are removed from sea water by animals needing calcium to make their shells. Many dry valleys are seen today which were cut by rivers that no longer exist. Many were temporary rivers formed by the melting ice of vast mile-thick glaciers. *Potholes* are sometimes seen in the bedrock of rivers. These are round, smooth holes formed by stones caught in whirlpools carving into the bedrock. Potholes indicate that the river was once fast-flowing, with rapids, cascades and waterfalls. During flood stage, a river valley may be filled to the top with powerful, fast-moving water. When the river returns to its normal level, the top of the valley is often found to be left wide, flat and fertile. This area is known as the *flood plain* and makes good farm land. But is not a good location for houses; it belongs to the river and being part of the river, will be filled with water during subsequent flooding periods. The *watershed* is all the land above a given point in a stream that contributes water to the flow at that point.

2. *Ground water*. When rain falls on the ground, some of it flows over the surface into rivers and some of it seeps into the earth to flow underground over waterproof (impermeable) rock until it reaches the surface again through springs, ponds or lakes and flows into rivers. This is called *ground water* and the top level of the ground water is called the *ground water table*. The level of this table varies with the seasons as it is affected

by the amount of rainfall and the water needs of growing plants. If ground water is flowing with any speed, it can be an active force of erosion. It is particularly important when carrying rock-dissolving chemicals such as CO_2 which forms carbonic acid. Ground water carrying carbonic acid is responsible for dissolving and carrying away much limestone to form many famous *caverns*. A *sink hole* is formed when the roof caves in on a hole formed by ground water. An area with many sink holes is referred to as *Karst* topography. Such areas are common in Kentucky and Florida, among other places.

3. *Wind.* Wind carrying sand is a force of both weathering and erosion as the grains of sand blast against exposed rock and cut in like millions of tiny carving knives. Wind is also an important mover of soil especially in the Great Plains where many farmers have lost entire crops as valuable fertile soil was carried away by wind. Wind erosion is greatest on smooth ground, less on rough ground and least on land which is covered by vegetation. *Dunes* formed by wind may be seen in any sandy area.

4. *Glaciers.* A glacier is a *moving* ice field. Glaciers covering large areas of land in which the ice moves out radially from the center are *continental* glaciers and are found today on Greenland, Iceland and Antarctica. Small glaciers found in the high, cold valleys of mountains are known as *alpine* glaciers. In order for glaciers to form, the winter snowfall must be greater than the summer melting, producing a continual accumulation year after year. When the snow accumulates sufficiently, it is compressed into a granular ice. After reaching a thickness greater than 200 feet, the ice has enough pressure to melt a thin layer on the bottom and produce a film of lubricating water. Weight at the thickest part squeezes ice out at the front, much as toothpaste is squeezed from a tube by pressure from the back, and the ice field is set in motion, thus forming a glacier. Often material on the edges breaks off into adjacent oceans, forming icebergs. The continental glacier on North America was about one mile thick. So also is the glacier now on Antarctica, which moves an average of 90 miles per year. If all Antarctic ice were to melt, the world sea level would rise 200 feet, provided the Antarctic continent did not rise up after the tremendous weight was removed or the ocean floor did not sink down under the new additional weight. These elevation shifts probably would take place to some extent.[1] Glaciers move forward. They do not move back, they melt back. The North American glaciers advanced and retreated four times, starting about 300,000 years ago and retreating for the last time about 17,000 years ago. Each of the four glacial periods lasted an average of 40,000 years. The exact cause of ice ages is not known although a number of theories have been advanced.

Glaciers, both alpine and continental, do not have the powerful erosional forces of rivers. While rivers can actually cut deep valleys out of a plain glaciers are mainly limited to smoothing, polishing, rounding and scour-

---

[1] Gordon deQ. Robin, "The Ice of the Antarctic," *Scientific American*, Sept. 1962 Vol. 207, No. 3.

ng those valleys and moving boulders and soil from one place to an-
ther. Glaciers round out V-shaped river valleys by a process of *glacial
lucking.* As the ice moves into the valley, it freezes into cracks along the
ock banks. The rock is broken by this process and carried away as the
lacier continues on its forward journey. After the ice has melted, a broad-
ased U-shaped valley remains as evidence of the great ice sheet.

The North American ice sheet covered only a northern portion of the
Jnited States. A line indicating its southern boundary may be drawn from
ast to west, starting at New York City, west to Pittsburgh, down the Ohio
River and up the Missouri River, with a line projected from the end of
he Missouri through Seattle to the West Coast. Most of the land north
f this line should show various glacial evidences as listed under project
ELD GEOLOGY. Glaciers are very difficult for young people to compre-
end, and facts concerning them should be repeated often to increase
amiliarity and credibility.

Mention of erosion automatically brings conservation to mind and this
opic should certainly be discussed at camp. The national conservation
ovement was initiated by Theodore Roosevelt and material giving infor-
ation and conservation projects will be found listed under RESOURCE
ATERIAL.

Finally we come to forces at work to build up the earth. Since the earth
now in a period of erosion, erosive forces can be observed and studied.
here is little opportunity to observe forces of building. Comparatively little
known about these and many ideas are still theories. One major evidence
f building is seen in mountains, of which there are four major types:
olcanoes, folded, fault block, and erosional.

Volcanoes start as openings in the ground through which molten rock
ours intermittently. All rock flowing from a volcano is called *lava* and
ay form *basalt, felsite* or *trap,* along with pumice and obsidian. The six-
ile-high Mauna Loa, in Hawaii, is a volcano built up by lava flows and
probably the highest mountain in the world: about 14,000 feet above sea
vel, 19,000 feet below sea level. (See MAPS, CHARTS AND MODELS.)

Folded mountains develop in chains or ranges and usually have the great-
st elevation above sea level. The Himalayas are folded mountains and
iclude the 29,141-foot peak of Mount Everest, highest elevation on earth.
hese mountain ranges are developed by horizonal compression in the
rust, causing the surface to buckle and fold up.

Fault block mountains include most of those found on the West Coast.
hese mountains, according to the theory, are huge blocks of granite with
ots that extend far down into the crust and float on semi-fluid plastic
ck theoretically present there. These West Coast mountains are still
rowing, for as material is eroded from the tops, the mountains become
ghter and must readjust by rising up and floating at a higher level. The
adjustments are made as a series of very small moves but they are felt
the surrounding area as *earthquakes,* resulting in shock waves which

pass through the rocks and record on *seismographs* around the world. Even when there are no earthquakes, seismographs show slight changes in the crust, probably due to changes in atmospheric pressure.

Erosional mountains are the Appalachians and other East Coast mountains. These are older structures than those on the West Coast and started as giant folded mountains, about 300,000,000 years ago. Rivers cut into the peaks for millions of years and eventually brought them down to a level plain. The rivers worked fastest in the peaks of the mountains because during folding, the rocks of the summits were bent back, cracked weakened and left most vulnerable to erosion. After the level plain was formed, the rivers continued cutting down, carving valleys under the places that were once towering summits. The deepest valleys go down about a mile and the walls towering above the valleys are now called mountains

The largest features on earth, the continents and oceans, are those about which we know the least. Many theories attempt to explain why we have these great ocean depressions. One, first proposed by Alfred Wegener early in the century, is now coming back into favor and will be described here Wegener was one of many people who noticed that if the American continents were moved across the Atlantic, they would fit like a jigsaw puzzle into the coastline of Europe and Africa. It was also noted that Africa, India South America, Australia and Antarctica may have been joined together in a single land mass called *Gondwanaland*. Indeed, geological and fossil evidence collected then and now supports this idea of a single supercontinent existing up until 150,000,000 years ago. Studies made in Antarctica during the International Geophysical Year further support the theory.

The fact that many of the world's great mountain ranges are located on or parallel to continental coastlines is another curiosity that has long challenged geologists. Wegener suggested that sections broke away from the supercontinent and drifted apart on the semi-fluid rock below the crust thus opening the Atlantic and Indian Oceans and forming our present continents.

In its original form this *Continental Drift Hypothesis* was controversial and insufficient. There are, however, three modern developments which lend new favor to a revised version of the hypothesis: 1. The hypothetical plastic zone below the crust on which the continents could float, 2. The discovery of mid-oceanic ridges in the Atlantic and Indian Oceans, and 3. Evidence of thermal convection currents moving up, across and down through the mantle at a rate of about one inch per year. Based on these findings, the modern hypothesis assumes that the primeval earth cooled by convection currents bringing heat through the mantle to the surface of the planet along with the light granite material of continents. The currents caused the granite to collect in masses just as inorganic scum collect in masses on a pond. The granite scum would pile up over the rising currents forming continents while the heavier basalt material would be pulled down by descending currents forming trenches and the surrounding ocean basins. The ocean trenches known to exist today are believed to be located over descending convection currents of mantle rock and the ridges mark the regions of rising currents in the mantle. Present coastal mountain ranges could have been caused either by granite pile-ups over vertical currents or by continents colliding with one another.

Scientists do not presume that the supercontinent of 150,000,000 years ago was the original position of land on earth but the result of some earlier movements of the granite scum which it would be impossible to trace. As with convection currents in most fluids, those in the earth should change their pattern from time to time and when they do various continental masses would be moved into new positions on the surface. Such changing patterns in the currents would help account for the breakup of the supercontinent and the periodic occurrence of mountain-building eras.

Some early versions of this hypothesis included a suggestion that the moon may have been thrown out of the molten earth to form the Pacific Ocean basin. This raises more questions than it answers and has fallen into disfavor. Although science is making slow progress on these fundamental questions, much discussion concerning them is well within the realm of speculation. What has been said here, although presently widely accepted, must certainly be considered speculative until more information can be gathered.

The earth still holds many mysteries for exploration and explanation. Even 2,000 years ago, Isaiah showed some familiarity with the opposing forces of building and erosion when he wrote:

> *Every valley shall be lifted up,*
> *And every mountain and hill be made low;*
> *The uneven ground shall become level,*
> *And the rough places plain.*
> —Isaiah 40:4, Revised Standard Version

ANIMATED DIAGRAMS

One of the difficult goals of geology at camp is to develop understanding of the slow processes which occur over millions of years. Having campers make animated diagrams, or moving pictures, is one way to speed these processes and make them more realistic. The same technique may be applied to many phenomena in other fields such as movement of warm and cold fronts, electrons in a vacuum tube, and eclipses. The basic method is the same for all and two examples are shown below.

MATERIALS

Assorted colors of construction paper, scissors, crayons or paint, staples or tape, modeling knife.

PROCEDURE

Draw the main diagram as shown in FIG. 5-2A with spaces marked to be cut out. Cut out marked areas with model knife, including slots at top and

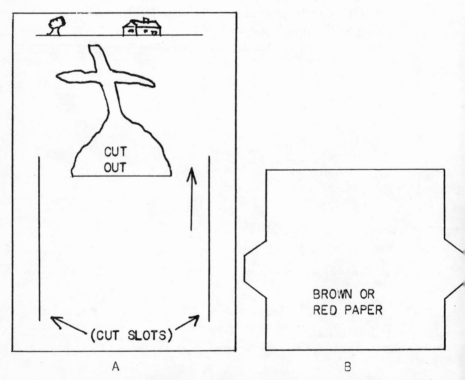

FIG. 5-2.   Animated diagram of dikes and sills (vertical and horizontal intrusions of molten rock)

bottom. Cut second sheet as shown in FIG. 5-2B, place under diagram and color in appropriate areas which should come into view as B moves under A. Insert tabs of B into slots of A and place third piece of paper under B as backing piece to be stapled or taped to top piece A, allowing B to move freely in the center. Completed "moving picture" may be used by campers to illustrate the geologic (or other) process under discussion.

Encourage campers to use their imaginations. Show them the basic technique of animation. Explain the diagram under discussion; but suggest that they do not have to make theirs exactly as yours, and think of a different way to explain the same principle. Also encourage them to think of new diagrams and processes to which this technique may be applied. They may like to experiment with these ideas. They provide good rainy day or individual activity.

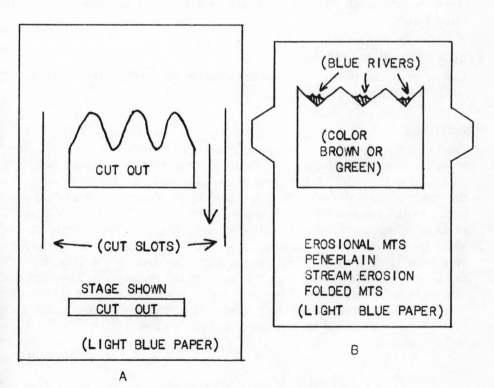

FIG. 5-3. Animated diagram illustrating formation of erosional mountains from folded mountains

MAKING ARTIFICIAL FOSSILS

Any remains, impression or trace of a prehistoric plant or animal is considered a *fossil*. There are three major groups of fossils: 1. Unaltered remains, such as insects in amber (resin), mammoths in ice, shells, teeth, bones. 2. Altered (petrified) remains, in which the organic tissues have been replaced, cell by cell, by mineral matter carried in water. The most common petrifying minerals are calcite, silicon and pyrite. 3. Casts and molds, impressions of shells, leaves, footprints, tracks and trails (such as those left by a crawling worm or snail). A mold is the impression left in the rock. This impression may become filled with mud or mineral matter which hardens and forms a cast.

Don't be deceived by the *pseudofossil*, or false fossil. It is called a *dendrite* and usually takes a form in the rock which looks like a branching tree. They are caused by mineral solutions (manganese dioxide or iron oxide) seeping into cracks and being deposited in the rocks. Many rocks may be dated by the fossils found in them.

The impression-type fossil, formed in mud and usually found in sedimentary rock, is the most common and widespread. This project is a simple one providing each camper with his own artificial impression fossil to bring home.

RECOMMENDED MATERIALS

Plaster of Paris, plastic pail, water paint or food color, ferns, leaves or shells to make impressions.

PROCEDURE

Each camper should select or collect the item he wishes to fossilize. Then scoop out a small hollow in the ground. Prepare plaster in plastic pail, add plaster to water until a fairly thick (heavy cream) mixture is obtained. As the mixing proceeds, add paint or coloring to plaster. Pour plaster into each ground hollow and have campers place specimens on top of plaster, pressing them in slightly. It will take your plaster "sedimentary rocks" about twenty minutes to harden. This time may be used to discuss types of fossils, their formation and importance. In nature, the leaf or shell would be decayed away in time, leaving only the impression. The campers may serve as agents of decay by removing their specimens from the plaster before it has completely set. Any hardened plaster remaining in the pail may be easily removed by bending the flexible plastic sides.

REPRODUCING FOSSILS

Fossils may be found which are publicly owned and cannot be moved; or the campers may find a fossil and bring it back to camp from a trip. In both of these cases it would be desirable to make reproductions of the fossil. In the first case, a reproduction is the only way to get a sample of the fossil. In the second case, reproductions may be made so each boy on the trip will have a sample of the fossil to bring home.

There are many types and sizes of fossils and consequently many methods of reproducing them. The two methods given here have been chosen because they are simple, dependable and will fit most circumstances. There are many substitutions possible in both materials and methods.

METHOD 1

For large or small impression-type fossils located in bedrock which cannot be moved. This method has been successful with large dinosaur tracks.

RECOMMENDED MATERIALS

Plaster of Paris, plastic pail, vaseline (petrolatum, fat, or other lubricant), pottery clay or Ceramite. Note three types of clay which can be used. The least expensive, pottery clay, must be kiln dried, and is not for very large fossils. Ceramite plastic clay is baked twenty minutes in oven at 250 degrees. It is made by Ettl Art Center, Glenville, Conn. Mexican pottery clay is the most expensive but dries hard without kiln or oven firing.

PROCEDURE

Coat fossil well with lubricant, pour in plaster. If fossil is extremely shallow, build up collar around it of mud or cardboard to hold plaster. Remove hardened plaster. This is your cast, remainder may be done at camp. Prepare clay and roll it out. Use rolling pin for large ones. Press plaster cast into soft clay firmly but gently, and remove. The clay should now have an impression similar to the original fossil. The plaster cast may be used repeatedly for any number of clay reproductions. A light coat of lubricant on plaster may make it easier to remove from clay.

METHOD 2

For small impression-type fossils at camp.

RECOMMENDED MATERIALS

Any soft clay or Plasticine, Plaster of Paris, plastic pail or paper cup, water color or food color.

PROCEDURE

Form a mold by pressing the fossil into the clay (or vice versa) or wrapping clay around fossil. Raise edge of clay to form collar to hold plaster. Mix plaster, adding some appropriate color to the mixture. Remove fossil from clay and pour plaster into remaining mold. Hardened plaster cast may be removed by simply rolling moist clay off. As the clay never has to harden for this method, it may be used repeatedly.

EARTH'S MAGNETIC FIELD

The knowledge that a lodestone (magnetic rock) would always point north was brought from China to Europe by Marco Polo. This discovery made possible navigation over open waters; but over the years, it has raised as many questions as it has answered. The foremost question is why the earth has a magnetic field with poles at the top and bottom. There are presently three lines of thought: 1. The field is due to permanent magnetism developed in the iron content of the earth by some force during earth formation. 2. The field is electrically produced either by currents in the atmosphere or by the rise, fall and rotation of the fluid rock under the crust. 3. Einstein attempted to explain both gravity and magnetism as interrelated forces in his *Unified Field Theory* based on the four-dimensional world he recognized in *Relativity*. Although many scientists now feel this theory is futile, some are still working on it. To make matters more difficult the "Mariner" spacecraft has indicated that our sister planet Venus does not have a magnetic field.

We do know that the sun has a general magnetic field about twice the strength of the earth's and that sunspots have their own magnetic fields averaging 4,000 times stronger than the earth's. Such findings come from daily observations made by telescopic magnetograph at Mount Wilson. Perhaps these studies or the new science of magnetohydrodynamics (MHD) will give us new insight into the magnetic field surrounding our earth. Building and using the compass described below will teach some facts about the magnetic field and compass use for navigation.

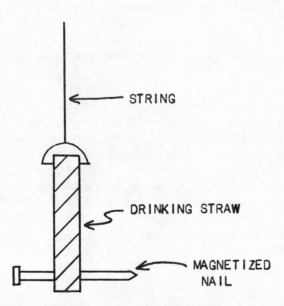

STRING

DRINKING STRAW

MAGNETIZED
NAIL

FIG. 5-4.   Homemade compass. Use where there are no strong air currents.

PROJECT 59

MATERIALS

Nails or iron wire, soda straws, thread, low-voltage DC supply (batteries or board described in Chapter 9), insulated wire (may be induction coil from Chapter 9).

PROCEDURE

Wrap wire neatly around a pencil, withdraw pencil leaving coil of wire. Place nail or wire to be magnetized inside coil and attach wires to source of direct current for a few seconds. If nail does not magnetize, connect wires for longer period. Too much time, however, will burn out the batteries of transformer and rectifier. If these become warm, wait until they cool down.

Hang thread in room with no strong air currents, attach three-inch straw and push magnet through straw until it balances. (See FIG. 5-4.) When needle has stopped turning, make a mark on the end pointing north. This is the north-seeking pole of the magnet.

USE

Campers may make more magnets and see the effects on their compass needles. Compare the direction of north as determined by the compass and by the North Star (see Chapter 4). Polaris is located over the North Geographic Pole; that is the point through which the earth's axis of spin passes. Like the axle of a wheel, the *geographic poles* (N and S) are at the center of spin. The *magnetic poles* are to the side of the axis. What's more, the magnetic poles change position slowly over the years. For some parts of the country, the magnetic pole is as much as twenty degrees away from the geographic poles. The difference between compass north and geographic north is known as *magnetic declination* and is written as 20 W, 15 E, etc. Have campers determine their magnetic declination by comparing compass with Polaris (Polaris is one and one-quarter degrees from the true geographic pole).

Zero declination is on a path running north and south between 88° and 80° longitude. A chart showing magnetic declinations is available from the U. S. Coast and Geodetic Survey. (See MAPS, CHARTS AND MODELS.) Lines of equal declination on such charts are called isogonic lines. As hikers and navigators use maps based on geographic, not magnetic directions, it is vital that they know the magnetic declination of their area so that compass readings may be adjusted for true directions. This point should be emphasized with campers and it should be demonstrated, using a map, that being off direction by 20 degrees for any great distance will deliver one far from his desired destination.

DEMONSTRATING CRYSTAL GROWTH

In strict scientific terms, a crystal is any solid that has a definite geo-metric shape due to an orderly arrangement of atoms. This includes most solids. The amateur geologist is most concerned, however, with mineral crystals which are shaped distinctly and large enough to be visible to the naked eye or magnifying glass. (The crystalline structure of many solids is only visible to the X-ray.) Crystals form because atoms arrange themselves into definite patterns which grow in size as more atoms are added. Crystals of metals are built up of atoms, salts are built of ions, and carbon compounds are built of molecules. Exactly why the atoms arrange themselves in these patterns remains one of the yet unsolved mysteries of science. However, the crystal shape of a given substance is always the same because it is always composed of the same atoms or molecules. Thus a quartz or calcite crystal will always have the same shape and this may be used as one means of identification.

A modest amount of rock hunting will soon reveal that the same mineral may be found as a perfectly formed crystal or as a shapeless chunk. As the liquid mineral solution cooled during its formation, two conditions determined the development of crystals: 1. *Rate of cooling.* Crystals take time to form, and the slower the solution cooled and remained liquid, the larger the crystals could grow. Very rapid cooling would form microscopic crystals which, being indistinguishable, would appear as a large chunk. 2. *Growing room.* Crystals cannot grow if there are other rocks in the way or other crystals also attempting to grow. The following demonstration makes it possible to grow crystals within minutes, to actually watch their growth and see how the above conditions affect them.

MATERIALS

Salol (Phenyl salicylate, granular, a drugstore item), alcohol, 10-power magnifying glass (or microscope), glass sheet (or micro slide), light.

PROCEDURE

With magnifying glass: Salol is used because it is a crystalline solid with a low melting point of 109° F. Place a pinch of Salol on the glass and hold over a light bulb to melt the powder. Remove from heat as soon as it has melted and place glass on blocks of wood or other support so there is an air space between bottom of glass and table top. Observe the melted Salol through a magnifying glass as it cools. Take care not to breathe too closely on it or heat from breath will retard cooling. If crystals do not begin to form within a couple of minutes, disturb the molecules by touching a nail or other object to the edge of the molten substance. Crystals will now begin to grow from this point toward the center. As they develop, find some with perfect shape. (Salol crystals are diamond-shaped.) Notice that

Geology   151

if a crystal grows into another crystal or object, its shape is destroyed. Because this solution is so concentrated, the final solid will show few perfect crystals even though many perfect ones did start to develop.

With microscope: Dissolve a pinch of Salol in an inch of alcohol in a test tube by shaking tube vigorously. Place a few drops of the solution on a micro slide and observe through microscope or magnifying glass as it evaporates. If crystal-growing activity has not started after three to four minutes, it may be stimulated by touching solution as before or dropping a grain of Salol into it. Notice that this time the solution is not as concentrated as the pure Salol was and crystals have more room for growth. Use of a micro-projector arrangement would make it possible to show this crystal growth to all members of a group at once.

USE

The importance of this activity is that it speeds up to a few minutes processes which may take months or years in nature. Pose the original questions to the campers: How do crystals form? Why do some form perfectly while others, of the same substance, form only chunks? Let them do the work above under your guidance and see how many of the answers they can discover for themselves. Have them draw Salol crystals. This activity can be a real indoor exploration under the true meaning of science.

GROWING PERMANENT CRYSTALS

Following these directions, campers may grow permanent crystals much as they are grown in nature by the evaporation of warm solutions containing various salts. The directions given may be used with any of the three salts named. These salts have been selected for their availability, speed and general success in growing crystals under less than ideal conditions. Least expensive is table salt. Also very inexpensive is alum which grows crystals somewhat larger and faster than table salt. Most expensive of the three is Rochelle salt, which grows the longest crystals.

MATERIALS

One of the following salts: table salt (sodium chloride), alum (ammonium aluminum sulfate), or Rochelle salt (potassium sodium tartrate). Saucers or small bowls, hot water, Pyrex jar, pan or flask.

PROCEDURE

PHASE 1: Pour about a cup of hot (not boiling) water into the Pyrex container, add the salt selected, stirring continuously until no more salt will remain suspended in the water and it begins to settle to bottom of container. The glass container is recommended so the entire contents may be carefully observed and the point noted when the solution has become saturated with the salt. Stop adding salt but continue stirring for a minute to make sure that the few visible grains will not dissolve.

Cover Pyrex container and allow solution to cool to room temperature. Pour small amount of cooled solution into shallow bowl which is located in a place where it will not be shaken or disturbed. Stopper the remaining solution in Pyrex container (or it may now be put in any clean glass jar) and set aside to save. As water begins to evaporate from bowl, solution becomes more concentrated and salt atoms begin to collect together. Within twelve hours these should be visible as very tiny *seed crystals*. Some of these crystals should reach an eighth of an inch within two days. As they reach this size, remove them from the solution and place them on some tissue paper. *Caution:* All bowls containing growing crystals should be placed where there is the least variation in temperature (including day-to-night). An electric refrigerator which is not subjected to vibration is the ideal location, but usually not available at camp. Bowls may be placed in a tank of water which will help keep an even temperature. Try to use a room where temperature changes are the least in camp. As your solution changes temperature, it also changes concentration and your crystal may alternately grow and dissolve to small extents.

PHASE 2: Now take the original jar of solution which you had set aside and pour some of the solution into a clean bowl or jar. It is very likely that some salts have settled out of the solution to the bottom of the container.

Take care that none of these grains are poured out into the clean bowl. Select a large, well formed seed crystal and place it in the new solution. Leave the bowl or jar uncovered and allow water to evaporate as before without being disturbed. This time the atoms will collect on the seed crystal and enlarge it. Growth of the seed crystal will be slowest but will continue longest in a jar. Growth will be fastest in a bowl but in a few days, other tiny crystals will begin to form in the solution and the large crystal will have to be removed at about this time to prevent it from colliding with another crystal, in its growth, and being deformed. Not touching the solution will help prevent these small crystals from forming. In the camp situation, the faster bowl method is recommended. By the bowl method, crystals between one-half and one inch should be obtained within a week. There are other methods for growing more perfect crystals (such as suspending seed by string in growing solution) but these require a fairly constant temperature and, more often than not, will not succeed under camp conditions.

USE

This activity is a good follow-up to the crystal growth demonstration with Salol. It provides the camper with a crystal which can be observed as it grows slowly, examined for shape and added to a permanent collection. Compare the shapes of crystals grown from all three salts. Note how this property may be used for identification. Alum and Rochelle crystals grown this way should not be considered perfect specimens as the side against the bottom of the bowl does not grow properly. For further details on this subject see: Holden and Singer, *Crystals and Crystal Growing*, Garden City, New York: Doubleday, 1960. $1.00.

SUGAR CRYSTALS

Growing sugar crystals is a good way to learn about crystals and get something to eat at the same time. The final product is also known as rock candy.

RECOMMENDED MATERIALS

Sugar, hot water, glass, cotton thread or string, paper clips.

PROCEDURE

Many people have been unsuccessful in growing sugar crystals because they do not realize the large quantities of sugar that will dissolve in water. The ratio is about two parts of sugar to one of water; for example, two cups of sugar, one cup of hot water. This problem can be minimized by adding water to the sugar instead of vice versa.

Half fill a container (preferably Pyrex glass) with sugar, add a very small amount of hot (nearly boiling) water, stir to get all sugar in suspension. Continue adding small amounts of water and stirring until sugar remains in suspension and does not settle to bottom of container. This will be a thick syrup in which you may still see many sugar grains floating. Allow to cool. Pour into glass and hang thread in solution with some weight on the bottom. Paper clips are convenient for this, but clean them before use. (See FIG. 5-5.) Place glass where it will not be disturbed and where there is circulation of air. Cheesecloth over the top will help keep out dust.

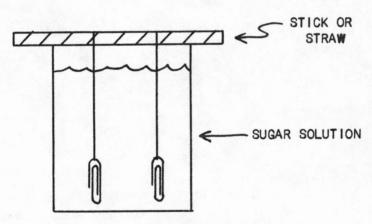

STICK OR STRAW

SUGAR SOLUTION

FIG. 5-5.   Setup to grow sugar crystals

RESULTS

As water evaporates, sugar will become more concentrated and begin settling out onto thread and bottom of glass. Signs of this should be seen within twelve hours. Allow crystals to grow for a week or more. Then campers may remove them, study them, and eat them.

IDENTIFYING MINERALS

What is the difference between rocks and minerals? The earth is made of rock, and *most* of these rocks are made of combinations of minerals. Minerals are specific substances which always have the same properties and chemical composition. They are the building blocks of rocks. A *mineral* may be defined as a naturally occurring substance of inorganic origin with definite physical and chemical properties. By this definition, oil and coal would not be minerals because of their origin in decayed prehistoric plant and animal life. Water would be considered a mineral. It is of inorganic origin and has definite physical and chemical properties.

Minerals are formed by the cooling or evaporation of warm solutions containing metals, salts or other impurities. If the solution cools slowly enough, large crystals will grow. Details on mineral and crystal development are included in the projects on crystals. The ability to identify some minerals is prerequisite to rock identification which, in turn, is prerequisite to understanding the geological processes which have occurred in a given area.

RECOMMENDED MATERIALS

Pocket knife, magnifying glass, penny, hydrochloric (muriatic) acid and dropper.

PROCEDURE

Minerals seen in rocks are usually tiny grains all mixed together. Before attempting to identify these tiny mineral fragments, campers should have an opportunity to examine large pieces of the pure minerals and thus become acquainted with their properties. Large pieces of the most common minerals shown on the chart may be obtained before camp and an indoor activity may be the discussion of mineral properties and practice in using these properties in identifying unmarked samples.

USE

The mineral chart (FIG. 5-6) lists properties of the most common minerals. They are called rock-forming minerals because they are found in the most common rocks. The first five minerals are the most widespread and will certainly be known on sight by the end of camp. The three most important properties of identification are listed here in the order in which they should be checked.

1. Luster: Luster is either metallic or nonmetallic. Minerals which look like iron, copper, silver and gold, etc., have metallic luster. All others are nonmetallic. Some of the nonmetallics may be described as having a glassy luster, among them quartz and fluorite.

MINERAL	CHEMICAL COMPONENTS	COLORS	HARDNESS	PROPERTIES & USES
		A. NON-METALLIC LUSTER		
QUARTZ	SiO_2	COLORLESS, ROSE, SMOKY, MILKY, AMETHYST (VIOLET) +	7	GLASSY. USED IN JEWELRY & ELECTRONICS
FELDSPAR	$NaAlSi_3O_8$ +	WHITE, BUFF, PINK, GRAY	6	BLOCKY. USED IN SOAP POWDER. & PORCELAIN
MICA	$AlSiO$ + +	TRANSPARENT, GRAY, BLACK (PURPLE CALLED LEPIDOLITE)	2.5	ELECTRICAL INSULATORS
HORNBLENDE	$CaNaAlSiO$+	BLACK	5.5	COAL-LIKE APPEARANCE
CALCITE	$CaCO_3$	TRANSPARENT, WHITE, GRAY, GOLD +	3	FIZZES IN ACID. MINERAL IN LIMESTONE & MARBLE
HALITE	$NaCl$	COLORLESS, WHITE	2.5	ROCK SALT. CUBIC. GLASSY
GARNET	$FeAlSiO$ +	RED, BROWN, YELLOW, GREEN	7	TINY BARRELS, GLASSY
FLUORITE	CaF_2	CLEAR, BLUE, GREEN, WHITE + +	4	GLASSY
GYPSUM	$CaSO_4 \cdot 2H_2O$	GRAY, WHITE, COLORLESS	2	PLASTER
TOURMALINE	$AlSiO$ + +	BLACK, PINK, GREEN +	7	JEWELRY
		B. METALLIC LUSTER		
MAGNETITE	Fe_3O_4	GRAY - BLACK	6	REMOVE FROM SOIL & SAND WITH MAGNET. IRON ORE
PYRITE	FeS_2	PALE BRASS YELLOW	6.5	FOOL'S GOLD. SOURCE OF SULFUR

FIG. 5-6. Mineral chart. First five are the most common rock-forming minerals.

2. Hardness: The hardness scale goes from 1 (soft) to 10 (hard). Examples: Talc = 1, feldspar = 6, quartz = 7, diamond = 10. Hardness is determined by scratching one mineral on another and brushing away any powder formed in the process. If mineral A scratches B, A is harder. Two minerals of equal hardness will scratch each other. Hardness tests may be made by scratching an unknown mineral against a known mineral. They may also be made using an unknown mineral and any other common substance of known hardness. Commonly used are: penny = 3, knife blade = 5.5, window glass also 5.5. Example: quartz and fluorite often look alike but quartz will scratch window glass while fluorite will not.

3. Color: As with rocks, color is highly variable in minerals and is the least useful of these three properties in making determination.

4. Special properties: Many minerals have properties peculiar to themselves. Calcite will fizz and bubble if acid is dropped on it. Mica peels easily into thin translucent sheets. Some minerals glow under ultraviolet light. Other properties which will be found in mineral books include: streak, specific gravity, chemical analysis with blowpipe, bead, flame, magnetism, cleavage, and radioactivity.

Minerals included in the chart are generally common, but if some are not found in your area, they should be replaced by others that are. The chemical formulas shown are not complete because minerals often include traces of foreign elements causing color changes. The difference between clear quartz and purple quartz (amethyst) for example, is only the addition of a trace of manganese.

IDENTIFYING ROCKS

Rock types are keys to processes of geologic folding, pressing, faulting, erosion, melting and even volcanic activity which have taken place in your area. Since the conditions and processes which form different rocks are known, the identification of such rocks begins to reveal the geological history of the region going back millions of years.

RECOMMENDED MATERIALS

Geology hammer (pick), magnifying glass, pocket knife. See COLLECTING TECHNIQUES.

PROCEDURE

Campers should have an opportunity to identify rocks at camp before going into the field. Provide a box of assorted, unlabeled rocks found in the area, rocks that they may handle, examine and identify while referring to the rock charts included in this section. These charts are based upon two most important and easily recognized properties by which rocks may be identified: *texture* and *mineral content.* Texture is determined by the size of mineral grains in the rock. Large grains or chunks represent coarse texture, small or indistinguishable grains, fine texture. Mineral content is determined by the identification of minerals which make up these grains or chunks. Color may vary from place to place and can only be a secondary property; but it may be helpful within the confines of a local area. Show examples of fine- and coarse-textured rocks so campers may become familiar with these properties and train themselves to look for them.

The rock charts shown have been arranged, where possible, on various continua. The texture continuum is shown in all three, although in metamorphic rocks it is more of a sudden change than a continuous one. Rocks included are common, but not found in all parts of the country. You may wish to omit ones not found in your area or replace them with others which have not been included. Young geologists will be busy enough learning the rocks of their own region without bothering immediately with rocks found elsewhere which they may never see.

USE

IGNEOUS ROCKS (FIG. 5-7). Important properties: Texture and mineral content. Granite always contains three minerals: quartz, feldspar, and mica or hornblende. Pegmatite is often good source of crystals. Note that as rate of cooling becomes faster, texture becomes finer (smaller grains or crystals).

SEDIMENTARY ROCKS (FIG. 5-8). Important properties: Texture and content which may be stones or minerals. Hardness continuum is not true

ROCK	TEX.-TURE	COLORS	MINERAL CONTENT	RATE OF COOLING	DESCRIPTIVE NOTES
			A. INDIVIDUAL GRAINS, CRYSTALS OR FRAGMENTS VISIBLE		
BRECCIA	COARSE	GREEN-GRAY + +	FELDSPAR, QUARTZ + +	SEDIMENTARY IGNEOUS	SOLID ROCK IN THROAT OF VOLCANO BROKEN INTO SMALL PIECES & THROWN FROM VOLCANO BY ERUPTION. CEMENTED TOGETHER BY VOLCANIC DUST AND ASH.
PEGMATITE		LIGHT	FELDSPAR, MICA QUARTZ	VERY SLOW	VERY LARGE CRYSTALS FROM 1" TO MANY FEET
GRANITE		PINK, BUFF, GRAY + +	FELDSPAR & QUARTZ MICA OR HORNBLENDE	SLOW	ALL MINERAL CRYSTALS ABOUT SAME SIZE
TRAP		GREEN-GRAY	FELDSPAR-OLIVINE +	MEDIUM	GENERAL NAME...MAY BE APPLIED TO ALL DENSE DARK IGNEOUS ROCKS
			B. INDIVIDUAL GRAINS NOT VISIBLE		
BASALT		BLACK DARK GREEN	FELDSPAR, OLIVINE+	FAST	SOLIDIFIED LAVA - FOUND IN DIKES, SILLS & OTHER INTRUSIONS
PUMICE	FINE	BUFF - GRAY	GLASS	VERY FAST	SOLID ASH-LIKE LAVA CONTAINS TRAPPED VOLCANIC GAS. FLOATS IN WATER
OBSIDIAN		RED - BLACK	GLASS	VERY FAST	"NATURAL GLASS"- LAVA WHICH COOLED SO FAST THAT NO CRYSTALS WERE ABLE TO FORM
PORPHRYTIC		ADJECTIVE USED TO DESCRIBE SPECIAL CONDITION FOUND IN ABOVE ROCKS.			SCATTERED LARGE CRYSTALS AGAINST A BACKGROUND OF SMALLER CRYSTALS. PORPHRYTIC GRANITE, BASALT, ETC.

FIG. 5-7. Igneous rock chart

ROCK	TEXTURE	HARDNESS	CONTENT	HOW FORMED	NOTES
	COARSE ────────────────────────────→ FINE	HARD ────────────────────────────→ SOFT			
CONGLOMERATE			ROUNDED PEBBLE – LIKE STONES. MUCH QUARTZITE AND FELDSPAR	STONES CARRIED BY RIVERS AND DEPOSITED IN MUD	ALSO CALLED "PUDDINGSTONE". HELD TOGETHER BY BROWNISH MUDS OF SAND OR CLAY.
TILLITE			BOTH SHARP AND ROUNDED STONES OF ALL SIZES. MUCH QUARTZITE	STONES CARRIED BY GLACIER & DROPPED UPON MELTING OF THE ICE	HELD TOGETHER BY A COARSE MUD CEMENT. LARGER BOULDERS MAY SHOW GLACIAL SCRATCHES
SANDSTONE			QUARTZ GRAINS	SAND CARRIED BY RIVERS & DEPOSITED	COARSE OR FINE SAND CEMENTED TOGETHER. SURFACE LIKE SAND‐PAPER
LIMESTONE			CALCITE	BUILT UP IN SHALLOW SEAS FROM SKELETONS OF TINY ANIMALS	TAN TO GRAY. FIZZES IN ACID. MAY CONTAIN FOSSILS
SHALE			CLAY, MUD & SILT	FINE MUD & SILT CARRIED BY RIVERS & DEPOSITED	CAN BE SPLIT INTO LAYERS. OFTEN HAS ALTERNATING DARK & LIGHT LAYERS. SANDSTONE DEPOSITED IN SUMMER, SHALE IN WINTER

Fig. 5-8.   Sedimentary rock chart

ROCK	ROCK FORMED FROM	MINERALS	COLORS	NOTES
A. SIMPLE METAMORPHIC ROCKS - DIRECT CHANGE OF SEDIMENTARY ROCKS - ONE BASIC MINERAL				
QUARTZITE	SANDSTONE	QUARTZ	PALE WHITISH SHADES	MORE-COMPACT THAN SANDSTONE - CRYSTALLINE - ONE OF THE HARDEST ROCKS
MARBLE	LIMESTONE	CALCITE	WHITE, PINK, GRAY, BLACK + +	FIZZES IN ACID. CRYSTALLINE. MAY HAVE INTERMIXED COLORED BANDS
SLATE	SHALE	CLAY	RED, GRAY, GREEN, BLACK + +	SPLITS INTO LAYERS. MAY BE TINY MICA FLAKES VISIBLE. USED FOR FLAGSTONES
B. COMPLEX METAMORPHIC ROCKS - GREATLY CHANGED, NEW MINERALS FORMED - MANY MINERALS				
PHYLLITE	SHALE GRANITE + +	FELDSPAR QUARTZ MICA + CHLORITE +	VARIABLE	FINE TEXTURE. SILKY LUSTER IRREGULAR LAYERS
SCHIST	SLATE FELSITE GRANITE +	MICA GARNET HORNBLENDE+	DARK VARIABLE	THICK LAYERS. FLAKES OF MICA COME OFF ON HANDS
GNEISS	SHALE GRANITE CONGLOMERATE +	GARNET FELDSPAR QUARTZ HORNBLENDE MICA +	VARIABLE	IRREGULAR BANDS. MEDIUM TO COARSE TEXTURE

FIG. 5-9. Metamorphic rock chart

for entire country but may be for your area. Omit if there is danger of confusion.

METAMORPHIC ROCKS (FIG. 5-9). Important properties: Texture, minerals and cleavage. Cleavage has to do with the ability to split the rock easily into layers. Slate and schist are both easily cleavable. The simple metamorphic rocks are usually harder and more compact due to slight melting and pressure than were their sedimentary ancestors. Quartzite is one of our hardest rocks and is often found included as stones in sedimentary formations. The complex metamorphic rocks bear little resemblance to their original igneous or sedimentary ancestors and the pressures which they have undergone often form semiprecious minerals such as garnet, epidote, chlorite and staurolite which are often found in these rocks. Schists are named for their most common mineral. Thus we may have mica schist, quartz schist, chlorite schist.

The schists, pegmatites and some sedimentary rocks are among the most common locations of semiprecious mineral crystals.

COLLECTING TECHNIQUES AND EQUIPMENT

When a group goes out to collect rocks or minerals, it is important that there be sufficient equipment for everybody to do some digging, chopping or chiseling at the same time. Don't dampen anyone's enthusiasm for geology by making him wait a long while for a tool. For trips to mines that can be reached by car, you may take heavy equipment such as shovels and other extra tools. But for hiking trips, try to anticipate your needs and travel lightly. A hiking trip can usually be managed with a geology hammer in a belt sheath, small magnifying glass and possibly a cold chisel. You need something in which to carry specimens, food, clothing and equipment. On short trips of less than a day, I use an army surplus canvas bag designed for gas masks. It has pockets inside and plenty of room for lunch, extra clothes and specimens. For day trips a rucksack is more comfortable, balances better and provides the needed extra room for more supplies. If you are covering the same ground both going and coming, you may pick up the specimens on the return trip when the pack will be less full.

MATERIALS AND USE

Geology pick. This is the proper name for a rock hammer. There are two types. One has a chisel edge opposite the head, used for prying rocks, and is good for people who will collect mostly rocks. The other has a sharp point opposite the head, making it suitable for digging out mineral samples. Be sure to get a belt sheath to carry the pick. Before attempting to identify any rock, always use the pick to break the rock in half. This exposes a clean surface in which the minerals may be more clearly seen. Do not attempt to identify rocks from features seen on an outer, weathered surface.

Cold chisel. Useful in removing crystal from rock. Do not attempt to chip crystal out of rock. Chip surrounding rock away from crystal until crystal falls out.

Magnifying glass. A one-inch-diameter lens is suitable for minerals and is less apt to break in the field than a larger one. Ten-power magnification is good. Try to obtain one with an outside metal or plastic case, into which the lens may be pushed for protection.

Ultraviolet minerals may be detected and exhibited with least expense by using an argon glow lamp (G.E. Type AR-1) available from radio supply stores for less than two dollars.

Shovel or trowel. The waste piles of mines are often rich sources of minerals and crystals. They are composed of crushed rock which was not hauled away. A shovel or trowel will help in turning this rock over and getting down where other collectors have not been. Turn slowly and with a sharp eye.

Bags. Bags for a hike have already been described. A small paper bag for each camper will be sufficient for trips to mines. Have names written on bags before collecting starts.

Marking specimens is necessary on a hike, so location of rocks will be known after the trip. Rock samples may be numbered with a bright crayon and the numbers then keyed to locations kept in a notebook. Pieces of numbered paper may be wrapped around small specimens. You may wish to use *mineral sample bags*, made of cloth with attached tags. They are available from Ward's for about ten cents each. (See RESOURCE MATERIALS at end of this chapter.) The bags may be permanently numbered and used repeatedly. Be sure a notebook is part of your equipment. One or two small jars or plastic vials may be carried for soil and sand samples.

Pocket knife. Among its many uses a knife is valuable as a hardness indicator. The knife blade has a hardness of 5.5. If it scratches specimen, specimen is soft, 1 to 5. If specimen scratches knife, specimen is hard, 6 to 10. This crude hardness check is often helpful in identification.

Washing. Rocks and minerals which are going to be displayed should be brought back to camp and washed or soaked in warm soapy or detergent water. A brush may be used on the harder rocks. Take care not to soak minerals such as halite, which are soluble in water. Most rocks and minerals will not present this problem as very few are soluble.

Numbering. Probably the best method of permanently numbering rock specimens is with plaster of Paris. Mix plaster of Paris and paint a spot of it onto the specimen. Print number in ink on dry plaster and coat with varnish or clear plastic spray. This is a simple method and much more satisfactory than trying to keep numbered tapes attached to rocks.

Where to look. Obtain a guide to mines and minerals of your area from the state, a local mineral store, or the Geological Survey. Visit mines recommended by local collectors. Mountain streams and rivers are often good sources of minerals which the water has loosened and released from bedrock along the banks. Many mountain paths become streams in wet weather. They are often covered with minerals and sand grains which have been weathered and eroded out of the mountain rock. Wherever a geology trip goes, be sure to keep safety and caution foremost.

MAPS, CHARTS AND MODELS

Listed here are various types of maps and charts used in geology and directions for constructing topographic models. For maps available from government agencies, the agency name and address is given.

1. *Topographic Maps.* Geological Survey, Washington, D. C. 20025. These are detailed maps which show topography and elevations of the land by the use of contour lines. They are thirty cents each and are generally used for geological study and hiking. For free detailed information write Geological Survey and ask for: A. Topographic maps descriptive folder, B. Topographic map symbols, C. Index to topo maps of U.S. at scale of 1:250,000, D. Index to topo maps of your state. Remember: *Elevation* is distance above sea level; *height* is distance between the top and the general ground level. Thus a mountain may have an elevation of 6,000 feet above sea level; but the top may only be 4,000 feet above the base at ground level.

2. *Nautical Coast and Harbor Charts.* Coast and Geodetic Survey, Washington, D. C. 20025. These charts show coastline and harbor details along with ocean depths going out from the coast. These depths indicate the underwater topography of the coast. Often the edge of the continental shelf may be identified on the charts by a sudden increase in depths. River beds now drowned under the ocean may also be recognized. For free information write the Coast and Geodetic Survey asking for: A. Information on nautical charts, B. Index diagrams of the coastal sections in which you are interested. For a slight fee, you may obtain the following introductory information: A. Chart No. 1, *Nautical Chart Symbols,* twenty-five cents; B. Chart No. 1210TR, *Nautical Training Chart,* fifteen cents.

3. *Surficial Geologic Maps.* By the use of colors and markings, maps indicate surface features such as glacial deposits, scratches, boulder and soil types.

4. *Bedrock Geologic Maps.* By the use of various colors, these maps show the types of bedrock underlying the soil throughout the area covered. They are helpful in identifying outcrops of rock through soil. For full information on surficial maps, and other charts and pamphlets on geology, write the Geological Survey and request its free catalog, *Publications of the Geological Survey.* Maps mentioned will be found in the table of contents of the catalog under "Maps and Charts." Also included under this heading is a list of state agencies from which other geological maps may be obtained.

5. *Soil Maps.* U.S. Government Printing Office, Washington, D. C. 20025. Soil survey reports and maps are available for many counties in the country. A list of surveys available may be obtained by requesting free catalog PL 46, *Soils,* from the Printing Office.

6. *Nautical Charts of International Waters.* U.S. Navy Hydrographic Office, Washington, D. C. 20025. Charts of the high seas and ocean depths. Contour lines may be added to show bottom topography. Request free *Catalog of Nautical Charts* from above office. Chart No. 5244 includes most of the North Atlantic ($1.20).

7. *Relief Models.* You may take topographic models showing surface relief of camp, a mountain, or other physical features. Use a topographic map of the area to determine elevations. A good material for making such models may be made with two parts salt and one part flour, adding just enough water to hold the powders together. Plaster tends to crack when used for this purpose. The model may be built on a cardboard base. Plywood will provide better support and help prevent damage. Decide upon horizontal and vertical scales. (They need not be the same. Many models have a vertical exaggeration.) Cut straws or toothpicks to the scaled heights of various elevations on the map and stick them in the proper locations on the base. These now act as guides for hilltops, rivers, and other physical features. The salt-flour mixture may be spread on the base being raised up to cover the top of each straw marker. The dry model may be painted in natural colors or in colors coded to various features. Many things beside topographic relief may be shown on the completed model, such as trails, plant distribution, animal homes, soil types, bedrock, buildings and roads.

FIELD GEOLOGY

Usually three final products result from a complete geological survey of an area: 1. Bedrock map showing and naming various bedrock and mineral formations by shading a base map in different colors; 2. Surficial map showing features which are visible on the surface such as soil types, glacial deposits and scratches, water and possibly outcrops of bedrock. Both of these maps are often done over a topographic map of the region. You could even use a road map. 3. Written report describing the topography of the area, vegetation, rock exposures, drainage, surface features, glacial effects, soils, any economic importance of rocks and minerals present, and the geologic history of the region.

You may or may not wish to go into all the above detail; but any amount of field geology will be an exciting and rewarding way of using and reinforcing a basic knowledge of minerals, rocks and formations. Regardless of the amount of field study planned, first obtain a topographic map of your area and bedrock—surficial maps if available. (See MAPS, CHARTS AND MODELS.) For details on taking samples see COLLECTING TECHNIQUES AND EQUIPMENT. It is accepted as general practice to trim specimens to flat rectangles—measuring three by four by one inches. This is done with chisel and hammer. Be sure to include notebook and compass in equipment. Try to accomplish as much as possible in the field. Don't trust your memory. Write, sketch or photograph on the spot. It is often helpful to assume that the region was originally flat, bare rock and to explain all present-day features with this basic assumption in mind.

Following is a list of the most common features which should be watched for during a field geology survey:

A. Bedrock
   1. Dikes and sills—vertical or horizontal intrusions of igneous rock into bedrock.
   2. Folding, joints (cracks) and faults (movement of bedrock).
   3. Outcrops. Identify rocks and minerals and locate on map.
B. Weathering of rock by methods described in introduction: ice, plants, temperature extremes, oxygen, carbonic acid and water.
C. Erosion of soils by methods described in introduction: streams (regardless of size), ground water and springs, wind, glaciers.
D. Soil
   1. Amounts of sand, gravel, silt, clay and organic matter.
   2. Minerals included in sand.
   3. Origin: weathering of local rock, glacial deposit, water deposit, other.
E. Fossils—most likely found in sedimentary rock areas
F. Glacial evidence
   1. Polish on rocks.

2. Striations (scratches) on rock, usually in north-south direction.

3. Outwash plains: broad flat plains of sand and gravel deposited by rivers pouring out of the melting ice front.

4. Kettle ponds: steep bank ponds in outwash plain formed by remaining block of ice being surrounded by sand deposits. When block melts, hole (pond) remains.

5. Valley smoothing and widening.

6. Sheep rock hills (roches moutonnées): bedrock core, gentle north side of glacial gravel and boulders, steep south side due to glacial plucking. Often bare cliffs on south side.

7. Till: any deposit of glacial soil usually containing mixture of sand, gravel, stones and boulders.

8. Erratic boulders: unusually large rocks dropped by glacier, often balanced or perched on smaller boulders. Usually are not the same type as bedrock.

9. Eskers, kames and drumlins: three types of sand and gravel hills dropped by glacier. Eskers are long and look like railroad bed. Kames are irregular rounded knolls or hummocks. Drumlins are oval and have a profile similar to a whale. Not higher than 200 feet, they point in the direction of glacial movement and may have a small rock core.

For more information on field geology and identification of formations, see Wolfe and Lahee in BIBLIOGRAPHY.

OVERNIGHT EQUIPMENT

A geology survey of an area may well be reason to stay out over night. Those who like to rough it and live off the land will not require the advice given here; but most people enjoy having some rudimentary comforts even in the wilderness. For these people, the following suggestions are offered.

EQUIPMENT FOR GROUP

Cook kit (contains large pans, kettle, etc.), cooking forks and spoons, can and bottle opener, hatchet or axe, knife, toilet paper, lantern or candles, matches. Cooking may be done individually over Sterno stoves; or for the group on gas stoves, over open fire, or in a pit or ring of boulders covered with metal grill. Take along napkins, first aid kit.

PERSONAL EQUIPMENT

Sleeping bag, raincoat or poncho, mess kit and silverware, flashlight, insect repellant, toothbrush, towel, soap, other toilet articles, sweater, jacket, sufficient changes of socks and underwear, high shoes or hiking boots, canteen.

FOOD

Extra and perishable food may often be purchased near the campsite. Check on this point. Sugar cubes, tea, cocoa, canned meals (stews, spaghetti, beans) or dehydrated or freeze-dried foods available from camping suppliers, bread, fruit or raisins, eggs, peanut butter and sandwich supplies, canned juice. Foods which may be bought near the campsite include frankfurters, bacon, milk.

PROCEDURE

Since the primary purpose of science trips is not cooking out, the canned and prepared foods have been recommended to save time during the daylight hours. No scientific equipment has been included in this list. The list presupposes the ideal situation of having a base camp located near the car so that large items may be used as needed and weight is no problem. If there is no base camp that may be reached by road, the list will require considerable revision. Shelter may consist of an available cabin, tent, or lean-to made of canvass, poncho or boughs, or you may use the sky. When you travel away from the base camp, plan your equipment and clothing carefully. Travel light but be prepared for all probable needs. Water in mountain streams is usually safe, especially if boiled. If you have any doubt about water, drink only fruit juice and carbonated beverages. Finally, don't hesitate taking an overnight trip. You'll enjoy it, the campers will love it and there are usually fewer problems out in the woods than there are back in camp.

INDIVIDUAL MINERAL-ROCK COLLECTIONS

Here is a simple scheme to encourage campers to become familiar with the most common minerals and rocks of the area. It works on the idea of a stamp album. You provide labeled blanks and the collector fills them in

RECOMMENDED MATERIALS

Oaktag, rulers, pencils or pens, cement.

PROCEDURE

Determine the most common minerals and rocks in your area. At the start of the season, have campers prepare a piece of oaktag as shown in FIG 5-10, writing in the name of the state or region, their own names, and the names of the minerals you have selected. During the season, see to it that they have an opportunity to find these samples either in camp or on trips. They should break them down to proper size, wash them and cement into correct blank. The reward is a completed collection of rocks of the area which they can take home and use as guides to rock identification there.

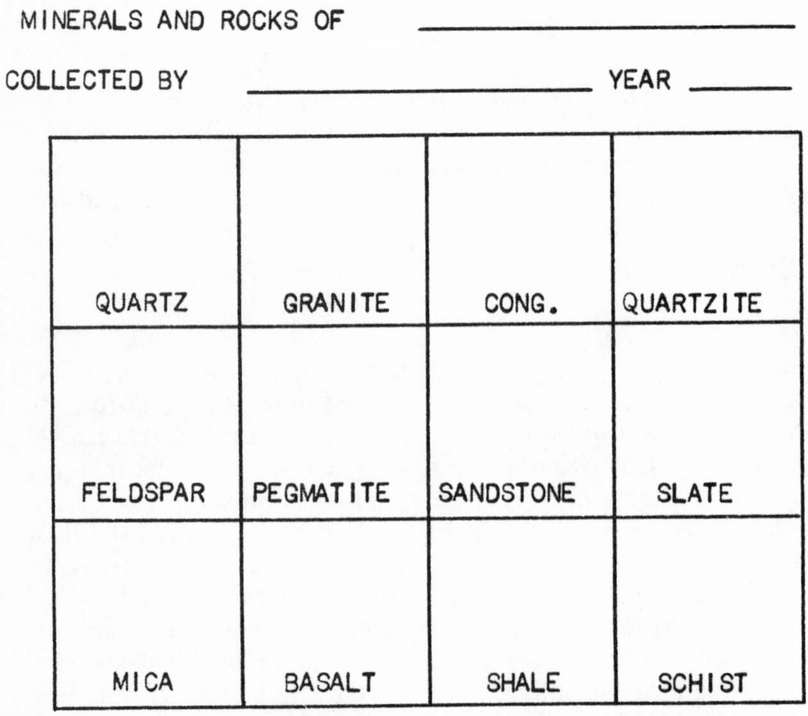

MINERALS AND ROCKS OF _____

COLLECTED BY _____ YEAR _____

QUARTZ	GRANITE	CONG.	QUARTZITE
FELDSPAR	PEGMATITE	SANDSTONE	SLATE
MICA	BASALT	SHALE	SCHIST

FIG. 5-10.   Labeled oaktag to which specimens may be cemented

THE SPINTHARISCOPE AND RADIOACTIVITY

The spinthariscope is an instrument used to observe flashes of light (scintillations) produced when radioactivity particles strike a luminescent screen. As with most atomic instruments, this does not show atoms but rather the effects caused by atoms on another substance.

MATERIALS

Clock, watch or compass with luminous dial. Magnifying glass of about ten power.

PROCEDURE

Luminescence, be it chemical, physical or biological, is the production of cold light by exciting atoms and causing the electrons to jump from one shell to another. Each time the electrons change position, a tiny spark of light is produced. Materials which glow after being exposed to light are *phosphorescent*. Those that glow only during exposure to light (such as ultraviolet or an electron beam) are *fluorescent*.

Modern luminous paints contain two sources of light. One is a phosphorescent chemical such as strontium thiosulphate. Exposure to light raises the electrons in this substance to a higher energy shell. When light is removed, they return to original shells, producing light in the process. The other source of light is a fluorescent chemical such as zinc sulphide. This is similar to the material used to coat television tubes. It glows when struck by an electron beam or ultraviolet rays. It has no afterglow. Mixed with the zinc sulphide is a highly radioactive mineral such as mesothorium (thorium 228 isotope, 200 times more radioactive than radium). The radioactive particles constantly being shot off by this substance strike the zinc sulphide atoms, change their electron positions and cause them to produce tiny scintillations of light.

Leave the luminous dial in a dark room until the bright phosphorescent glow due to light exposure can no longer be seen. This may take an hour or more. After this, the remaining glow will be that caused by the radioactive substance on the zinc sulphide. Have the room in total darkness and allow your eyes to become adapted to the dark by waiting about five minutes. Examine the luminous paint through the magnifying glass. The tiny sparks, each caused by a radioactive particle colliding with a zinc sulphide atom, will be clearly seen just as in a commercial spinthariscope.

The magnifying glass used should be at least ten-power. The *magnifying power* of a lens may be determined by dividing the number ten by the focal length in inches. Find focal length by using lens to focus image of light bulb onto paper. The distance from the lens to the paper is focal length.

Note: Some luminous dials contain only a phosphorescent chemical.

Such dials do not glow for long in the dark and must be frequently re-exposed to light. Since they do not contain a radioactive material, they will not show scintillations. If the first dial you try does not work, assume this to be the reason and try another. (See also Chapter 9, GEIGER COUNTER.)

WORLD GLOBE FOR TWENTY-FIVE CENTS

Here is a project that is instructive and inexpensive, yet provides the camp or camper with a nine-inch-diameter world globe in color for twenty-five cents. The outline maps are already printed and colored on a twenty-three-by-thirty-inch sheet available as Sheet Number 3093 from the U.S. Coast and Geodetic Survey, Washington, D. C. 20025. They cost twenty-five cents each. Making the world globe is easy and results are satisfying.

RECOMMENDED MATERIALS

Sheet No. 3093 "Lambert Globe," model cement, scissors. Stand may be made from wood base and dowel.

PROCEDURE

Instructions included on sheet. Sheet includes six long bands which are cut out, cemented at ends to form loops, and cemented side-to-side to form a sphere. Disks are provided to cement onto top and bottom. Bands and disks are printed in three colors on extra-heavy paper and globe is finished when they have been fitted and cemented together.

A stand may be constructed using a block of wood which has been hand-rubbed with stain. Drill a hole in this base at an angle of 23½°, representing the tilt of the earth's axis, and fit a length of dowel into the hole. Cut a round role in the bottom of the globe, fit it over the dowel and place a pin or tack through the top of the globe into the top of the dowel.

USE

The finished globe may be used as any other globe and is particularly helpful in weather, astronomy and geology.

GEOLOGY AND CRAFTS

The cutting, polishing and mounting of precious and semi-precious stones is known as *lapidary* science (or art, depending on the point of view). Geology excursions may provide campers with minerals which they would like to cut, polish and mount as a ring, tie clip, cuff links, pendant, earrings, charm, or key chain. These mountings are available at little cost and a variety of them may be kept on hand at camp. Stones are held to the mounts with cement, preferably jeweler's cement. The simplest item is to cut and polish a small stone and cement it into a *bell cap* with a chain attached (by a *jump ring*) for a key chain. Bell caps are available by the dozen for less than a dollar. Further information may be obtained from catalogs listed at the end of the chapter.

MATERIALS

Lapidary equipment may be conveniently purchased as kits containing: diamond saw for cutting minerals (note: saw does not have teeth, just diamond bits embedded in edge), motor, grinding wheels of various grits, container to drip water on grinding wheels or oil on saw, water soluble oil for cutting, dop sticks and dopping wax used as handle for small gems while grinding, felt wheel and red rouge for final polish, clamp to hold stone while cutting.

PROCEDURE

The procedure of preparing the rough stone for a ring is described here as an example. Using the saw, a *slab* with two flat sides is cut out of the stone. The slab is roughly shaped with a coarse grit grinder. If it is small, it is attached to a *dop stick* with wax for easier handling. The stone is polished with successively finer grit grinders, and finally polished with the felt wheel and cemented into place on the ring mounting.

Tumble polishing is another method which eliminates all above equipment but is not as versatile. Small stones are placed in a jar or barrel with a sand-like grit and the jar is turned continuously by motor for a week or more. The stones come out rounded, smoothed and polished. The silicon carbide grit is replaced with finer types as polishing progresses. Jewelry made of such stones is known as baroque jewelry for its unusual abstract, nonsymmetrical shapes.

RESOURCE MATERIALS FOR GEOLOGY

Magazines

Earth Science. Bimonthly, $2.50 per year. Box 1357, Chicago, Ill.   60690.

Rocks and Minerals. Bimonthly, $3 per year. Box 29, Peekskill, N. Y.

Gems and Minerals. Monthly, $3 per year. Box 687, Mentone, Calif.

Pamphlets and Charts

Government agencies, state and federal. See Project MAPS, CHARTS AND MODELS.

American Petroleum Institute, 1270 Avenue of the Americas, New York, N.Y. 10020. Free wall charts on oil and geology.

Teaching Soil and Water Conservation (PA-341), excellent project pamphlet free from Division of Publications, U. S. Dept. of Agriculture, Washington, D. C.   20025.

Assistance in identifying difficult specimens may be obtained from a local science museum or college geology department.

Project Ideas in the Earth Sciences. Free booklet from Geological Survey, Washington, D. C.   20025.

Films

Films from the following sources are free, user pays return postage. It is suggested that the free film catalogs be obtained from:

Shell Oil Company, Public Relations Department, 50 West 50th St., New York, N. Y. 10020. Films on oil formation, exploration and recovery.

Bureau of Mines, Graphic Services, 4800 Forbes Avenue, Pittsburgh, Penna. 15213. Large selection of films on mining and mineral resources of various states.

The Restless Sea, free film from local Bell Telephone business office.

Atomic Energy Commission, Public Information Service, Washington, D. C. 20025. Large selection of films. Request "Popular Level Film List."

Supplies

Ward's Natural Science Establishment, Box 1712, Rochester, N. Y. 14603. Request geology catalog preferably on camp or school stationery.

Grieger's, Inc., 1633 E. Walnut Street, Pasadena, Calif. Complete free catalog of lapidary and geology supplies, mineral and rock specimens.

I. Goldberg & Co., 429 Market Street, Philadelphia, Penna. 19106. Catalog of camping supplies and surplus equipment.

Chapter

6: Plants

SUGGESTED REFERENCES

Zim and Martin, *Trees*. New York: Golden Press, 1956.

Zim and Martin, *Flowers*. New York: Golden Press, 1950.

Watts, May Theilgaard, *Tree Finder*. Naperville, Illinois: Nature Study Guild, 25¢.

Watts, May Theilgaard, *Flower Finder*. Naperville, Illinois: Nature Study Guild, 50¢. The Watts booklets are very complete and useful. Easily carried in the field, they may be used in place of or in addition to the Zim books.

Storer, John H., *The Web of Life*. New York: New American Library, 1961.

Hillcourt, William, *Field Book of Nature Activities and Conservation*. New York: G. P. Putnam's Sons, 1961. $4.95. A hard-cover book that every counselor should have.

BECAUSE of the vast number of species involved, plants and animals could easily be the most difficult subjects that one could possibly attempt to teach at camp. College biology courses are of little help in biology field work. If the counselor attempts to teach himself field biology, he will soon become overwhelmed by the vast amount of material available and will make little progress. The solution to this problem is simple and twofold: 1. Be provincial. Concern yourself only with those species commonly found in your part of the country during the summer months. Make a list of the common plants and animals found in the area. Get assistance with your list from books, local nature groups, state university, state forest service, fish and game service and other resources listed in this chapter and the next. Arrange the items on your list according to phyla. 2. With your list, go through the suggested nature books and become familiar with the identity, characteristics and habits of your entries. Ignore anything not on the list. The information need not be known by heart. You can always look it up again and it is no crime to use a reference book for information in front of a camper. In fact, such times provide an opportunity to show campers how to find such answers for themselves.

The classifications in this chapter and the next have been designed especially for camp work. Each phylum includes characteristics of the phylum and a list of common species, their identification, habits and habitats. These classifications should form the foundation for further study and work at camp with plants and animals.

Much of the activity in these subjects will consist of field trips along various trails to observe and collect. The activity projects described here are in addition to such field trips. The counselor should have a definite subject or purpose for each field trip. Some such subjects are suggested in the projects.

More than any other subject, the study of plants depends upon, and will help to further develop, keen methods of observation. Campers will learn to look for small differences to tell plants apart. They will learn to look under leaves as well as on top, to feel the bark, count pine needles, study stem structure. Development of acute observation takes time, but it should be one of the constant goals of the science program.

Plants are important because they are the food makers of the earth. Every animal depends upon plants for his food either directly or indirectly; none can live on soil, water and sunlight. Only plants can make living organic matter from inorganic materials. In the process of *photosynthesis,* green plants use water, carbon dioxide, sunlight and soil minerals to produce sugar, carbohydrates (more of the plant) and oxygen. This is the food used by animals.

What about picking plants? There are definite laws against picking some wildflowers. Even in other cases, it is always better to take only a part of a plant, usually the leaf, for a specimen rather than the whole thing. If the plant is one of the small, simple ones, *one* entire plant may be desired for mounting. In either case, before any part of a plant is removed be sure that there are enough additional growths of the same type of plant in the area to insure its propagation. This principle of individual responsibility for conservation should be made known to campers. Only pick a plant when you can leave many more behind to continue the species. The safest things to collect *en masse* are tree leaves. Enough of these can be collected from several trees to supply individual camper collections.

Still on the subject of conservation, it has been pointed out by one author[1] that conservation can be made much more of an everyday reality for youngsters rather than a meaningless verbalism. Take, for example, the student in the classroom of a large city school. He is not going to be a forest ranger and he may never see a farm. In each of the following choices, it is not difficult to see which would be a more practical example of conservation for him: a) contour farming, or the wastebasket at the front of the room overflowing with half-used paper; b) forest conservation, or the person who reduces the length of a pencil by half every time it is sharpened; c) conservation of our vast mineral resources, or taking a bicycle or wagon in out of the rain to prevent rusting; d) care of watersheds and reservoirs, or the person who operates a lawn sprinkler so half of the spray lands on the road. Basically, conservation amounts to old-fashioned thrift and care. It is our individual waste that causes our collective loss of resources. This is something that all counselors can work on with campers throughout the season.

In plant-hunting, probably the greatest variety of vegetation can be found on a climb up a good-sized mountain. FIG. 6-1 shows the different

[1] Pearl A. Nelson, "Conservation Begins in the Elementary School Classroom," *Elementary School Science Bulletin,* March 1963, No. 77.

ICE

SNOW

LICHENS

MOSSES

ALPINE PLANTS

GRASS MEADOWS

BUSH CONIFERS

TREE LINE

CONIFEROUS FORESTS

DECIDUOUS FORESTS

TROPICAL FORESTS

FIG. 6-1. Plant communities found at various mountain altitudes. Conditions at base and summit are determined by specific climate, season and altitude. Each 1,000-foot change in elevation is climatologically approximately equal to a 300-mile (4°) latitude change.

plant communities that exist at various elevations on mountains. There are mosses, lichens and wild flowers on top of Mount Washington in New Hampshire that would be found at sea level only if one traveled to the Arctic. Each type of plant community attracts a different animal community. This study of interrelationships of plants, animals and environment is called *ecology*. The plant groups at top and bottom of your mountain will of course be determined by its geographical location and height.

INFORMATION OF IMPORTANCE: PLANT CLASSIFICATION

PHYLUM I: THALLOPHYTES

These are the simplest of plants, with no true root, leaf or stem, no circulatory system, no seeds or flowers. Many have an anchor, or "holdfast," which holds the plant to ground or rock. Leaflike structures, if present, have openings reaching all cells through which food, gases and wastes may pass.

1. *Algae* have green chlorophyll and can produce food by photosynthesis. Many are aquatic, and some phosphorescent, causing water, especially sea water, to glow at night. Algae are classified by color:

A. *Blue-green algae* prefer warm water, and are often a sign of water pollution.
B. *Green,* with five thousand species, are most common. They are often found in stagnant fresh-water pools. The *protococcus* forms common green film on rocks and trees and is often mistaken for moss. *Spirogyra* are long green filaments found in ponds and streams, and often called pond scum.
C. *Brown,* mostly salt-water "seaweeds," include kelp.
D. *Red* too are mostly salt-water; used for agar, a laxative and a culture medium.
E. *Diatoms* are microscopic plants with a silicon shell, found in brooks, pond mud, slippery brownish coating on rocks, and stems in ponds and streams. They are most common in spring and fall.
F. Animal-plant group includes algae which contain chlorophyll but can move about. See Phylum I under ANIMALS: FLAGELLA.

2. *Fungi* are not green, have no chlorophyll. They cannot produce food and must get organic food from other decaying plants. They include *mushrooms;* molds including *bread mold; yeasts,* the smallest fungi, next to bacteria in size; *shelf fungi,* found on trees; *orange sulfur mushrooms;* and *puffballs,* which when dry and brown can be squeezed to make the spores come out like smoke. A fungus causes many dead stumps to glow at night in the woods. This common phosphorescent phenomenon is called *fox fire* and is probably due to slow oxidation by fungi in the presence of water. It may also account for many of the "ghosts" seen in the woods in the days of superstition.

3. *Bacteria,* related to fungi, have no chlorophyll. They occur everywhere. Some are helpful, others harmful. While they cause food spoilage and food poisoning, they also ripen cheese, and produce vinegar and antibiotics. They can be seen only with a microscope of 300 to 500 magnifications. They are classified by shape: rod-shaped *bacilli,* spiral *spirilla,* and disc-shaped *cocci.*

4. *Lichen* are algae and fungi living together. The fungus provides shelter and moisture for algae which carry on photosynthesis and provide fungi with organic food material. Lichen survives the harshest environments from the Antarctic to the tropics, and is the only plant to live on completely bare rock, which it starts weathering into soil for the growth of moss, grass, and other life. They may be crusty *(crustose),* leaflike *(foliose)* or shrublike *(fruticose)* on trees, rocks and ground. Two common types include *rock tripe* (foliose), brown patches held to rock by a central holdfast; and *reindeer* (fruticose), a rubberlike small shrub-type lichen found on the ground, the algae growing like a cloak around fungi within stem. Various crustose forms are closely attached to rocks.

PHYLUM II: BRYOPHYTES

These have no roots or circulatory system. Roots are replaced by thread-like rhizoids (root hairs) which can absorb moisture to osmose a short distance through the upper cells. Most live in damp, shady areas, but a few mosses live at high elevations in direct sunlight. They reproduce by alternation of generations.

1. *Liverworts* are small, broad, flat, green plant bodies sometimes bearing capped stalks containing spores. There may also be a ribbon-like plant body. The least-noticed group of small common plants, they grow flat on earth, trees, rotting wood, ravine walls, or moist rocks on stream banks.

2. *Mosses* consist of an upright stem surrounded by masses of tiny leaves. In their life cycle, one generation consists of the conspicuous leafed plants living close together. Some stems are antheridia and bear sperms, others are archegonia and bear eggs at the top. Sperm is splashed by raindrop or swims in water film to fertilize egg. From the top of its stem, the fertilized egg grows rapidly into an elongated stalk with a capsule at top bearing spores. This capped stalk is the second generation (sporophyte). When the cap dries and bursts, spores scatter. Some germinate to form the *protonema,* a threadlike branching structure running over and under soil. Protonema is the first structure of the first generation, and the buds along it grow into new moss plants. Then the protonema disappears and plants are ready to fertilize again for the second generation. Mosses form natural germination beds for the seeds of larger plants in harsh environments such as rocks. It is easier to distinguish between different mosses when capsules are present. *Sphagnum* or peat moss has leaves one cell thick with openings that take in

and hold water. This water-absorbing property of sphagnum is used by nurseries for shipping plants and starting seeds and cuttings.

PHYLUM III: PTERIDOPHYTES

Pteridophytes have distinct roots, leaves and stems, with water-conducting tubes in the stems. A dominant form of life during the Carboniferous period, they reached heights of ninety feet. They reproduce by alternating generations, similar to mosses.

1. *Ferns* have a leaf called a frond, which when immature is a tightly coiled fuzzy structure called a "fiddlehead," and which unfolds during the spring. Only the leaf is visible above ground; the stem is a horizontal underground rhizome which may branch out to form a "fairy ring" of visible fronds. Reproduction is similar to mosses except that the most conspicuous generation is the spore-bearing one (sporophyte). The egg- and sperm-bearing generation is the *prothallus,* a tiny fingernail-sized plate. The familiar second-generation fern plants grow from this; only fertile fronds bear the black spore cases each carrying about sixty-four tiny spores capable of germinating to form a new prothallus. Fern beds make excellent cover for small animals.

2. *Horsetails* have straight, hollow stems with branches growing out in circular whorls. They are found in barren, sandy areas, and the fibers contain large amounts of silicon from the sand. *Scouring rush* is used by Indians and others to scour pots and pans. People have made the mistake of chewing these and finding the silicon grains painfully imbedded in the tongue and mouth.

3. *Club mosses (lycopodium)* bear no relation to true mosses. They are ground creepers on horizontal surface-running stems. Many are evergreen and bear spores in conelike structures. They include ground cedar and ground pine.

PHYLUM IV: SPERMATOPHYTES

Seed-bearing plants with distinct roots, leaves and stem, spermatophytes produce their seeds in cones or flowers. Adapted for a land habitat, they have connecting tissues capable of transporting water to great heights— over three hundred feet in the case of redwoods. They do not require water to transport sperm to egg as in the previous two phyla.

1. *Gymnosperms* include all coniferous evergreens. The needles fall off after two to three years, but not all at one time as with deciduous trees. There are two kinds of cones. The pollen cones (male), small and short-lived, appear in the spring covered with yellow pollen. Seed cones (female) are large and woody and may live for two years. Pollination occurs in spring, the pollen being blown onto the scales of the seed cones. Seeds develop at the base of each scale for a year or more. The cone then opens, the seeds fall out with the light scale membranes attached, and are carried away by the wind. Conifers include the *pine* (identified

by number of needles in cluster), *spruces* (four-sided needles that can be twirled in the fingers), *cedars* (scalelike stem), *hemlock* (two silver lines on under side of needle), the *fir* with its pungent fragrance, and the *larch*, with needles in tufts. Twenty-five million firs and spruces are used each year for Christmas trees.

2. *Angiosperms*, the dominant plant form of the present age, have over 250,000 species. They bear seeds in a flower which becomes a fruit, and are the only plants with flowers. The flower contains a stamen, whose pollen grains contain sperm, and a pistil bearing ovules which contain eggs. Seeds develop in ovary at base of pistil. An ovary containing seeds may enlarge to become a fruit, such as a grain of wheat, an apple, squash, tomato or watermelon. Below are two groups of angiosperms.

A. *Monocotyledons* are named from having a single cotyledon in the seed, and usually have parallel-veined leaves. The flower parts in groups of three. The group includes all *grasses, lilies* and *palms.* Many are self- or wind-pollenated. There is a brief and inconspicuous flowering period. Along with timothy and blue grass, the grasses include the world's most important food crops: corn, oats, wheat, barley, rye, sugar cane and rice.

B. *Dicotyledons* have two seed leaves. Leaf veins may be pinnate (like a feather) or palmate (netted). The flower parts are in groups of four or five. All deciduous trees, most wildflowers, and fruits, vegetables and cultivated plants are dicotyledons. For this large group, field books on trees and wildflowers should be on hand.

SEED GERMINATION

Seeds develop in the flower of the angiosperms. The seed is the means by which such plants continue from one generation to another. The seeds will remain dormant until provided with favorable growing conditions (heat, light, water, and air). When such conditions are found, the plant will begin growth, using food stored in the seed until it develops leaves for manufacturing its own food. This resumption of growth by a seed embryo after the dormant period is called *germination*. As a project, it is so simple and troublefree that each camper may germinate his own seeds and study their growth.

MATERIALS

Glasses or saucers, paper toweling or tissue, bean or pea seeds. If seeds are not available, a box of whole peas may be purchased in a grocery store. These germinate very well and at fifteen cents a pound are much less expensive than packaged seeds.

PROCEDURE

Each camper should stuff a glass with paper toweling. Place three seeds between paper and glass about an inch down from the top. Keep paper moistened with water daily. This may also be done in saucers but growth is more difficult to observe. Keep glasses in warm lighted area. To make one complete science session, this activity may follow a discussion of flowers and seed development.

Germination will start within a week and should be observed daily. Note that regardless of seed position, root always turns down and stem up. Although not completely understood, these phenomena have names. *Geotropism* means downward response to gravity; *hydrotropism*, response to water; *phototropism*, response to light. There is also *thigmotropism*, the twining growth movement of ivys and vine climbers. If one glass is turned upside down for a few days, the stem will curve back up and the root down. If plants are in a window, they will probably bend toward the light.

Peas and beans have been suggested because they are dicotyledons and upon germination the seed splits in half forming two seed leaves which will feed the plant until larger leaves develop.

USE

Plants may be allowed to continue growing through the season or they may be dried and mounted when the seed leaves are at the peak of development. Instructions for mounting will be found under LEAF COLLECTIONS.

Campers may also try to germinate wild seeds collected around camp such as the dandelion, milkweed, and acorn.

MAKING LEAF PRINTS

Another item that campers can take home as a tangible result of the summer science program is a collection of identified leaf prints. The collection need not be large. It may contain as few as four different leaves; but it should include representative types such as simple and compound, and those with parallel veins and palmate veins. It will then be useful at home for identifying leaves and trees.

Prints may be made photographically or with ink. The photographic method works best for pine-needle clusters and may be done following directions in Chapter 3 for PHOTOGRAMS. Deciduous leaves are best done with ink as described below.

MATERIALS

White paper, various tubes of water color block-printing ink, two brayers (rubber rollers for water ink), inking plate (sheet of glass or sheet metal). Art materials are available at J. L. Hammet Company.

PROCEDURE

Use freshly picked leaves free from defects caused by insects or weather. Squeeze some ink out onto the inking plate and spread out with one of the rubber rollers. Water color ink is used rather than oil because it can be easily washed from hands and tools. When a thin layer of ink is obtained on the plate, carefully place a leaf on the ink and smooth out any unevenness in the leaf surface. Roll over leaf with rubber roller (which will also have ink on it) so both sides of leaf are inked.

Select a piece of white paper twice as large as leaf and crease down the center. Very carefully remove leaf from ink plate and center on one half of white paper. Once again smooth out any wrinkles in leaf. Fold the other half of the paper over on top of the leaf and roll over top of paper with the clean rubber roller. (This roller never touches ink.) Gently lift up top half of paper and inspect resulting leaf print. The leaf and all veins should show clearly. There will be two prints, one on each half of paper. Since leaf may smudge while being positioned on bottom half, the top print is usually better. Cut paper in half, select the better print, and label with such information as name of tree, type of leaf (simple or compound) type of veins (pinnate, palmate or parallel), location found, date and name of camper.

With additional rollers and inking plates, prints can be made in many colors. A pleasant effect may also be obtained by spreading two colors beside each other on the same plate. Wash rollers and inking plates immediately after the printing session is over.

PRESSED-LEAF COLLECTIONS

Leaf prints are an excellent method of preserving many details of leaves for future identification, but only pressed leaves can show all the fine details of the original specimen. Campers may not want to press leaves to bring home, but the camp should build up a collection of pressed specimens of each variety found in the area. Such a collection will be useful for study discussion and identification purposes. Pressing leaves is simpler than making prints but the results are more fragile and probably wouldn't withstand the ride home in a trunk. A systematic collection of pressed leaves is called a *herbarium*.

MATERIALS

Newspapers, absorbent paper (paper towels), 12″ × 18″ construction paper (standard herbarium paper is 11½″ × 16½″; shirt cardboard may also be used), masking tape or Scotch frosted tape.

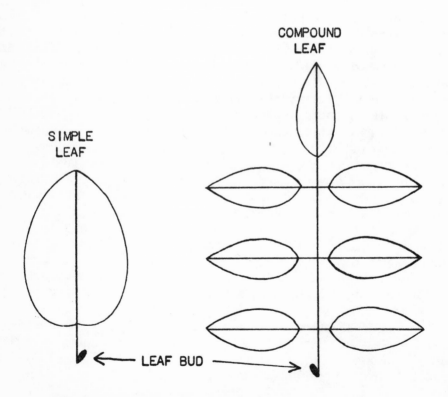

COMPOUND
LEAF

SIMPLE
LEAF

←—— LEAF BUD ——→

Fig. 6-2.   Difference between simple and compound leaves

There are two steps: drying the leaves and mounting the leaves. Leaves to be dried should be carefully selected, free of insect defects and of the desired color. Leaves must be held flat while drying so they will not curl or wrinkle. Stack leaves with layers of newspaper and sheets of paper towel in the following order from the bottom: newspaper pad folded about 12″ × 15″, paper towel, leaf, paper towel, newspaper, paper towel, leaf, paper towel, newspaper, etc. Paper towels are used on both sides of leaf to absorb moisture and prevent newspaper ink from defacing leaf. Place a flat board on top of the stack and add weights—books or cases—on top of the board so leaves will be kept tightly pressed. Leave in dry, well-ventilated place until leaves are completely dry (at least a week).

The flat, dry leaves are removed and each is placed on its own 12″ × 18″ piece of mounting paper. Hold in place with ⅛″ wide strips of cloth tape or masking tape or regular strips of Scotch frosted tape. The older transparent Scotch tape should not be used as it dries in time and peels from the paper. Label each sheet in lower right-hand corner with name of specimen, date, location found, name of collector. When the time comes for storage, herbarium sheets should be stacked on a flat surface or in a box with some moth balls or flakes scattered around to discourage animals that might use the herbarium for a dining room. Specimens from all phyla should be included in the herbarium. This technique is not limited to deciduous tree leaves.

Note: Many people confuse leaves and leaflets. A complete leaf always has a *leaf bud* at the base of its stem. Leaves may be *simple* or *compound*. The two types are shown in FIG. 6-2. A simple leaf has only one large green blade. A compound leaf has many blades called leaflets on a stem with one leaf bud where the stem joins the branch. Look for the bud to make sure you have a complete leaf.

FIELD TRIPS TO FIND AND COLLECT PLANTS

A camp project might be to find, collect and preserve plant specimens from each plant phylum. Field trips may be taken for this specific purpose. Interested campers may want to make individual collections that they can bring home. Most of the plants found may be pressed and mounted as described in PRESSED-LEAF COLLECTIONS.

MATERIALS

Pocket-size pruning shears, pocket knife, note pad, shoulder bag (available at surplus for about a dollar). Miscellaneous equipment is referred to below.

PROCEDURE

No plant should be picked unless there are plenty left behind to carry on the species. Plants must not be allowed to dry out before being pressed. With thallophytes and bryophytes, it is usually easiest to keep them moist until you return to camp by placing them in jars with wet sponge or moss in the bottom. The jars will have a humid atmosphere and will keep the small plants of these two phyla moist and green until they can be properly pressed.

For the larger plants and leaves listed as pteridophytes and spermatophytes, it is usually easier to press in the field as they are collected. This is conveniently managed by carrying a large spiral notebook, eight by ten inches, with hard board covers. As leaves are collected, they are placed between separate pages and the book is tied, clamped or held tightly together. When collecting specimens, notes should be made as to the environment in which they were found. Such notes may be written on the same page with the leaf when the spiral notebook press is used. Leaves should be removed and placed in a standard press when the group returns to camp.

Shelf fungi found on trees are probably the only plants that do not have to be pressed. Allow these to dry hard in warm air and cement or tie onto herbarium sheets or cardboard. Delicate water algae are best mounted by floating the plant in a tray of water. Slide the mounting paper up under the algae, remove from water, cover with wax paper and press to dry. When dry, remove wax paper. Usually no cement or tape will be needed to hold algae to the herbarium sheet. Many pressed leaves can make attractive prints for framing and glass table tops.

A representative plant collection should be able to include the following without any trouble: algae (water and land), shelf fungus, lichen, moss, ferns, club moss, conifer needles and cones, deciduous tree leaves (and seeds or nuts), grasses and leaves or flowers of a few wildflowers. See PLANT CLASSIFICATION for details on locations and plant structures.

Note: Take an evening walk in woods to find glowing phosphorescent wood. This *fox fire* will be found on decaying tree stumps. See FUNGI in PLANT CLASSIFICATION.

GLASS BEAD MICROSCOPE

The glass bead microscope is more permanent and portable than the water drop microscope and can be made for less than one cent. In the 1600's, Anton van Leeuwenhoek used to study plants and animals with glass bead microscopes made by grinding the glass bead down slightly to form a flattened lens. With the flattened bead, he lost some power but increased the clarity. For simplicity, our beads will not be ground flat, thus we will have increased power but also increased chance of distortion. Performance of this microscope, then, is very similar to but not identical with Van Leeuwenhoek's.

MATERIALS

Corrugated cardboard (cut from box), black plastic electrical tape, poster board, rubber bands, cement, 5/64" drill, microscope slides, 5-mm solid clear glass beads (Cenco No. 14225 cost $8.25 for one pound, containing about three thousand beads.)

PROCEDURE

The black plastic tape should be prepared in advance as follows: Drill 5/64" holes right through the roll of tape about 1 ½" apart. Do not allow drill to enter cardboard core and take care that sides of holes are smooth and

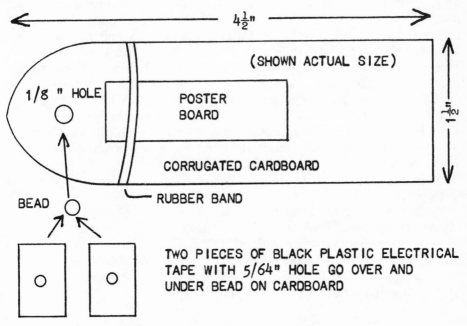

FIG. 6-3.   Construction of glass bead microscope

clean. Cut rounded rectangle of corrugated cardboard as shown in FIG. 6-3. Make a ⅛″ hole to receive the bead (a ⅛″ hole paper punch is useful here). Look through the glass beads for one that is not scratched or cloudy and push it into the ⅛″ hole in cardboard holder. Cut two patches of tape containing holes in center, center one hole under bead and press tape onto cardboard. Hold up to light and center second hole over top of bead. When light can be seen clearly, press tape onto cardboard. These smaller holes reduce internal light reflections in the bead and increase the image sharpness.

A piece of poster board is cemented to corrugated cardboard to keep the microscope slide at approximately the proper distance from bead for focus. Wrap rubber band around cardboard to hold slide in place.

There should be a well-prepared permanent slide on hand to test the microscope as follows. Slip slide under rubber band with specimen toward the glass bead. Hold the microscope in hand horizontally and bring it up close to your eye, so eyelashes touch cardboard. Slide should be on side away from face. Look through microscope at a bare incandescent light bulb. (Other light may be used but the incandescent gives the sharpest image.) Move slide slowly with free hand back and forth for position and in and out for focus. If microscope does not work properly, re-center glass bead under tape holes or replace with another glass bead.

USE

This microscope has a magnification of about seventy power and will bring into the visible range many of the larger microscopic specimens. The cells in an onion membrane show up very well. Peel the various fleshy layers from an onion that has been sliced in half. On the underside of each layer is a very thin, delicate membrane. Carefully peal a piece of this membrane, place it on a microscope slide and examine with glass bead microscope. Some parts of the membrane will be only one cell thick and the various cells can be clearly seen like bricks in a wall. The membrane should be moist for best results. Add a bit of water if needed. With a toothpick or glass rod place a tiny drop of iodine on the onion membrane and examine again. Iodine will stain the nucleus and cell wall of each cell a darker color so they may be more easily seen. All living things are made of such cells. Plant cells have hard walls, animal cells have softer walls. If campers see no more than this with the glass bead microscope, the project will be worth while.

You may be able to get some pollen grains by touching a slide to the stamens of a flower. These may be seen under the microscope.

Dry or semi-dry protozoan mounts (Chapter 7) can be seen with the glass bead. Some show better when stained. You can also try paper fibers, insect wings, human hair, thin leaves and blades of grass, pond scum algae, and many other natural phenomena.

GROWING BREAD-MOLD FUNGUS

Fungi and bacteria grow best in a warm, humid atmosphere. The principle behind the many methods of preserving food by canning, pasteurizing, freezing and refrigerating is to kill all bacteria present and prevent new ones from entering the food or from having the proper conditions for growth and reproduction. By purposely providing the needed conditions, we can grow some interesting fungi in a very short time. The most common food fungi are bread mold (*rhizopus*) and *penicillium*.

MATERIALS

Saucer, paper towel or tissue, plastic food wrap, bread, magnifying glass.

PROCEDURE

Bread mold is a white cottony fungus that will grow on almost any common food. It may be easily grown by providing a warm, humid atmosphere and some food material (bread). Fold a piece of paper towel and place in a saucer. Moisten towel with water, place a piece of bread on towel and introduce fungus spores by shaking a dusty cloth onto bread. (Or you may leave the bread out in the air for few days previous to the experiment.) Cover saucer with plastic food wrap to keep moisture from escaping. Bread should not be soggy wet. Place in a warm area away from direct sources of light. The fungus will develop first as a white cottony mass on the bread. The cobwebby white filaments will reproduce rapidly and in a few days the stems will develop knobby black spore cases. This is the mature stage. The spore cases will ripen and burst, releasing thousands of spores to

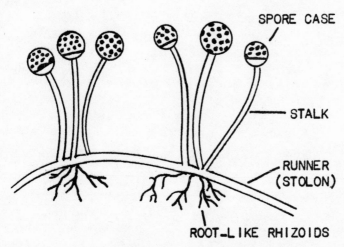

FIG. 6-4.   Enlarged view of rhizopus bread mold. When ripe, each spore case bursts, releasing up to 70,000 spores.

grow new plants. Growth should be observed daily with a magnifying glass Some of the fungus may be placed on a microscope slide and examined under the glass bead microscope. A drop of water may help to hold it in place on the slide. Mature stage of rhizopus is shown in FIG. 6-4. Because the individual rhizopus plants are quite large, they are easily examined under a magnifying glass.

Penicillium is a green cottony mold fungus most common on decaying fruit. Your black bread mold may be joined by the blue-green penicillium The mold may be grown by placing pieces of fruit or jelly in the moistened saucer environment as was done for bread mold. The individual penicil lium plants are much smaller than bread mold and will only be visible under a microscope of about 300 power. Under such power, the spore cases will be observed to grow in chains rather than separate knobs as on bread mold. Penicillium is used to ripen certain cheeses and is the source of anti biotic penicillin.

Note: Both rhizopus and penicillium are harmless fungi, but the con ditions under which they grow are also ideal for other fungi, some of which may not be harmless. *Aspergillus fumigatus* is a blue-green mold similar in appearance to penicillium which may cause reaction in man if ingested by breathing or swallowing. *A simple precaution is in order: Do not breathe close to molds or touch with bare hands. Wash hands after observations are made.*

MYSTERY BOX

The mystery box is a continuing project of the science program. Located in the dining room or other conspicuous place, it is a constant reminder and interest arouser for your science program. It may be a small wooden box with glass front or just a mystery shelf. Some unusual nature item with an interesting story should be placed in the box for a few days to a week. Even live animals may be included for an hour or two. Then at mealtime or campfire, you can identify the object and tell the story behind it. Any science object is eligible. Some suggestions: insect gall, skull or other animal parts, fruit of some plant, rock with conspicuous mineral, cocoons, frog eggs, pressed leaves, mosses, ferns, lichen, track cast, insects.

A larger version of the mystery box is the mystery tree. This is suitable for the science museum—a tree fixed to the floor and ceiling, with various specimens located in their natural positions under, on, above and around the tree. A "Can you find them?" list of all objects included may be posted on a nearby wall. This is an exhibit to which campers can continually add specimens.

MAKING PHOTOMICROGRAPHS

It is not difficult to produce striking photomicrographs (photographs through a microscope). Directions are similar to those given in Chapter 4 under TELESCOPIC PHOTOGRAPHY and reference should be made to that project. Since individual set-ups will depend upon the materials available, these directions are sketchy and describe general principles involved.

MATERIALS

Microscope (the ten-dollar imported microscopes are adequate for most camp uses. See catalogs of Radio Shack, Lafayette Radio and Edmund Scientific.), source of strong light beam (flashlight, projector or home-made), elevator tripod, camera (View camera or single-lens reflex are easiest to use.), film, microscope slides.

PROCEDURE

A set-up that we have used with considerable success is shown in FIG. 6-5. Illumination is a major problem but not difficult to solve. Mirror illumination is usually not satisfactory. There should be a source of high-intensity light directly under the microscope stage. Looking around for available parts, we made our light using a bright automobile bulb and socket, a magnifying lens, the metal cover from an old radio I.F. transformer, and a

FIG. 6-5.   Setup for photomicrography using view-type camera and home made light under microscope stage for illumination

transformer for power. Bulb and socket were installed in one end of the metal can, the lens fitting tightly in the open end. With bulb turned on, lens was moved in and out until light came to focus where microscope stage would be. The bulb was given a slight overload of voltage to increase brightness. Assembly can be held to stage with a sheet-metal clip. This is one system of illumination; it shouldn't be difficult to think of others using available materials. This light is bright enough (and tightly enclosed) to permit use of the microscope as a microprojector. Put in slide, turn on light and focus on screen of white paper. This procedure is excellent for group viewing.

Photos are made by aiming the light beam through the microscope tube, through a camera and onto the film. The beam travels in a straight line and, as with the telescope, the camera must be carefully positioned so the light reaches the film and doesn't get caught someplace on the side of the camera. Checking the focus and positioning of the projected image is easiest on a view or press camera or a single-lens reflex. If these are not available, a simple camera may be used, but first remove the back and hold a piece of wax paper or tissue paper behind the lens where the film would be. Focus and position the microscope image on the wax paper, then, without moving microscope or camera, install film, replace the back and take pictures. The camera should be held firmly by a tripod, preferably the elevator type so height can be precisely adjusted. When shooting, turn room lights off and drape black cloth over junction of microscope and camera lens to shield out extraneous light.

Almost any film may be used. There should be sufficient light to use Plus-X. If not, Tri-X should get the picture, even under poorest illumination. For sheet film, Royal Pan will work well. The negative image will be quite large and making prints will be no problem.

USE

For your first photomicrographs try the old standby, onion cells. (See GLASS BEAD MICROSCOPE.) Onion cells are easy to focus and illuminate. From here you can do any microscopic subject including the protozoans. Flower pistils (illuminated from above) make dramatic pictures and are very satisfying because the illumination problems are a bit different. The top-stage illumination may require longer exposures.

Note: For cinephotomicrographs (movies through microscope), project microscope image onto white paper or screen and use movie camera to photograph image. (A close-up lens may be needed.) Using a standard microprojector, excellent results have been obtained in making motion pictures of the flow of blood corpuscles through capillaries in the tail of living goldfish. Protozoans also lend themselves to this technique.

Comparing microscopic photography and telescopic photography, the latter is usually more difficult because of the bulk of the telescope. Photomicrography is a more flexible and more easily controlled operation. Both subjects make excellent projects for a small group of campers to work on through the summer.

GAMES

Campers enjoy the competition of games. The games described here require a minimum of preparation. They may be used for an entire session or to fill in extra time at the end of a session. The first game is well suited as a fill-in and is the only one particularly adapted to indoors.

WHAT AM I?

After the method of "Twenty Questions," but without a necessary limit as to number. Counselor may start game by being "it" and saying "What am I?" or "I am a mineral, what am I?" Campers ask questions which are answered by "Yes" or "No." The one who guesses the identity is new "it." In variations of this game, each camper may receive a slip of paper assigning his secret identity; or the game may be played outdoors and mystery must involve some nature object within sight.

PLANT OR ANIMAL?

Place two goal lines about one hundred feet apart on ground. Divide group into two teams, the Plants and the Animals. Teams may be selected by counting 1, 2, 1, 2, etc. All those with same number are on same team. Teams form lines facing each other. Counselor calls name of plant or animal. If it is an animal, all plants chase animals until they are safe behind their goal line. If plant is called, then animals chase. Those who are tagged become members of the opposing team that tagged them. Sample items called may be: bat, robin, oak, copperhead, spinach, green frog, green leaves, red pine, red beets, red fox, red squirrel, deer. A variation: One team is true and the other is false. Make statements such as "All snakes lay eggs." If false, false team chases true team. Have statements prepared in advance.

NATURE HUNT

The group goes to an area rich in nature materials and divides into two teams. Each team takes one side of the trail. Counselor announces an item to be found. The team finding the item in the area on its side of the trail first scores point. Players need only locate item and call counselor, they need not pick it. Trail sides should be switched half way through the game to assume equal opportunity. Each item should be discussed briefly after it is found. Particularly discuss marks of identification. Team with most points wins game.

PROSPECTING

Give each camper a four-foot length of string with ends tied together to form a loop. Loop is placed on ground to form a square or circle. Each camper then prospects his enclosed "property" for all nature items he can find, starting with different types of grass. (It is not necessary to identify these by name.) The person with the most items is winner. Items should be gathered together and discussed after game.

SCAVENGER HUNT

This may be played between individuals or in teams. Each team is given a list of things to be collected and a paper bag in which to place them. Set specific time limit or signal and penalize groups not back on time. Winning team has largest number of objects. Sample items: acorn cups, parallel-veined leaves, bird feather, two-winged insect, granite, lichen. As a variation, Hillcourt suggests the "sealed letter" hunt. Instructions read as follows: "Our Indian chief has not slept for twenty nights. The witch doctor of our tribe has promised to cure him with his famous sleeping brew, but needs your help. Bring him the following ingredients within thirty minutes from the moment you read this: ten dandelion seeds, two bird feathers, four dead flies, bit of rabbit fluff, ten white pine needles, live frog or toad. . . ." (Extend the list to include about twenty items.)

OTHER PLANT PROJECTS

Some other projects that may be done in studying plants are:

GERMINATING IRRADIATED SEEDS

Seeds which have been exposed to radioactive rays are easily obtained. (See the Edmund Scientific Catalog, "Atomic Seeds.") Radiation changes the genes of the plant and its inherited characteristics. Often these changes result in better, faster-growing plants. These seeds may be germinated with normal seeds in the SEED GERMINATION experiment to compare differences, or they may be placed in pots to enable a longer and more complete observation period.

SCIENCE TRAIL

The camp nature or science trail need not be an elaborate operation. In most cases it is only used for two months and is neither used nor kept up during the rest of the year. Since many changes may take place between camp seasons, it is probably best to have a simple trail with markings that can be easily changed. Because campers generally do not use the trail by themselves but are accompanied by a science leader, explanatory signs may be kept to a minimum. The only signs that might be needed are those pointing to items of interest that are located away from the trail and might be missed during the field trips. Simplest labels are shipping tags coated with varnish or clear plastic spray and tied to twigs. The trail should pass through as many types of environment as possible: woods, field, marsh, pond, stream, rocky areas. Signs or tags may point out locations of various nearby animal homes.

NATURE MAP OF CAMP

This is a wall map showing camp and major buildings. Locations and names of plants and animal homes are plotted on it. It may be the center of a major nature display showing specimens of items listed on map. Include co-ordinates across top and side (A,B,C, and 1,2,3) as on road map. Stakes with co-ordinates may be placed around perimeter of camp. Measuring and surveying instruments of Chapter 8 may be used in preparing map. This will be a continuing project taking more than one season.

MICROCOSMIC ENVIRONMENT STUDY

Interested campers may make a detailed and documented study of the science lore of a small section of camp. Graphs, charts and lists may be kept on such factors as temperature, wind directions, precipitation, barometric pressure, cloud cover, forecasts, overhead stars and constellations, animals observed, plants observed, soil profile down twelve inches, type(s) of soil, whether sand, silt, or clay, and amount of organic material present, bedrock formations, number of stones per square yard, drainage and topography. A map of area can show land formations, locations of plants and animal homes. The study may also include diagrams, photographs, drawings and specimens gathered and preserved from the area. Such a project may be undertaken as the basis for a science fair project for the following school year.

RESOURCE MATERIALS FOR PLANTS

(Also see ANIMALS.)

Pamphlets and Charts

Request list of conservation education publications from: Educational Servicing Section, National Wildlife Federation, 1412 Sixteenth Street, N.W., Washington, D. C. 20006. Many free publications available. Mention use at a camp

Request catalog of publications from: Division of Publications, Office of Information, U. S. Department of Agriculture, Washington, D. C. 20025. Mention camp work.

Request "Natural Resources Educational Packet" from: Garden Club of America 598 Madison Ave., New York, N. Y. 10022. An excellent collection of material giving useful information and many other references.

Request "Bibliography of Teaching Aids" from: American Forest Products Industries, Inc., 1816 N Street, N.W., Washington, D. C. 20006. Many outstanding free materials including large full-color posters such as "Forest and Trees of United States" and new "Growth of a Tree."

Request "Forest Service Film Catalog" and "Materials to Help Teach Forest Conservation" from: Forest Service, U. S. Department of Agriculture, Washington, D. C. 20025. Single copies of all publications available free. The Service will also send you enough "Smokey Bear" posters for each cabin in camp.

Request "Audubon Nature Bulletin List" and "List of Publications" from: National Audubon Society, 1130 Fifth Ave., New York, N. Y. 10028. You will have a valuable resource if you purchase all sixty-five Nature Bulletins, $5.95 plus postage.

Sixty "Turtox Service Leaflets" are available from: General Biological Supply House, Inc., 8200 South Hoyne Ave., Chicago, Ill. 60620. Free to secondary school and college teachers of science; $1.80 for elementary teachers and students. Another excellent resource.

Request "Bulletin 1102, List of Publications" from: Department of Extension Teaching, New York State College of Agriculture, Cornell University, Ithaca N. Y. Listing of hundreds of valuable science and nature leaflets. Every camp should especially have E 191: "Poison Ivy and Poison Sumac."

Additional information may be obtained from your state forest service located in the state capital. Also request list of publications from Agricultural Experiment Station at your state university (list of stations included in U. S. Department of Agriculture catalog).

Films

The U.S.D.A. has about 250 films available for free loan. Subjects include agriculture, forestry, conservation, and others. Request catalog from: Motion Picture Service, Office of Information, U. S. Department of Agriculture, Washington, D. C. 20025.

Forest Service Films: See above.

Chapter
7: Animals

Zim and Cottam, *Insects*. New York: Golden Press, 1956.

Zim and Hoffmeister, *Mammals*. New York: Golden Press, 1955.

Zim and Smith, *Reptiles and Amphibians*. New York: Golden Press, 1953. Other titles in the Golden Nature Series include *Seashores, Fishes* and *Birds*.

Burnett, Fisher and Zim, *Zoology*. New York: Golden Press, 1958.

Carson, Rachel, *The Edge of the Sea*. New York: New American Library, 1959.

Peterson, Roger Tory, *How to Know the Birds*. New York: New American Library.

Morgan, Ann Haven, *Field Book of Ponds and Streams*. New York: G. P. Putnam's Sons, 1930. This hard-cover book will be invaluable at fresh-water camps. Includes all plants and animals found in or near fresh water.

SUGGESTED REFERENCES

THE ANIMAL KINGDOM is large and varied and so is our list of suggested references; but none of the books, except Morgan, costs more than a dollar, so the total expense is not great. As with plants, the counselor's first job will be to go through each book checking off those species found in his local region. This will greatly narrow the field and simplify further study.

The objective of animal study at camp is to know what animals exist in the area and to learn about their habits and interaction with the other elements of their environment. Accomplishing this objective does not require keeping animals in captivity. In fact, the best policy in this respect is: *Catch, study, release.* Even this is best limited to the cold-blooded vertebrates and simpler animals. Birds and mammals are best studied in their natural habitats. The catch-release policy prevents the science museum from becoming a zoo or a morgue and most other counselors will willingly bring in animals they find knowing that they will be released shortly and not spend the remainder of the camp season in a jar.

The animal classification on the following pages has been carefully prepared for camp use by including facts about many common woodland animals and the type of environment where each is likely to be found. The classification should be the foundation for most animal study with older campers and the major headings might well be displayed in the science museum along with representative specimens that have been caught and preserved at camp. Since many people avoid the animal world for fear of unknown hazards, we have included in the classification most of the hazards that are real. It will be found that there are very few. Remember that most animals are defensive and avoid man if at all possible. Also, when catching animals, it is not a bad thing to wear gloves. Leather pigskin will suffice in most cases.

INFORMATION OF IMPORTANCE:
ANIMAL CLASSIFICATION

PHYLUM I: PROTOZOANS—SINGLE-CELLED ANIMALS

Most protozoa are microscopic. They live in fresh and salt water, in soil —in fact in most places, including the bodies of other animals. Reproduction in most cases is asexual, by cell division, and these single cells carry on all the life processes of other animals. There are over 30,000 species; all other animals are multicellular. Fertile soil has about 200 pounds of protozoans per acre within the top twelve inches. They are classified by means of locomotion:

1. By *cilia,* or hairlike projections around the cell body, which wave and propel the animal through the water. These include the *paramecium* (slipper-shaped), *stentor* (trumpet-shaped), *glaucoma,* which is similar but smaller than the paramecium, and *vorticella,* with a spring-action stalk.

2. By *flagella,* whiplike tails used for locomotion. Many of these are animal-plants because they contain chlorophyll, these including the *euglena,* the *volvox* (a round colony of cells) and *chlamydomonas,* with two flagella.

3. By *protoplasmic* flow, the animal moving by stretching the protoplasm of the body in wavelike forward extensions. Examples: the *ameba,* which is often overlooked even under the microscope, due to its simple jellylike structure. (Termites have amebas in their bodies, which enable them to digest wood.) *Heliozoans* are a fresh-water form with radiating spiny axopodia; *radiolarians* are similar in appearance but marine. *Foraminiferans,* also marine, form hardened shell-like structures up to a few inches in size. Both radiolarians and foraminiferans deposit on the ocean bottom large amounts of "skeleton" material which becomes fossilized as sedimentary rock. These are key fossils used to date rocks and to plot rock profiles for the location of oil.

PHYLUM II: PORIFERANS—SPONGES

All live in water—some in fresh but mostly in salt water. They are permanent colonies of cells, reproducing asexually by regeneration or budding, or sexually by fertilized eggs. Water enters by the many pores, and leaves by one opening, the osculum, at the end.

PHYLUM III: COELENTERATES—STINGING
TENTACLES ON MOST

All are water animals, mostly salt water, with a radial structure having no front or back. They may reproduce asexually by budding or regeneration, or sexually by fertilized eggs. Their baglike structure has a large mouth opening at one end, surrounded by telescoping tentacles which can stretch or contract to capture food.

1. *Hydra,* often called the fresh-water jellyfish, is the only common fresh-water coelenterate. It attaches to stems and leaves of water plants, and may extend to a half inch or contract to pinhead size. It feeds on tiny fresh-water crustaceans (see ARTHROPODS). Fertilized eggs lie dormant through the winter and continue development in the spring.

2. Salt-water members which swim include *jellyfish* and *Portuguese man-of-war.* Some of these have tentacles able to extend 100 feet.

3. Salt-water members which spend most of their lives attached to rocks or shells include *sea anemones, corals, sea plumes* and *sea fans.*

PHYLUM IV: ROTIFERS—CILIA "WHEEL" AROUND MOUTH

Appearing in both fresh and salt water, these are a common microscopic animal in pond water. The ring of beating cilia around the mouth is used for sucking in food and also for propeller-type locomotion. There is a complete digestive tract. They reproduce by fertilized eggs which may hatch during summer or lie dormant until the following spring. Rotifers are often found attached under the leaves of water plants in ponds. They may have the ability to resume normal activity following great temperature extremes —freezing and drought. They have an extendable, sliding, telescopic tail.

PHYLUM V: PLATYHELMINTHES—FLATWORMS

Most live either in fresh water or as parasites in the bodies of other animals, and only a few species are nonparasitic. They reproduce asexually by budding or regeneration, or sexually by fertilized eggs.

1. *Planaria,* the most common fresh-water species, is less than a half inch long. Nocturnal, they avoid light, living under rocks and logs in streams and swampy areas. These are popular laboratory animals for regeneration experiments, since when they are cut, both pieces will grow into new animals.

2. Parasitic species include the *tapeworm,* which enters the body in undercooked beef and lives in the intestine; and the *liver fluke,* which enters in raw fish, and makes its home in the bile ducts of the liver.

PHYLUM VI: NEMATHELMINTHES—ROUNDWORMS

Also known as *nematodes,* their various species are found in water, in soil, and parasitic in the bodies of other animals. They reproduce only sexually by fertilized eggs. While some are as long as two feet, the most abundant forms measure less than one inch. The smooth, round body has a mouth at the blunt end.

1. *Threadworms* (a common name for roundworms) are abundant in soil, about fifty pounds of them in the top twelve inches of one acre. Most are nearly microscopic; are commonly found in the mud on the bottom of pools, ponds and streams. The *vinegar eel* is a species which develops in vinegar to which no preservatives have been added.

2. Parasitic species: The *ascaris* lives in intestines of young mammals, enters the body as eggs on infected vegetables, water or soiled hands. The *hookworm* enters through bare feet from warm soil, and travels by the blood stream to lodge in the intestines, where it pierces a blood vessel and secretes a substance which prevents the blood from clotting, causing anemia. The *trichina* enters the body in undercooked pork and infects muscles.

PHYLUM VII: ANNELIDS—SEGMENTED WORMS

With bodies consisting of ringed segments, annelids reproduce sexually by fertilized eggs. The largest number live in salt water, but many species live in fresh water, moist soil, or as parasites in the bodies of other animals.

1. The *earthworm* occupies a central position in the animal kingdom between the very simple and the very complex. Its well-developed nervous system permits response to light, touch, sound and moisture, and it "breathes" through a skin which must always be moist for this purpose. Frequently surfacing at night and after heavy rain, they are called night crawlers. The worms will burrow deep into dry ground for moisture. In one acre of soil there may be several million earthworms weighing one-half ton with burrowing most intense in the top six inches. In one region, Charles Darwin estimated 50,000 per acre. The worms bring soil and plant food into the gizzard, where food is ground down with gravel as in birds, and the soil passes on out of the body. By this process the worms in an acre of land may turn over twenty tons of soil per year, keeping it aerated and loose. Used soil often forms temporary little ropes called castings. Eight tiny bristles under each segment of the worm aid locomotion. There is a smooth, unsegmented "girdle" near its front which produces material for making a cocoon, which contains eggs and is slipped off the front of the body. If cut, the front end of a worm will grow a new tail by regeneration. This works best if the cut is made beyond the twentieth segment from the front, since all vital organs are between there and the head, while the rest of the worm is one long intestine. Occasionally both ends will become new worms.

2. *Bristleworms* all have short or long bristles along the body. Very tiny bristles place the earthworm in this category. The *tubifex*, a tiny red worm with inconspicuous bristles, lives in ponds with its head buried in a tube made of sand. The *nais*, with rather long, conspicuous bristles, is a common worm found in the mud of streams and ponds. It may be an inch or more long and is commonly referred to as a bristleworm.

3. *Leeches*, also called bloodsuckers, are external parasites. They will eat tiny animals, but prefer to suck blood from larger animals. A leech bite is not dangerous to humans unless there is accidental infection. The average bite takes a half ounce of blood, and the saliva of the leech con-

tains a chemical that prevents coagulation of the blood as it sucks. Found in fresh-water streams and ponds and in warm, moist land areas, leeches are extremely sensitive to vibrations and shadows in the water, and will investigate looking for food.

PHYLUM VIII: ECHINODERMS—SPINY-SKIN MARINE ANIMALS

All are salt-water, commonly found in tidal pools at low tide in any season, sometimes under rocks. Reproduction is sexual, the fertilized eggs becoming wormlike larvae which develop into the final adult stage. Structure is radial, with no front or back, and most have tube feet with suction disks. Many are capable of regeneration.

1. *Starfish* can reproduce by regeneration if broken parts contain a portion of the central disk. Attaching to clams, mussels and oysters with its tube feet, the starfish will pull the shell open with arms after the victim's muscles tire and relax. It then pushes its stomach inside out into the victim, digests food, and returns its stomach to its body. The orange spot is a sieve plate through which water enters to extend and operate the tube feet.

2. Among the other echinoderms, the *sea urchin* has a mouth on its under side with five teeth used to scrape the vegetation off rocks, and a spherical body covered with spines. The *sand dollar* is disk-shaped, with five-pointed design on the top surface. *Sea cucumbers* are in this category, as are *sea lilies* (crinoids). The latter are attached to rocks by a long stalk, mostly in warm southern waters. They were more common in the Paleozoic era, 500,000,000 years ago, when many became fossilized.

PHYLUM IX: MOLLUSKS—MUSCULAR FOOT AND SHELL

Many of these occur in salt water and fresh water, and there are some land species. All have a muscular foot, and most have an external shell which grows in rings or coils with the animal. They are classified according to the location or shape of the foot.

1. *Gastropods* (meaning stomach-footed) include *snails* as their most common member, and these can be marine, fresh-water, or land animals. The snail secretes a slimy substance as it moves, which protects its foot and provides a track to facilitate its operation. The tonguelike structure is lined with tiny teeth used to cut plants and bore holes into wood and shelled prey. The eyes are on two large tentacles. Most species lay eggs in masses of protective jelly. *Slugs* may best be described as snails without shells, and are often found on land under rocks and rotting logs.

2. *Pelecypods* (hatchet-footed) are all bivalves. *Mussels,* the only fresh-water members, commonly called fresh-water clams, fasten themselves by secreting silklike threads. *Oysters* anchor permanently. *Clams* and *scallops* are more mobile. They burrow into mud and extend two siphon tubes to the surface, through which material is taken in and expelled.

3. *Cephalopods* (head-footed) all live in salt water. The foot is divided into many tenacles covered with suction disks. They swim by shooting jets of water, and are also able to eject an inky fluid. Like chordates, they have a single-lens eye. *Squid* and *cuttlefish* have ten arms, the *octopus* eight. The *nautilus* is also a cephalopod.

PHYLUM X: ARTHROPODS—JOINTED LEGS, HORNY EXOSKELETON, SEGMENTED BODY

This is the largest phylum of animals, with over a million species. Most molt or shed their horny exoskeleton periodically to permit growth, and the new one underneath stretches and hardens.

1. *Crustaceans* are mostly aquatic, the marine species including *lobsters, crabs, shrimp, barnacles, ostrocods* (tiny, some luminous), *hermit crabs* (which have soft abdomen, use empty shells), *sand hoppers, sand fleas,* and many *copepods,* which form plankton. Fresh-water species include *crayfish* (which swim backward, are nocturnal, and can be found under rocks along a pond), *Caledonia shrimp, fairy shrimp,* and *cyclops.* (Cyclops eggs lie dormant through the winter, develop in pools of melted snow, and hatch into one of the first animals in the summer food chain.)

2. *Millipedes* have four legs on each body segment. These plant-eaters live in dark, damp places under stones and logs, the same as centipedes.

3. *Centipedes* have two legs per body segment, two antennae, and two poison claws on front used to paralyze insect prey for food. Some may sting humans.

4. *Spiders* share the same class as *scorpions, ticks, mites, daddy longlegs,* and *horseshoe* or *king crabs.* The last is a "living fossil" related to the ancient trilobites of 400,000,000 years ago. *Spiders* have eight legs, two body sections. Their bite is painful, for the most part not poisonous to man, although effective in poisoning insect prey. They lay eggs in silk cocoons.

5. *Insects* number about one million species. All have three body sections—head, thorax and abdomen—with six legs on the thorax. Most have two or four wings, two antennae, spiracles on the abdomen for breathing, and compound eyes, and lay eggs. A yellow, green, red, or colorless "blood" fills the body cavity. Pumped by an open tube at the top of the body, it carries food, gases and wastes. There are over thirty orders of insects. For the ten major orders, see INSECT COLLECTIONS, Project 87.

PHYLUM XI: CHORDATES—INTERNAL SKELETON WITH SPINAL CORD (VERTEBRATES)

Structural features shared by all chordates are a central heart, and well-developed eye with single spherical lens (although many cannot see colors). There are never more than four appendages or "legs."

1. Fishes. *True fishes* have skeletons of bone, true teeth, gills, and paired fins on the sides, and are covered with transparent scales. Most have an air bladder which contracts to dive and expands to rise. They re-

produce by fertilized eggs, except for rays, dogfish, some sharks, and some small tropical species, which are live bearers.

A. *Sharks, rays* and *skates* are not true bony fish, as those above, but have a skeleton of cartilage, and toothlike scales in place of true teeth. They have existed for 100,000,000 years. Rays and sharks prefer warm water, but are often found farther north than expected. Skates and skate egg cases are commonly found along northern shores.

B. *Lampreys* are not entirely true fish, having cartilage skeletons and lacking scales, jaws, and paired fins. Found in salt water and inland lakes, they live on fish blood. A large suction disk surrounds a mouth bearing horny teeth. The lamprey fastens this disk onto its prey, bores into the flesh with its teeth, and remains attached, sucking blood, as long as the fish can swim. Fish found floating on the surface with holes in their sides indicate the work of lampreys.

2. *Amphibians* lead a double life. Starting out in the water, they have gills and eat plants. When grown, they spend some or all of their life on land, breathing with lungs or through a moist skin and eating animals. They are valuable in controlling insects. The skin is bare, with no scales, and usually moist. Most are found in moist places, but there are no marine amphibians. They are cold-blooded, and may hibernate buried in mud. Most reproduce by fertilized eggs, usually in water. Given time, the skin color of most will change to match surroundings. There are two main groups:

A. Tailless amphibians include frogs and toads. *Frogs* are streamlined, smooth, prefer water; toads are slow-moving, have rough, warty skin, and prefer land. *Toads* living in quarries of light-colored rock may turn whitish. Skin is shed and swallowed about six times a year. It is estimated that a toad eats 10,000 insects in three months.

B. Tailed amphibians include *salamanders* and *newts*. They avoid direct sunlight, and many are nocturnal, found under damp logs and rocks. Most toads, pickerel frogs, and some salamanders exude an unpleasant liquid through their skin, which discourages other animals from eating them.

3. *Reptiles* are covered with scales (tiny plates). They have a dry, cool skin, not slimy. Most lay eggs, but a few bear young from internally hatched eggs. Most are harmless and beneficial. All breathe by lungs, and are cold-blooded. Now relatively few in number, reptiles ruled the earth about 175,000,000 years ago. Five groups:

A. *Snakes* move by hooking scales against rough ground or by wriggling from side to side. The tongue is used as a sense organ for feeling and smelling. They see to the side rather than straight ahead, have no eyelids, and cannot hear. A snake cannot chew food. It must be swallowed whole, and powerful digestive juices dissolve it. Many will give a harmless bite if caught, and leather gloves are protection against this; but they usually become tame when accustomed to human handling. The *Florida king snake* is immune to copperhead and rattlesnake venom, and often eats these snakes.

B. *Poisonous snakes* include only four varieties in the United States: the *rattlesnake, copperhead, cottonmouth water moccasin,* and *coral.* Many harmless water snakes are killed because some people think every water snake is a cottonmouth. Poisonous snakes have two hollow fangs which inject the poison, and enlarged heads containing poison sacs. They bite about 1,000 people per year in the United States; an average of two do not survive.

C. *Lizards* may be called "snakes with four feet." They have hearing and eyelids, and (unlike salamanders) have scales and claws. The *gila monster* of Arizona is the only poisonous lizard. Many lizards can break off their tails if caught and go free to grow a new one.

D. *Turtles* are from one of the oldest animal families, going back more than 150,000,000 years. They have no teeth, but a horny beak. All lay eggs buried in sand. They hibernate in mud during the winter. Some are known to live more than 100 years. Most turtles are harmless and easy to keep. But beware of the *snapping turtle.* Its powerful jaws can break a broomstick. It has rough, heavy skin, and very small undershell (plastron).

E. *Alligators* and *crocodiles* are becoming less numerous in southern swamps, and are now protected by law. Alligators are usually found in fresh-water marshes along the Gulf Coast. Crocodiles prefer the salt-water marshes of southern Florida.

4. *Birds* are warm-blooded, winged, covered with feathers, and have sharp eyesight and hearing. Most birds cannot see straight ahead but must look to the side. Many have hollow bones, and special adaptations of beaks and feet. All lay eggs. Baby birds eat their own weight in food daily. No teeth are present. Food is stored in crop while being collected, and is later ground with sand or gravel in the muscular gizzard, as with the earthworm and many insects, before going to the stomach. When migrating, birds often follow coastlines or rivers, and may also use the stars and sun for navigation. There are many theories about migration, one being that birds living in the north in glacial periods were pushed south by the ice, and now return each year as the snow line recedes. (The only sure reason that they fly south in the winter is that it is too far to walk!) Here is a simple bird classification: water birds, shore birds, birds of prey, woodpeckers, and perching birds. Of the birds of prey, the *goshawk, Cooper's,* and *sharp-shinned* hawks are the only hawks that generally steal chickens; others eliminate rodents. Perching birds include most of those generally referred to as songbirds. Birds are most active during the spring, and not particularly conspicuous during the summer camping season.

5. *Mammals* are warm-blooded, and have some fur or hair on the body. They have milk glands for feeding the young, and a highly developed brain. All mammals in the United States are live bearers, and most live on land.

Before we consider the various mammals, a word is in order about rabies, or hydrophobia, since this virus disease may be carried by any warm-blooded animal and transferred to another through saliva. Its possibility should be kept in mind when warm-blooded animals are handled or found in the woods. It takes two forms in animals: *furious rabies*, and *paralytic rabies*. The furious form is easily recognized, but the paralytic form may be deceptive. It is characterized by a paralyzed dropped jaw, and fearlessness of man. The animal is unable to bite, and the resulting lack of nutrition is apparent from its fur and general appearance. Such animals have been known to wander into camp, and should not be approached by campers wanting to care for them. Foxes are the most common carriers in the wild. Others include skunks, bats, coyotes, and raccoons.

Now let's proceed to consider some of the various types of mammals.

A. Egg-laying mammals include the *spiny anteater* and the *duckbill platypus,* both of Australia.

B. Marsupials are pouched animals, whose young are born when partly developed and cared for in the pouch. The *opossum* is the only one in the United States. The *kangaroo* and others are found in Australia.

C. Insect eaters, such as moles and shrews, use underground tunnels. *Moles* usually dig their own, *shrews* use prepared tunnels. Many moles have little or no vision, but very sensitive snouts. Both animals eat more than their own weight daily, the menu including insects, worms and slugs. Both have glands on their sides which give off a pungent odor and discourage enemies from eating them; many are found dead but uneaten. Shrews are tiny and fierce. The short-tailed shrew has poisonous saliva to overcome its enemies, and this can cause swelling and discomfort in a man.

D. *Bats* are the only flying mammals. ("Flying" squirrels do not fly but glide.) They are nocturnal, sleeping during the day hanging upside down by hooked claws, or a hooked thumb on the front of the wings. Insect eaters, they consume large numbers of mosquitoes. They have poor vision, and use a high-frequency echo-sonar system for hunting and navigation. In flight they can catch food by using the forearm "wing" as a net. Bats dart at all moving objects, such as a ball tossed into the air, and are very maneuverable in flight.

E. *Rodents* are the largest, most widespread order of mammals. They have two prominent incisor teeth above and two below. These incisors grow continuously to compensate for wear due to cutting wood. If the animal stopped gnawing, or if one incisor broke, its opposite, not receiving normal wear, would grow on and stab the opposing jaw. Most rodents are plant eaters. *Squirrels, mice, rats, muskrats, beavers, chipmunks, woodchucks, pocket gophers* and *porcupines* are rodents. The porcupine cannot throw his quills, but he can slap with his tail.

F. *Rabbits* are not rodents; they have four incisors in the upper jaw. There is little difference between the *hare* and the rabbit. Hares are usually larger with longer legs, never dig burrows, and may use woodchuck holes in severe weather. The *snowshoe hare* changes color by molting, shedding brown summer fur for white winter fur. The *cot-*

tontail is a hare. Hares fight with their hind legs, usually while running away. These animals may carry *rabbit fever* or tularemia and transmit it to humans by bite, handling, or through the bite of a tick or flea. The disease in humans, not uncommon, is characterized by fever, chills and weakness. Observe wild rabbits from a distance.

G. *Whales, dolphins* and *porpoises* are not usually encountered at camp, but many campers will want to know about them. The blue whale is the largest animal in existence, measuring up to 100 feet and weighing 150 tons. Dolphins, not porpoises, are usually found in marine exhibits. Some believe the dolphin to be the next most intelligent animal to man. Experiments are now in progress on teaching them to communicate.

H. Carnivores are meat eaters. Of nocturnal habits, they hunt smaller mammals, birds and fish. The group includes *cats, dogs, wolves, bears, otters, skunks, weasels, mink, badgers,* and the *bobcats* (which can be distinguished from the domestic cat by their very short tails).

i *Raccoon* is masked, with a ringed tail and human-like hand with opposable thumb for grasping. He is a good fisherman, and his tracks are often to be seen on stream banks. He eats everything, and washes some of his food, either to clean it or to aid in swallowing.

ii. *Coyote,* a very smart animal, is a good rodent controller. This species can mate with the dog.

iii. *Foxes* are also intelligent, are rodent eaters, and like the coyote and crow, are adapted to living near man. Many colors are possible within the same litter. They are the commonest carriers of rabies among wild animals. They have scent pads on their paws. which give off an odor commonly mistaken for that of a skunk.

I. Single-toed herbivores are plant eaters, and include the *horse.*

J. Two-toed herbivores include *sheep, goats, cows, deer,* and two rare species, the *elk* and *moose.* Most are cud-chewers. They gather grass quickly, swallow it, and store it in a special section of the digestive system comparable to the crop of birds and insects. When they are alone and free from danger, the food is brought up and chewed thoroughly.

i. *White-tailed deer* prefer young forests and brush. Since they eat leaves, twigs, fruits and plants, many starve in the winter. Hunting helps keep the deer population in line with food supply. "Tame" deer, especially bucks, are not dependable; and fawns should be left alone. Only the bucks grow antlers, and these they shed each year as do all antlered animals. (Horned animals do not shed their horns.)

K. Primates have eyes in the front of the head which permit three-dimensional vision, an opposable thumb, and a large and well-developed brain. The group includes *apes, monkeys* and *man.*

TRACK CASTS

Plaster casts of animal tracks are easy for any camper to make and provide another science project that can be taken home after the season. One of the best places to look for a variety of well-formed animal tracks is along the banks of some watering hole. This may be the camp waterfront or some nearby pond. The nocturnal mammals come to these places at night to drink and leave excellent tracks in the bare sand or soil. The nearby water is helpful in preparing the plaster.

MATERIALS

Plaster of Paris, plastic pail, mixing spatula, strips of oaktag about four inches wide, stapler or paper clips, water. Optional are talcum powder and vaseline.

PROCEDURE

Each camper should select and identify the track he wishes to cast. Form a round collar from an oaktag strip, stapling ends together. Rub vaseline on inside of collar and place around track, pressing slightly into the soil. Sprinkle talcum powder into track to help make clean cast. Prepare a fairly thick mixture of Plaster of Paris by adding plaster to water in the pail. Consistency should be like heavy cream which is still light enough to flow, not drop from a pail. Add pinch of salt to plaster to hasten drying. Pour plaster into track and an inch or so into collar. Allow to harden. This will take about thirty minutes which may be spent discussing tracks, animals that made them, and hunting for other signs of animals. Allow leftover plaster to harden in plastic pail and remove by squeezing sides of pail.

When plaster has hardened, remove entire cast and collar from ground and return to camp where collar may be removed, soil brushed from cast or washed out with water. During the next science session, track casts may be painted.

OPTICAL ILLUSIONS

The subject of how our senses can deceive us is always a fascinating one and there are many simple experiments in this field which may be done at camp. Some optical illusions are *psychological*, caused by the way the brain interprets what is seen by the eye, and some are *physiological*, caused by the structure and operation of the lens and the retina of the eye. Not all people are affected by psychological illusions in the same way. This depends upon their past experiences. But most people are deceived by physiological illusions.

An illusion that has perplexed everybody at some time is the water *mirage* seen on distant hot road pavement. This illusion occurs when the sun overheats the pavement causing a layer of hot thin air to develop above the road. When a beam of light strikes a surface separating one medium from another, some of the light is reflected from the surface, as air to water, air to glass, air to mirror, cool thick air to warm thin air. The reflection of sun's rays from a warm air layer causes a shiny "wet" appearance above road. The word "mirage" comes from the same French root meaning "mirror."

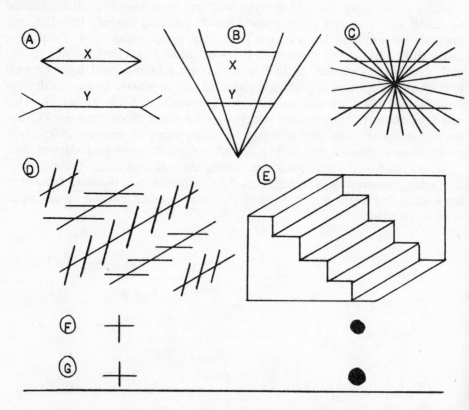

Fig. 7-1.   Optical illusions to be drawn

FIGS. 7-1 and 7-2 show other illusions that can be drawn or made at camp. Campers may make all of these and have an "Optical Illusion Kit" to bring home.

MATERIALS

White and colored paper, scissors, pencils and rulers

PROCEDURE

FIG. 7-1 shows illusions that can be drawn. In A and B first draw lines X and Y exactly the same length, then add other lines to see the illusion. In C and D draw parallel lines then put in additional lines. In E draw stairs as shown and notice how you can make them reverse from right side to upside down. Draw F and G as shown. Hold F at arm's length, close right eye and watch dot with left eye as you bring paper closer to face. At one point, the cross will disappear because it is focused on the *blind spot* of the retina where the optic nerve enters the eye and there are no light-sensitive rods or cones. Do the same with G. If you still "see" the straight line when the cross is not visible, it is because your brain is filling it in for you. There is no image of the line on your retina when focused on the blind spot.

FIG. 7-2 shows illusions that should be cut from colored paper. For A, first draw the perspective lines on a piece of white paper, then cut three

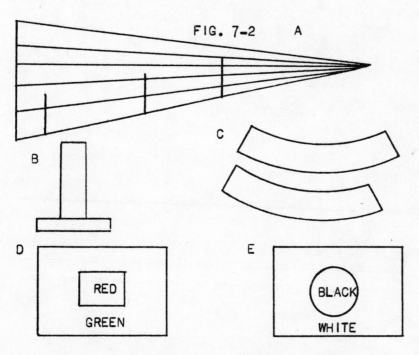

FIG. 7-2.   Optical illusions to be copied and cut out

strips of colored paper and place in vertical positions as shown. The "farthest" one always seems largest. Compare with moon illusion project in Chapter 4. Cut two strips of same size for B, vertical one always seems longer. Cut two arcs for C (about two-inch radius on compass, same for top and bottom of each arc). Bottom arc always appears smaller.

D and E demonstrate the negative afterimage seen when the retina is exposed to a certain color for at least thirty seconds. Cut from colored paper and paste together as shown. Under good light, stare at the colored image for at least thirty seconds, then at a piece of plain white paper. The complementary colors should "appear" on the white paper.

Positive afterimage may be demonstrated by looking at a bare light bulb, then staring into total darkness. An afterimage of a bright bulb will appear. If done in a lighted room, the afterimage will be negative, the light bulb appearing black.

Psychological illusions include FIGS. 7-1 A, B, C, D, E and 7-2 A, B, C. Physiological illusions include 7-1 F and G, and 7-2 D, E. For more on optical illusions, see Chapter 4, IS THE MOON LARGER NEAR THE HORIZON? and Chapter 3, MOTION PICTURES ON THREE-BY-FIVE CARDS.

CHICKEN INCUBATOR

It takes twenty-one days for fertile hens' eggs to hatch. If the camp season is long enough and if fertile eggs can be obtained from a nearby farm, this project would be an interesting possibility for your program.

MATERIALS

Cardboard box (about 12″ × 12″ × 12″), insulating fireproof wallboard or celotex, etc., porcelain lamp socket, cord and plug, two saucers or jar covers for water, small sheet of glass (about 4″ × 4″), thermometer, ¾″ × ¾″ wood (about 9″ long), plastic tape (¾″ or 1″ wide), two hinges with machine screws, nuts and large washers.

PROCEDURE

Construct incubator as shown in FIG. 7-3. All inner surfaces of box are lined with the insulating wallboard. In place of wallboard, you may line a larger carton with wrinkled newspaper and place the smaller carton in the center of this. Make two vent holes (you may need more later) and tack cardboard over each to be used as vent control. Install light socket

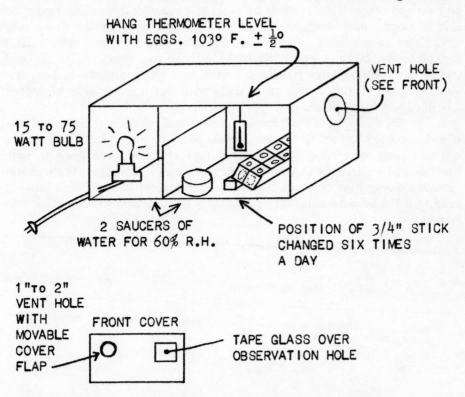

HANG THERMOMETER LEVEL
WITH EGGS. 103° F. $\pm \frac{1}{2}$°

VENT HOLE
(SEE FRONT)

15 TO 75
WATT BULB

2 SAUCERS OF
WATER FOR 60% R.H.

POSITION OF 3/4″ STICK
CHANGED SIX TIMES
A DAY

1″TO 2″
VENT HOLE
WITH
MOVABLE
COVER
FLAP

FRONT COVER

TAPE GLASS OVER
OBSERVATION HOLE

FIG. 7-3.   Plans for construction of chicken incubator

so bulb will be at least three inches from any surface. Install partition between bulb and egg section about eight inches high; but at least three inches from top of box. Hang thermometer so that bulb will be level with eggs and touches no part of box. Two saucers of water should be included to keep relative humidity around the sixty-percent level optimum for eggs. Prepare front cover with vent and observation window and hinge in place using machine bolts, nuts and large washers. In use, the front cover may be fastened closed with hooks, tape or string.

USE

Temperature to incubate eggs must be constantly within half degree of 103° F. It will be necessary to spend a few days testing different light bulbs from fifteen to seventy-five watts and adjusting the vents to find the correct combination to maintain this temperature. Start with fifteen watts. Excessive temperature will kill embryo but lower temperatures may be withstood for an hour or more. It will help to keep incubator in a room with little temperature variation. When incubator has held correct temperature for a couple of days, it is ready to receive eggs. These may usually be obtained by making previous arrangements with a nearby farmer. Not all eggs will be fertile so extras should be included. Do not wash eggs, place them in standard carton with *large ends up*. Position of eggs must be changed often. This is done by placing a quarter-inch stick under one side of carton and changing from one side to the other six times every day. Extra care should be taken on the third day and just before hatching, since mortality is especially high at these two times. After the eighteenth day, remove eggs from egg carton and place undisturbed on their sides to hatch. Sprinkle eggs twice daily with warm water after eighteenth day until hatching occurs.

A few days' supply of food might be obtained when eggs are purchased. If a dozen eggs are set in the incubator, you will have plenty to break an egg and examine contents every three days and still have some to hatch into chicks (which may be returned to the farmer). Embryos obtained from premature eggs may be studied and preserved in separate labeled jars containing a ten-percent solution of formalin (one part formalin, nine parts water).

MICROSCOPIC ANIMALS

Tiny animals easily seen with microscope or magnifying glass live practically everywhere. Careful examination of a quiet semi-permanent pool should reveal tiny white specks moving about which may be caught with jar and eyedropper for closer examination under magnification. Since the animals in such a pool are likely to be well scattered, it is common practice to bring them to the laboratory so they may reproduce and become more concentrated. A culture of tiny animals may be made as follows.

MATERIALS

Jar of pond or stream water, hay or grass pulled close to roots, or yeast cake or malted milk, microscope (The ten-dollar imported microscopes are adequate for most simple camp uses. See catalogs of Radio Shack and Lafayette Radio.), micro slides.

PROCEDURE

It may be well to use all three methods described here to allow for variables in the local habitat.

Method 1: Place about a dozen pieces of dry grass in jar of pond water containing some pond scum or pieces of pond plants. Since the protozoa come from the grass as well as the water, this method may be used with any fresh water if pond water is not available.

Method 2: Crumble a yeast cake into jar of pond water containing scum and plants.

Method 3: Sprinkle a small amount of mashed malted milk powder or tablet on top of pond water containing scum and plants.

Prepare a number of cultures and keep in medium light during day (not direct sunlight) where temperature will be between 64° and 70° F. Temperatures below 59° F. and above 77° F. may kill cultures. Jars should not be covered. If ameba are desired, water should include scrapings from stalks and underside of water plants.

After two or three days, you will notice white specks moving about in the water. These may be captured by deft use of a medicine dropper and placed on micro slide for observation. Your most common animal will probably be the paramecium. For details on identification of animals see ANIMAL CLASSIFICATION, PHYLA I, IV, and X (Cyclops, Water Flea and Fairy Shrimp). The most common animals in such a culture will come from these three phyla. If your culture contains some mud from the pond bottom, you may find some of the worms from Phyla V, VI and VII. Rapidly moving paramecia may be slowed down by adding a drop of corn starch or gelatine solution to slide.

Your animals may be studied under the microscope for a longer time if the drop of water is placed in a *well slide,* easily made by depositing a ring of Duco cement on a slide and allowing to dry thoroughly. The well becomes a tiny pond environment for the animals and plants.

Most of these animals eat smaller protozoa or bacteria, which are provided by fermentation of grass, yeast or malt in your cultures. In turn, they become food for larger animals (worms and snails) which become food for fish to be eaten by shore-living animals and man. The creatures under the microscope, then, are the beginning of a long and vital food chain.

INDIVIDUAL INSECT COLLECTIONS

Because insects are particularly active and plentiful during the camp season, their study may be an important part of the science program. There are many sources available to describe the proper methods of insect mounting, but insects properly mounted on pins must be stored in boxes and sufficient numbers of small shallow boxes are not generally available at camp. Campers may be contacted before the season and advised to bring such boxes if they desire to start serious collections. However, insect collecting for most campers will be introductory with emphasis upon groups of insects and not on proper mounting procedures. Mounting with improvised Riker mounts on cement will be more practical for most camps.

COLLECTING INSECTS

Nets: The camp should have an aerial net and aquatic dip net (also used for small fish). Sugaring: Mix a paste of brown sugar and molasses with something smelly such as stale beer or mashed over-ripe fruit. Paint mixture onto trees in afternoon, go back in evening with flashlight and jars and collect your guests. Light Trap: Construct a simple light trap as shown in FIG. 7-4. Any means may be used for supporting light bulb. Hang it from a stick, wire frame from lamp shade, etc. Funnel may be metal or oaktag, container may be large can or wide-mouth jar. It is possible to put killing material (carbon tetrachloride) in collecting jar but this sometimes results in damaged specimens.

KILLING INSECTS

Construct some killing jars as follows: Select a variety of jars, the largest being of the peanut-butter type. Pour half inch of Plaster of Paris into jar

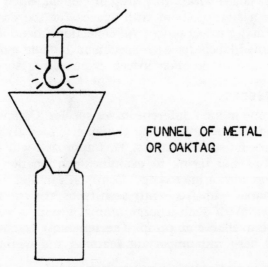

FUNNEL OF METAL OR OAKTAG

FIG. 7-4. Light trap for catching insects at night

bottom. When plaster is hard, saturate with carbon tetrachloride (also called Carbona) and keep jar covered so fumes will build up. Note: Although this jar is much safer than the cyanide jars usually used, carbon tet is deadly to humans if inhaled in large amounts. Use in ventilated area and avoid inhalation. Carbon tet is not flammable (it is used in fire extinguishers). One insect per killing jar is optimum.

PREPARING INSECTS

Wings of butterflies, dragonflies and moths must be spread and dried before mounting. If no spreading board is available, this may be done by placing insect upside down on soft wood (balsa wood), spreading wings and holding them in place with glass slides or strips of paper pinned in place. Allow insect to dry this way for a few days. This is actually the proper spreading method if insect is to be finally mounted in cotton.

If insects have dried in an undesirable position, they may be moistened again in a *relaxing jar* and re-positioned. Relaxing jar consists of jar or box with layer of sand or cotton on bottom. Moisten sand with water, cover with dry clean paper, add insect and cover tightly. Insect should be soft again in twenty-four hours.

Most of the harder insects require little preparation.

MOUNTING INSECTS

If boxes are available, insects may be properly mounted with insect pins and a supply of Nos. 2 and 5 pins should be on hand. Cotton and glass Riker mounts, 6" × 8", may be purchased for about a dollar from Wards. Simpler Riker mounts may be made by gluing nonsterile cotton batting onto a poster-board backing. Arrange insects on cotton and cover with plastic food wrap held with tape to back of poster board. Pins are never used with Riker mounts. A final method of mounting is simply to attach insects to poster board with a tiny drop of cement. Such a mount may be pre-labeled like a stamp album with spaces for the common insects of the area or the major insect orders. All collections mentioned above should have neatly printed labels for each specimen. Include moth balls or flakes in each box to discourage other insects from eating specimens.

IDENTIFYING INSECTS

There are over one million different insect species. Campers should realize this from the outset and adjust their thinking to identify insects by family or order, not specific species names. This approach will save many hours of book-searching and trying to examine identification marks that are meant to be seen with a microscope. Common families would be the bees and ants. Of course, with frequently seen types, the species name may be readily available. With such a large animal group, a good identification book[1] should be available at camp. The ten most common orders of insects are listed here with important features and members of each.

---

[1] Frank Lutz, *Field Book of Insects*. New York: G. P. Putnam's Sons, 1948.

TEN MOST COMMON ORDERS OF INSECTS

ORDER	FEATURES	EXAMPLES
A. Odonata	Carnivorous, hard chewing parts	Dragonflies, damselflies
B. Orthoptera	Herbivorous, chewing mandibles	Crickets, roaches, grasshoppers, destructive locusts
C. Mantodea	Carnivorous, chewer, very movable head, grasping front legs	Praying mantis
D. Isoptera	Social, strong toothed mandibles	Termites (amebas in body to digest wood)
E. Homoptera	Sucking mouth parts	Aphids, leaf-hoppers, cicadas, seventeen-year locusts
F. Heteroptera	Sucking mouth parts. Wings if present overlap back over abdomen.	True bugs, many aquatic species
G. Lepidoptera	Sucking mouth parts, scales on wings, caterpillar larvae	Butterflies, moths
H. Diptera	Sucking mouth parts, two wings	Flies (maggot larvae), mosquitoes (wiggler larvae)
I. Coleoptera	Hard body parts and wings, chewers	Beetles (grub larvae), many aquatic include whirligig
J. Hymenoptera	Many social, some have stinger at rear of abdomen.	Bees, wasps, ants

FIELD TRIP TO DISCOVER ANIMAL HOMES

Although most mammals will not make themselves visible during the daylight hours, campers can have an exciting time hunting for their houses.[2] For many animals, home is a place of shelter, food storage and raising the young. Some animals always insist upon the same type of home, others are not so fussy. The latter include squirrels, skunks, bobcats, mice and bears. Careful observation should turn up homes in the following areas:

Hollow trees: Raccoon, bats, bees, squirrel, opossum, porcupine, bobcat, mice, woodpeckers and owls.

Caves and rocks: Porcupine, lynx, snakes, bats, mountain lions.

Burrows: Coyote, wolf, fox, woodchuck, skunk, badger, prairie dog. The chipmunk hides his burrow by digging two entrances and then closing one up with the extra dirt that would have been left on the surface, to distract attention.

Tree nests: Birds, squirrels.

Lodges and bank dens: Beaver, muskrat. The lodges are built of mud and twigs in ponds, streams and marshes.

Forms: Rabbits (hares). Forms are round depressions in the ground lined with grass and used for raising young. The only holes used by most wild rabbits are woodchuck holes.

Brush thickets: Deer use dense thickets for shelter and protection.

Many of our invertebrates live under rocks, logs and bark.

---

[2] George Mason, *Animal Homes*. New York: Wm. Morrow & Co., 1947. $2.50. An excellent, well-illustrated book for people of all ages.

ANIMAL DISCUSSION USING AUDUBON CHARTS

Not every project requires manual exercise to maintain interest. Campers are willing to sit quietly and talk, if there is an interesting subject. Such a subject is the world of animals and its interest can be heightened by the special knowledge of the counselor, stories from campers, large colored pictures and possibly a live specimen. Such a session can deal with the many animals which may not be uncommon but are seldom seen.

MATERIALS

Audubon animal charts (20″ × 30″ full color) two sets, $3.50 plus fifty cents postage per set. If camp has captive snake, turtle, etc., this is the time to bring it out.

PROCEDURE

Concentrate on charts showing mammals, owls and birds of prey. These are the animals often talked about but seldom seen. Be prepared with some facts about each such as where it is found, what it eats, whether it is eaten by others, whether it hibernates, whether it comes out in day or night, what type of home, method of hunting, special adaptations or features. Develop discussion and involve campers by asking such questions. See what they think or know before you give any facts. This is a time to clear up mistaken ideas as well as to give new facts. Many campers will have stories to tell about animals.

One question that will come up is how nocturnal animals see in the dark. Somebody having seen cats' eyes reflect light in the dark may suggest that they "have a light in their eyes by which they see." Cats' eyes reflect green when struck by light because the retina is green. Alligators' eyes reflect pink for the same reason. The eyes of man do not reflect because the retina is black. Many nocturnal animals see well because their iris diaphragm opens very wide and admits more light than the human eye. Most animals do not see colors. The human retina has two types of sensors: *rods* which detect black and white, and *cones* which detect color. The cones are not as sensitive to light as rods and are concentrated in the center of the retina which we most often use for normal vision. If this area contained the more sensitive rods, as in animals, we might be able to see with fainter amounts of light. A third factor which may help animals see at night is *airglow*, described in Chapter 2.

Animals also have highly developed senses of sound and smell. Owls in a dark room can successfully catch real and imitation mice by sound alone.

FIELD TRIP TO OBSERVE AND CATCH ANIMALS

A camp project might be to observe and catch for detailed study and photographs at least one member of each animal phylum. Field trips may be taken for this specific purpose. Most of the invertebrates and cold-blooded vertebrates that may be caught can be kept for a day or two without special care and then released where they were caught. The warm-blooded vertebrates (birds and mammals) are best left in the wild to be observed but not captured. As insects are discussed in detail under their own heading, they will not be treated here.

MATERIALS

Hand trowel, aquatic dip net, wide-mouth jars (damp moss in some), plastic sacks, long dark socks for snakes, magnifying glass.

PROCEDURE

Most of the protozoans of Phylum I can only be seen under a microscope and are best observed after being cultured as described previously. Some may be seen in a jar of pond water under the magnifying glass as tiny white specks.

Attached under the leaves and on stalks of water plants in ponds, you may find hydra from Phylum III and rotifers (microscopic) from Phylum IV.

The flatworm known as planaria, Phylum V, may be found clinging under rocks and logs in streams and marshes. Try trapping planaria by hanging liver in water during night. They will be found on the meat.

Using the dip net, bring up some mud from a pond bottom and pour it out into a white porcelain pan, or just onto white paper. A wealth of animal life will be found by sifting through this material. Included will be many roundworms and segmented worms from Phyla VI and VII as well as insects and other life forms.

Snails, Phylum IX, may be found around water or climbing trees. Slugs will be found by turning over rocks and logs as will many other invertebrates.

The millipedes and centipedes, arthropods of Phylum X, will be found under rocks and logs and under bark of dead trees. Look quickly, as some are quite fast. The crayfish is best found at night under rocks along a pond with a flashlight.

Fish, Phylum XI, can be dipped up with the net. It is usually best to release these as wild fish require large tanks of cool water and do not keep well under other conditions. The frogs can also be dipped from their water-hole habitats. Salamanders and newts will be found in moist areas (often near ponds) under leaves, logs and rocks. They are often best hunted with a flashlight at night. Reach fast for these—they move quickly and they are slippery. The skin of worms and amphibians must stay moist. Put them in jars with wet moss. Habitats of snakes vary. Some like grassy areas while many prefer rocky places where they can dash into cracks for safety. Before you grab for these, be familiar with the poisonous snakes of your region; there probably aren't more than a couple of species. After a snake is caught point its head at an open sock and it will willingly go in for safety. Turtles may often be caught with the dip net. Note: After rocks have been turned over, they should be replaced as found to preserve the unique environment that exists under them.

The best policy to follow with animals is: *Catch, study, release.* Bring your catch back to camp, placing animals in suitable containers with moisture (if needed) and drinking water. A covered terrarium with moist moss is good for the worms and amphibians. Study and discuss the special structures that distinguish one phylum from another. Note special habits and adaptions of different animals. The animals should be released in a day or two near where they were first found. This is done not because their "friends" live there, but because that is the type of environment needed for their survival. Since most cold-blooded animals can go for short periods without food (a snake for a month or more), the catch-study-release policy permits study of animals without the unusual burdens of feeding and caring for them.

It may be worth preserving representative specimens from each phylum to become part of a permanent camp science exhibit. Each specimen should be placed in its separate neatly labeled jar containing a ten-percent formalin solution (one part formalin, nine parts water). Larger specimens should be killed by placing in a jar with ether-soaked cotton under cover. When placing large specimens in formalin, body cavity should be cut to allow preservative to contact all tissues. If formalin becomes clouded, it should be replaced with a new solution.

FIELD TRIP TO OBSERVE AND PHOTOGRAPH ANIMALS

While the simpler cold-blooded vertebrates and invertebrates may be caught and studied, it is usually best to study the warm-blooded vertebrates (birds and mammals) by observing and photographing them in their natural habitat. Trapping or caging migratory birds is illegal. The "harmless" traps sold for catching small mammals should not be used as these animals are very nervous and run around in the cramped quarters scraping their nose against the screening until released.

PROCEDURE

Birds are best observed around sunrise and sunset, sunrise being the more active period. It is not difficult to find campers wanting to take part in an early-morning bird walk before breakfast. Keeping the group small is usually the major problem. Six interested campers make a good group. It is well if each can be provided with binoculars. Observation should not be limited to birds. Also comment on plants and animals, many of which can still be seen at sunrise.

With the possibility of spotting animals, the group should proceed quietly. Visibility will be best if the rising sun is behind you, not shining in your eyes. As with all field trips, it is well for the counselor to go over the route beforehand so the location of interesting specimens will be known. If campers don't discover them, the counselor can. Even if no birds are seen, a bird walk should be a success because of other objects which the counselor knows can be pointed out and discussed.

Most mammals are nocturnal, coming out only during the night. Some such as deer, muskrat, beaver, woodchuck, and rabbit are quite active during sunrise and sunset and even on overcast days. Most of the nocturnal animals can be observed with a strong flashlight. The sealed-beam lantern with a good battery is excellent for this. You may wait for them at their watering hole, discovered during the day by tell-tale footprints; or you may wait in an area that has been baited with food to attract them. Once again the group of campers should be small and quiet. Turn on the light only when an animal has been located. Its picture may be taken with a flash camera. Although they may stand perfectly still, most animals will not be greatly bothered by the lights as long as there are no alarming noises from the group.

PHOTOGRAPHING

Pictures may be taken by arranging a trip-string to snap the shutter or by attaching a solenoid to the shutter and activating it with electricity by a push button. If you cannot arrange a method of tripping the shutter remotely or automatically, you can leave the shutter open (on a dark, moonless night) and arrange a device that will energize the flash bulb. A remote push button may do this manually or a mouse-trap tripping device may close the circuit for you automatically. The camera may be left on a tripod at a water hole or baited area, or aimed at the known residence of an animal.

Locating, tracking and photographing animals in the wild is an exciting project for campers and requires considerable ingenuity and careful advanced planning.

CARE AND FEEDING OF WILD ANIMALS

It has been our frequent suggestion in these pages that wild animals not be kept in caged captivity. This, of course, does not refer to zoos where there is a balanced selection of animals under the care of full-time experts and available for viewing by large numbers of people.

The most frequent animal dependents at camp are likely to be baby birds. Camping season is about the time birds begin their flying lessons. Many baby birds will spend a few hours to a day or two on the ground before they can fly. Often the parents push lazy birds from the nest to get them started. If such birds are seen at camp, these facts should be explained to all campers at mealtime. Nobody should pick the bird up. The parents are usually watching every move from a nearby tree and will feed the bird if it doesn't become airborne right away. If it's in the middle of the baseball diamond and doesn't seem likely to leave soon, move it gently and without fuss to a more protected spot. Its constant peeping will attract the parents to the new location. Campers are glad to co-operate with the baby bird's problem once they know the facts.

When necessary, the following foods are suggested for wild animals: For nesting song birds, mashed hard-boiled egg yolk, bread crumbs lightly moistened with milk, occasional cod liver oil. You may also try raisins, a banana, canned dog food, chopped lettuce, mealworms. Place food on narrow stick and poke well back in bird's throat. Birds need no water until old enough to sit on perch. Bird eats body weight in food daily. Feed every forty-five minutes except for nine-hour break at night. Older birds on solid food must be provided with gravel so food may be ground in gizzard.

Larger mammals will take much human food: greens and vegetables, meat, hard-boiled eggs, milk; also dog food. About a spoonful of cod liver oil per week is a good addition, and there should be a constant supply of clean water. Rodents are fond of sunflower seeds and grains. They must also have some gnawing wood or branches so their incisors will not grow too long. Never overfeed an animal. If feed is left over, reduce size of meals.

Most reptiles prefer live food. Snakes (depending on size) may be fed earthworms, mice, frogs or other snakes. They may also take unbroken raw eggs, and strips of liver. Snakes will take a good meal about twice a month. Like snakes, lizards are carnivorous with the main diet consisting of insects. They prefer water sprinkled on leaves rather than in a bowl. Most turtles are omnivorous, eating chopped fish, chopped greens and hamburger. Some must be under water to swallow their food.

Frogs, toads and salamanders also require live food such as chopped earthworms, mealworms and unaggressive insects.

Note: Mammal cages constructed of screening or hardware cloth stretched on a wood frame should always have the wood frame inside the screening so the animal cannot contact the sharp wire edges of the screen and cut itself.

OTHER ANIMAL PROJECTS

Some other projects relating to the study of animals are:

CONSTRUCTING BIRD FEEDERS

Some bird feeders and bird baths around camp will help attract birds to the area. Although birds do not need human assistance during the summer months, they will usually accept it if it is offered. Shelf feeders with bread and seeds and peanut butter, and seed stick feeders, are easily provided. Some campers should have charge of tending feeders and recording birds seen.

NEST COLLECTION

Toward the end of summer the nesting season is over and it is safe to collect unused nests. Identify these and make a permanent collection for the camp science museum. Identification will be most positive if the birds using nests were seen earlier in the season.

RAISING TADPOLES

This is sometimes attempted at camps. However, most frog eggs are laid before May and have fully developed by July. Tadpoles seen in summer are likely to be those of the green frog or bullfrog, which take one and two years respectively to mature. Such tadpoles may be interesting to study for a few days but should then be returned to their pond. You may feed them by placing a pinch of cornmeal on water.

EMBEDDING SPECIMENS IN PLASTIC

Any type of specimen, mineral, plant or animal, may be embedded in a block of clear plastic using inexpensive kits now available. Kit prices start at $1.00 (Ward's). Further information and materials may be obtained from: Ward, *Embedding with Bio-Plastic;* Turtox, Leaflet 33, *Embedding Specimens in Transparent Plastic*, and Castolite Company, Woodstock, Illinois, *How To Make and Use Nature Tiles* (25¢).

RESOURCE MATERIALS FOR ANIMALS

(Also see PLANTS)

Magazines

Audubon Magazine. Bimonthly, $5.00 per year. National Audubon Society, 1130 Fifth Avenue, New York, N. Y. 10028.

National Wildlife. Bimonthly, $5.00 per year which includes membership. National Wildlife Federation, 1412 Sixteenth Street, N.W., Washington, D. C. 20006.

Natural History. Ten issues per year, $5.00. American Museum of Natural History, 79 St. and Central Park West, New York, N. Y. 10024.

The Conservationist. Bimonthly, $2.00 per year. Room 335. State Campus, Albany, N. Y.

Turtox News. Monthly, free to teachers. General Biological Supply House, Inc., 8200 South Hoyne Ave., Chicago, Ill. 60620.

Pamphlets and Charts

From regional office of the Bureau of Sport Fisheries and Wildlife, Fish and Wildlife Service (See FILMS. Regional address may be obtained from the Department of the Interior, Washington, D. C. 20025.) Request "Conservation Notes" and circulars on National Wildlife Refuges and Federal Fish Hatcheries. Your regional director can also be of assistance with specific problems.

When the Unexpected Happens. Thirty-page first aid booklet available free in quantity from: Health Education Service, John Hancock Insurance Co., Boston, Mass.

How to Collect and Preserve Insects, by H. H. Ross. Excellent sixty-page booklet from Illinois Natural History Survey, Urbana, Ill.

Reptiles and Amphibians of the Northeastern States, by Roger Conant. Outstanding forty-page publication from Zoological Society of Philadelphia, Philadelphia, Penna.

Michigan Wildlife Sketches, by Bradt and Schafer. Outstanding text and illustrations on mammals. Includes tracks. From: Michigan Department of Conservation.

Additional information may be obtained from your state fish and game department located in the state capital.

Films

Hemo the Magnificent and *Gateways to the Mind.* Free through the local Bell Telephone business office. User pays return postage.

Request free film catalog from nearest regional office of Fish and Wildlife Service, Bureau of Sport Fisheries and Wildlife, Washington, D. C. 20025. Regional offices in Juneau, Albuquerque, Atlanta, Boston, Minneapolis and Portland, Oregon.

Request film catalog from: Canadian Embassy, 1746 Massachusetts Ave., N.W., Washington, D. C., 20006, or Canadian Consulate nearest you.

Supplies

Wild Cargo, 3230 Pembroke Road, Hollywood, Fla.

Quivira Specialties Co., 4204 West 21 St., Topeka, Kansas. Catalog 35¢. These two companies sell live animals of almost any description. If a live animal is desired, an indigo snake is good. Youngsters find a five-foot indigo interesting. They can hold it and it tames easily. Feed a live snake every two weeks. Florida kings are also good but sometimes refuse to eat in captivity.

General Biological Supply House, Inc., 8200 South Hoyne Ave., Chicago 20, Ill. (Turtox Products) This firm prefers catalog requests on school, college or camp stationery.

Ward's Natural Science Establishment, Inc., Box 1712, Rochester, N. Y. 14603, or Box 1749, Monterey, Calif. Request biology catalog. They too prefer requests on school, college or camp stationery.

Chapter

8: Mathematics

SUGGESTED REFERENCE Adler, Irving. *Magic House of Numbers.* New York: New American Library, 1958.

MATHEMATICS may be considered the Dr. Jekyll and Mr. Hyde of the sciences. Most of us know it in its everyday form as a utilitarian discipline for which we had to memorize endless tables and numbers to make sure we didn't get short-changed at the store. Who dares say that he finds this interesting, much less fascinating? But there is another side to mathematics—its study as a science in itself, the study of numbers, calculation and computers, the study of mathematics as a scientific tool of imagination, exploration and discovery. It is this latter face of mathematics that must be shown to campers, and shown a little, they will want to see more.

The reference book suggested above is not a math book. It is an unusual book of number puzzles and games that the non-mathematician can use and understand. Send some of your boys around camp to do the simple trick on page 74 of this volume, "Seeing into the Future," and you will soon have many more back to learn some others.

True, we use math for such menial tasks as paying the milkman, buying postage stamps and weighing cabbages. But let's not forget its other role as an instrument of exploration, just as important to the imaginative scientist as was the Santa Maria to the imaginative Columbus or the telescope to Galileo. The projects of this chapter have been prepared to stress this other role of mathematics so that more people may discover its true nature. If the understanding thus gained will serve as motivation to study this subject with greater zeal in school, this will be a happy side-effect for everyone concerned.

COMPUTERS, DIGITAL AND ANALOG

The two large divisions of computers are *digital* and *analog*. Not all computers fit into one of these categories; some are combinations of the two.

A digital computer is one that actually counts individual units. Such units may be number units, holes in a punched card, or electrical impulses. The transistor flip-flop circuits described under BINARY NUMBER CONVERTER are used in digital computers to count electrical impulses. The answers in a digital computer are usually given in exact numbers which may be written on a tape, shown by nixie tubes or binary on-off lights, or written by an electric typewriter. Digital computers are among the most versatile and costly of computers. Counting on the fingers and the *abacus* are simple methods of digital computing.

Analog computers do not count discreet units. They change numbers into some physical measurement and then calculate using that measurement. They work in units which are *analogous* to numbers. An electrical analog computer may convert numbers to volts, for example. A *slide rule* is an analog computer using lengths of wood to represent numbers. Electric meters used on instruments are analog computers which convert electrical units into estimated numbers which may tell volts, revolutions, wind velocity, or temperature. The answers on an analog computer usually are not given in exact numbers, but are estimated from the position of a dial or pointer on a scale of numbers.

Genuine electronic computers have one or more of the following advantages over the desk calculator or adding machine: They perform thousands of operations per minute; they have a "memory" section for storing information and instructions, usually some type of magnetic recording device such as tape; information can enter or leave the computer in the form of punched cards, magnetic tape, electric typewriter and other means such as direct pick-up devices; a control unit instructs computer in proper operations; and computer can learn not to make the same mistake twice. Of course, all this information must first be prepared and fed into the computer by highly trained people. Once the computer has been properly "programmed" it may carry on many operations without human assistance.

ADD-SUBTRACT STRING COMPUTER

The string computer is probably the simplest form of adding slide rule and the simplest form of analog computer. With this device, the calculations are made by the length of a string, rather than by the length of wood as in the slide rule.

MATERIALS

String, oaktag or cardboard, pen or pencil, ink or paint

PROCEDURE

See FIG. 8-1. Cut oaktag to size, 4″ × 8″. Draw line five inches long across center of oaktag and make marks along this line every half inch. Number the lines as shown. Both scales are used to show that two is equivalent to twenty or two hundred, etc. Punch a hole at each end of the line. Cut a piece of string to about sixteen inches and dip half of it into ink or paint so half the string is colored and half is white. When dry, thread string through the two holes, tie ends together and cut off excess string. The add-subtract computer is now ready for use.

USE

First pull the string around so the dividing line between colored and white string will be at zero. This dividing line in the string will serve as the index which points to numbers and answers. As you will see, your thumb also serves as an index. Example: Add 2 + 3. Move the colored index over to 2. Now grasp the string at zero with thumb and forefinger and move thumb and string to 3. Colored index should now indicate answer: 5.

Subtraction is done in reverse. Example: Subtract 30 from 50. Start colored index at 50, grasp string at 30 and pull thumb and string to zero. Colored index should now indicate answer: 20.

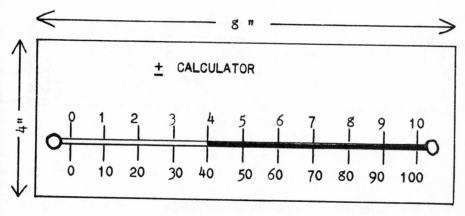

FIG. 8-1.   Computer using string to add and subtract

ADD-SUBTRACT SLIDE RULE

This project has proved successful with campers of all ages, but particularly the younger ones about ten years old. Basically it consists of two standard rulers which slide along each other so that one number (or length) may be added to another number (or length). Because it is a slide rule and does calculations by measuring lengths, this classifies as an analog computer, a definite length being analogous to a definite number.

MATERIALS
Oaktag, tape, ruler, scissors, pen or pencil

PROCEDURE
Two oaktag strips are needed, both 12" long, one about 1" wide, the other about 1¾" wide. Two smaller pieces of oaktag about 1" × 1" will also be needed. The long pieces should be cut carefully along ruler-drawn lines so the edges will be straight.

Lay the smaller strip over the center of the larger strip and fold protruding top and bottom edges of large strip up and over the top of the smaller piece in the center. Remove smaller piece and crease these folds down sharply with ruler or finger. Slide small piece back in under folds, place 1" × 1" piece on each end of rule and wrap tape around each end. If inner strip does not slide smoothly, draw it out and trim one edge carefully with scissors. There should be a slight friction in its movement.

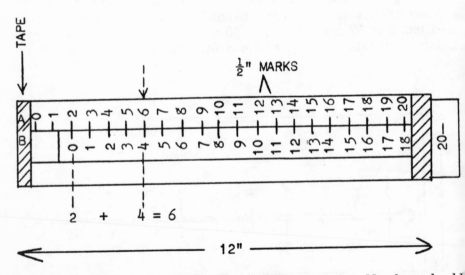

FIG. 8-2. Add-subtract slide rule shown adding 2 and 4. Numbers should be right side up on actual scale.

With the slide pushed all the way in, label the tape "A" and "B" for the two scales and, using a ruler, make short lines across scales A and B at half-inch intervals. See FIG. 8-2. With lines drawn, go back and number, starting with zero for the first. Finally, draw a second set of lines at half-inch intervals between each number.

USE

The slide rule in FIG. 8-2 is shown in position to add 2 + 4. Zero of scale B is placed under 2 of scale A. Then go down to 4 on scale B and find the total directly above on scale A.

In the same position, the rule will subtract 4 from 6. The answer is found on scale A above the zero. As is, the rule will add sums up to 20.

The rule may be used to add much larger numbers by imagining one or more zeros after each number. Thus 20 becomes 200, 12 becomes 120, 5 becomes 50. As shown in FIG. 8-2, the rule may just as well be adding 20 and 40 or 200 and 400. Just be sure you add the same number of extra zeros to the answer that you added to the numbers being added.

Halfway between 5 and 6, of course, is 5.5 or 5½. But if you add one zero to each number on the scale, this position becomes 55. To get the other numbers between 50 and 60, imagine that space to be divided into ten equal spaces. You may be able to draw lines for these spaces with a fine-pointed pencil. Exactly how much use you can make of this rule will depend upon the math background of the campers, but it is surprising that even those who have not had decimals soon learn to add zeros and interpolate numbers which do not appear on the scales.

MULTIPLY-DIVIDE SLIDE RULE

A slide rule to multiply and divide may be constructed in the same manner as the add-subtract slide rule, but with different scales. The scales used
for multiplying and dividing are based upon *logarithms*, invented by John
Napier and first published by him in 1614. Each number has a logarithm
equivalent and it is possible to multiply and divide numbers by adding and
subtracting their logarithms. You may try this with the logarithms given
below for the numbers 1 to 9.

NUMBER	LOGARITHM	NUMBER	LOGARITHM
1	.0000	6	.7782
2	.3010	7	.8451
3	.4771	8	.9031
4	.6021	9	.9542
5	.6990	10	1.0000

To multiply 4×2, you add. $6021 + .3010 = .9031$, which is the log of 8.
A complete log table or slide rule is needed to work with larger numbers.

MATERIALS

Oaktag, tape, ruler, scissors, pen or pencil

PROCEDURE

Construct the scale and slide from oaktag as explained under ADD-SUB-
TRACT SLIDE RULE. The multiplication scales should be placed along the
bottom edge of your other slide rule, if desired. There are two possible
methods for putting the numbers on your rule:

Method 1: Starting from the left side, measure off distances equal to
the above logarithms. This may be done in inches or centimeters, such as
0, 3.0, 4.7, 6.0, 6.9, 7.7, 8.4, 9.0, 9.5, 10. Number the lines and repeat the
scale again as shown in FIG. 8-3. Notice first number is 1, not 0.

Method 2: Measure the distances on the scale in FIG. 8-3 and transfer
these lines to your rule. Be sure to put lines on both A and B scales at the
same time.

USE

Now that the scale is marked in logarithm distances instead of uniform
distances, you use it in the same manner as the adding scale; but since it
is adding logs, the result will be multiplication. Example: Multiply 3×2.
Place 1 on scale B under 3 on scale A; go down to 2 on scale B and read
answer (6) above on scale A. Multiply 3×6. Scale is in same position but
you go down to 6 on scale B. Above it is 1.8. Using a slide rule, you must

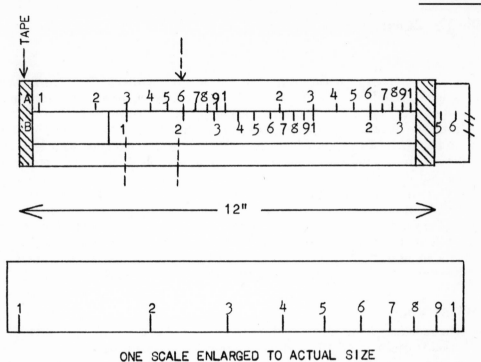

ONE SCALE ENLARGED TO ACTUAL SIZE

Fig. 8-3.   Logarithmic slide rule shown multiplying 3 by 2, or dividing 6 by 2

figure the proper position for the decimal point; in this case, of course, it is 18. Try 25×2. Place 1 of scale B under 2.5 of scale A, go down scale B to 2 and read answer (50) above on scale A.

To divide, you simply make a fraction and read the answer on scale A above the 1 of scale B. Example: $6 \div 2$. Place 2 of scale B under 6 of scale A, read answer (3) on scale A above the 1 index.

The slide rule was finally perfected in 1859 by Mannheim and today with the addition of other scales to find roots, squares, cubes, etc., it has become a convenient and essential tool of scientists, engineers and mathematicians. Note that it is not necessary to know about logs to make or use a slide. Although younger campers will not care about logs, they will still enjoy using the instrument.

NAPIER'S BONES

Businessmen of earlier days had considerable difficulty keeping mathematical records and doing rapid calculation. One of the earliest and most popular calculators developed to assist in this problem was the abacus. Even the abacus is awkward, however, when used for long multiplication problems. In 1617 John Napier, a Scottish mathematician who is mentioned above, published a book describing a multiplication calculator which he had developed and called "rods." The system later became known as "Napier's Bones" because they were often made of ivory. The same system had been used earlier in Persia and India, but Napier improved upon it and introduced it to the western world. Napier's rods were each about three inches long and three-eights inch wide, and businessmen would carry them in a small box ready for use. Ours will be larger for ease in construction, but the use will be the same as in the seventeenth century.

MATERIALS

The rods may be made from slips of oaktag or ¾-×-¾-inch pine rods. The wood is easier to handle and will be more permanent. Ruler, pen and ink or pencil. The finished rods may be coated with shellac, clear model dope or clear plastic spray.

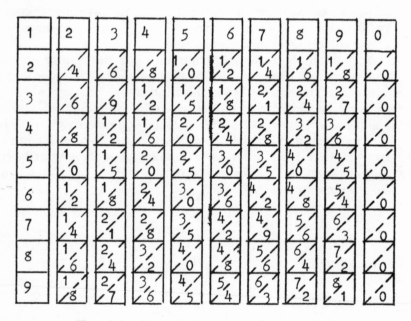

FIG. 8-4.   Napier's bones on oaktag or wood

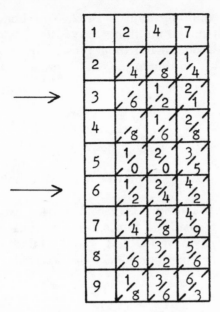

FIG. 8-5. Bones arranged to multiply 247 by 6

Ten rods will be needed for each calculator. Three-fourths of an inch is a good width; for ½" spaces, the rods should be 4½" long, for ¾" spaces, the rods will be 6¾" long. The 4½" rod should be long enough in most cases. FIG. 8-4 shows how the rods should be numbered. The left-hand rod shows index numbers (multipliers) and the top space in each other rod shows an index number (multiplicand). The numbers printed in the squares of each rod are the results of multiplying the top multiplicand by 2, 3, 4, etc. Notice that if a product has two digits, they are split by a diagonal line.

Use of the rods to multiply two digits is easily seen. Example: Place "Two" rod next to "Index" rod and you have all the products of "Twos": 2 × 4 = 8, 2 × 5 = 10, etc. Now let's do a more difficult problem: 6 × 247. Place the 2, 4 and 7 rods in order beside the index rod as shown in FIG. 8-5. Go down to 6 on the index and you have the numbers 1/2, 2/4 and 4/2. The numbers appearing in the same diagonal space must be added together, with any remainder carried over to the left as in a standard addition. This may be written as follows:

$$
\begin{array}{r}
124 \\
+\ 242 \\
\hline
1482
\end{array}
$$

The answer to this multiplication is 1482. Now imagine a problem with more than one digit in the multiplier, say: 36 × 247. This can be done without moving the bones from their present position. Multiplying by 3 gives a result of 741. Add this to the earlier product, so:

$$
\begin{array}{r}
1482 \\
+741 \\
\hline
8892
\end{array}
$$

The problem 247 × 36 = 8892 may be done with the rods by just adding a few simple numbers.

What if you want to multiply 33 × 5? You need two "three" rods. Napier solved this problem by using all four sides of his rods as you may do if you use wood. One rod may have the 2, 3, 4 and 5 tables on it while the other has 6, 7, 8 and 9. Providing four of each of these rods, you will have plenty for duplicate numbers.

BINARY NUMBER CONVERTER

Introduction to the binary number system opens a new world of numbers and often leads to the first real interest in mathematics for many people. Our usual number system is the decimal system and it uses ten numbers from 0 to 9. All other figures are combinations of these. The binary system uses only two numbers, 0 and 1, and all other figures are combinations of these. With the converter described below, it is easy to change decimal to binary and back again. The binary system had its first period of revitalization when electronic computers were first developed. With only two numbers, a 0 could be represented by having current off and a 1 indicated by having current on. The large computers were then designed around many small transistor units known as flip-flops. Each flip-flop could turn a circuit on or off according to the number of pulses it received, for example, from a telephone dial. The computer does all its calculation in binary numbers and the final answers are converted again to decimals.

MATERIALS

White paper, rulers, scissors, pen or pencils

PROCEDURE

On half of an 8½ × 11 piece of paper, draw the lines and numbers as shown in FIG. 8-6. Cut up each vertical line just as far as the horizontal line A — B. Fold these lower tabs up so they cover the row of zeros. On the under side of each tab (the upper side as they cover the zeros) write a "1." Now, when all tabs are down, the zeros are visible; but if a tab is raised, the zero is replaced by a "1." The tabs may be pointed as shown and slots cut under each decimal number. The ones in use may be tucked into these slots to hold them in place.

USE

Let's write the binary number for 5. You start at the top of the converter with the largest number that will go into 5, that is 4, and push up the 1 under 4. Now find the next largest number that will go into the remainder, 1. The number is 1 so you push up a 1 under 1. The binary number for 5 is 101. The binary number for 4 is 100. The binary number for 7 is 111. The binary number for 10 is 1010. (Read "One, 0, one, 0," not "one thousand and ten.") To convert from binary to decimal: Change 1100 to the decimal number. From the right-hand side of the converter, you push up 1100 and find the ones under 8 and 4. These are added together. The decimal number is 12.

Try adding binary numbers. In the binary system, whenever you add 1 and 1, you get 10, which means that you put down a 0 and carry 1 to the next column to the left. Example:

BINARY	DECIMAL
111	7
+ 101	+ 5
1100	12

Note above we had three ones in the left column, so one stayed while the others were carried.

11	3
+ 11	+ 3
110	6

101	5
+ 11	+ 3
1000	8

11	3
10	2
101	5
+ 1001	+ 9
10011	19

It is also easy to multiply with binary numbers. Example:

100	4
× 10	× 2
1000	8

For more binary projects and greater ease in calculating with the binary system see BINARY ABACUS.

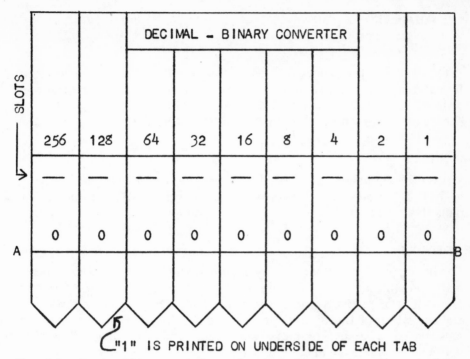

FIG. 8-6. Decimal-binary number converter. Cut along each vertical line up as far as line A – B.

BINARY ABACUS

Of all abaci, the binary abacus is simplest to build and easiest to use. It requires only two beads on each rod and does not require the mental arithmetic needed by the larger abacus. The binary abacus described below should be used with the BINARY NUMBER CONVERTER.

MATERIALS

Strips of wood about ¾" × ¾" thick, counting beads (Hammett's No. 743 or 744; Edmund's No. 60,088 or 70,226), drill, 2½" eight-penny finish nails, 1½" brads and wood glue.

PROCEDURE

The most complicated part of any abacus is the frame, for which there are many possible designs. The one shown in FIG. 8-7 is simple but sturdy. The length of pieces A and B will depend on the number of rows desired and the width of the beads used. For eight rows of Hammett beads, with rods spaced ¾" apart, these pieces are about 6½" long. Regardless of bead size, sides C and D are about 3¼" long.

The 2½" nails are used as rods. Place two beads on each nail. Measure along piece A at ¾" intervals and tap a nail into each location until it will just stand up. Get the opposite nail positions on piece B and drill very shallow holes just large enough to admit the head of each nail.

Fit piece B on the nail heads. Glue on sides C and D and put a brad through each corner. This completes the abacus.

Many substitutions are possible in the above materials. Coat-hanger wire may be used in place of nails to provide longer rods. Beads may be temporarily replaced with paper clips, buttons, or washers. Sides A and B may be attached to a 6" × 3" baseboard, thus eliminating sides C and D. A less permanent frame may be made of oaktag with straightened paper-clip rods.

USE

The abacus greatly facilitates the adding of binary numbers. The bead storage location is at the bottom of the rods, the number indicator is at the top of the rods. Let's add 101 and 111, starting with all beads down. First enter 101 by pushing up beads as shown in FIG. 8-8 A. Now add 111. With the abacus, numbers are always added from right to left just as when we add on paper. Pushing up 1 on the far right gives us two beads up; but this is not 2, it is 10. *Basic rule:* Whenever there are two beads up on a rod, both come down and one bead goes up on the next rod to the left. If the next rod results in two up then you continue pulling two down and pushing one up to the left until you arrive at a rod that does not have two up. After adding 1 to 101, the beads should be in position FIG. 8-8 B. Now add each of the other 1's separately. After adding 111 to 101, beads should be as in FIG. 8-8 C, which gives the final answer to this particular addition problem. Use your binary converter to change this number (1100) to a decimal (12).

Practice adding, then go on and try multiplying, subtracting and dividing. The binary abacus operates in the same manner as the binary computer. The computer uses electrical impulses operating flip-flop circuits to turn indicators on and off, corresponding to beads going up and down. If two impulses (beads) enter the same circuit, the circuit switches off (beads down) and pushes the additional impulse to the left, clearing those circuits, until it finds an open one and stays on (bead up). Here is a project that is not only instructive but can stimulate a great many lines of thought and investigation.

It is also possible to construct and use a binary abacus with only one bead on each rod.

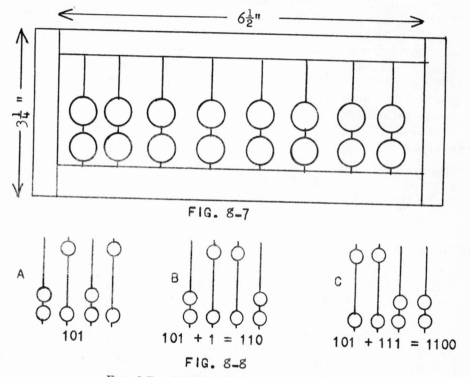

FIG. 8-7

A   101

B   101 + 1 = 110

C   101 + 111 = 1100

FIG. 8-8

FIG. 8-7.   Construction of binary abacus

FIG. 8-8.   Use of abacus showing "beads up" to indicate various numbers

BEAD ABACUS

Various forms of abaci have been in use for over two thousand years. Usually considered an Oriental invention, the abacus has been used by such widely separated peoples as the Greeks, Romans, Russians, Etruscans, Hindus, Chinese, Japanese and the Aztecs of Mexico. The abacus may be considered a digital computer because it counts individual digits in the form of beads. Another name for the "modern" abacus is the *swan-pan*. The abacus consists of parallel rods or wires which are threaded with beads or *counters*. The counters on each rod represent the numbers from one to ten. There are ten beads per rod on the Russian abacus, therefore each bead has a value of one. The Oriental forms use an additional cross piece or *reading bar*, dividing the beads into two groups, lower and upper. The lower group always had five beads per rod, each with a value of one. The Chinese abacus had two beads in the upper group, each with a value of five; while the Japanese had one bead in the upper group with a value of five. A good abacus operator can work faster than many who use desk calculators, especially in addition and subtraction.

The abacus described here is the Japanese type as that is the fastest and most efficient in operation and requires the fewest beads. This type of abacus is still used in many Oriental business establishments.

MATERIALS

Strips of wood about ¾" × ¾" thick, counting beads (Hammett's No. 743 or 744; Edmund's No. 60,088 or 70,226), drill, 1½" brads, wood glue, cutting pliers, coat hanger wire. (Or you may substitute paper clips straightened in vise or other heavy wire.)

PROCEDURE

See FIG. 8-9. Your dimensions may be different depending upon size of beads and number of rows desired. There should be a minimum of four rows; six should handle most problems. After deciding upon dimensions, prepare strips of ¾" × ¾" wood by cutting to proper sizes. Piece E may be a thin piece of wood with holes drilled through or a long piece of wire placed on top of the other wires; the wire is suggested. Mark pieces A and B at one-inch intervals and drill shallow holes (about ⅜" deep) into the wood at each mark. These holes will receive the rods. If E is to be a wire, measure down 2" from the end on C and D and drill shallow holes. Be sure these holes are at a slightly higher level than the holes in A and B so this wire will go over the other wires. Cut six 5" rods from coat hangers using pliers or hack saw. You will need two coat hangers to supply all rods for each abacus. Thread beads on rods, place rods in holes, cut 7½" rod and put in place on C and D. Glue wood ends together and secure each corner with a brad. Further strength may be obtained by using metal corner braces or angle irons.

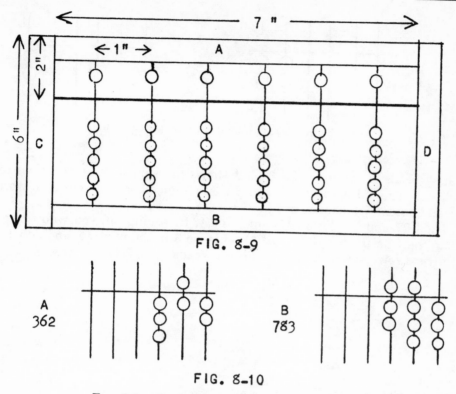

FIG. 8-9

FIG. 8-10

FIG. 8-9.   Bead abacus for decimal numbers

FIG. 8-10.   Use of abacus showing beads against reading bar to represent various numbers

USE

Hold abacus in front of you as shown in FIG. 8-9. Cross piece E is called the *reading bar* and only beads against the bar are counted. The beads on each rod equal 10. Each of the five beads below reading bar has a value of 1; the single bead above the bar has a value of 5. Numbers are entered on the abacus from right to left just as in standard addition. Much of the arithmetic is done mentally. The abacus is mainly a device to keep track of numbers as you do a problem. Now let's add 362 + 421.

Start with abacus set at 0, as shown in FIG. 8-9. All beads are away from the reading bar. Enter number 362 as shown in FIG. 8-10 A. Two beads go to bar in first column, the 5 bead and a 1 bead go to the bar in second column, and three beads to bar in third column . . . 362. Now as you enter the next number (421) you also are adding it to the 362. Push up one more bead in the first column, two more beads in the next column and in the third column there aren't four beads to push up so you add 4 to the 3 already there and get 7. Pull down the 5 bead and leave two of

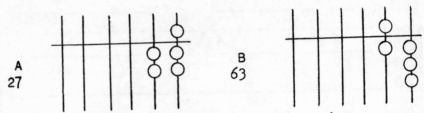

Fig. 8-11.   Use of abacus to represent numbers

the 1 beads at the bar. Fig. 8-10 B shows the sum now indicated on the abacus. To read it you count the beads. (Remember that some are worth 1 and others 5.) The answer is 783.

Add 27 and 36. Enter 27, Fig. 8-11 A. In adding 36, you want to add 6 to the 7 on the bar; 6 + 7 = 13 so leave 3 in the first row and add 1 to the next row. Now add the 3 and count beads (Fig. 8-11 B). Answer = 63.

PEBBLE ABACUS

The earliest abaci were not the well constructed, highly developed type shown here. They were rows of stones set along lines marked in sand. The pebbles were not necessarily kept within rows, they might be picked up and moved from line to line (to the left). This activity may be done as a preliminary or substitute to the bead abacus. It is also useful to show the different forms of abaci.

MATERIALS

Pebbles

PROCEDURE

Draw parallel lines in earth and place stones on lines. FIG. 8-12 shows the three common abaci forms.

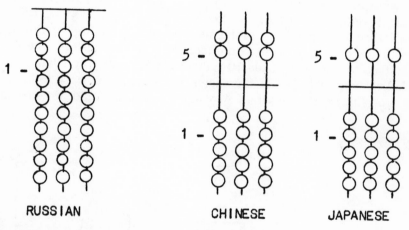

FIG. 8-12.   Three abaci forms showing values assigned to each bead

USE

Use as described under bead abacus. Subtraction is reverse of addition. Enter larger number first, remove beads to subtract smaller number. Count remaining beads for answer.

ELECTRIC ANALOG COMPUTER

Remember that analog computers do not count units, they change numbers into some physical measurement and then calculate with that measurement. The slide rule calculates with lengths of wood. This electric analog computer calculates with varying voltages. The electricity is controlled by potentiometers and read on a voltmeter with "0" in the center of the scale. FIG. 8-13 shows the front panel set up to calculate 5 multiplied by 5. Factors are entered on R 1 and R 2. This admits a certain voltage to the meter. R 3 is now turned until the meter once again reads "0". When the meter reads "0", the R 3 pointer will indicate the answer, 25.

Ability of the computer to multiply may be seen in the schematic FIG. 8-14. All controls are shown in "0" position. Notice that no current will reach meter if either R 1 or R 2 is at "0" (provided R 3 is also at "0"). Move R 1 up half way (5) and half the total voltage is available for R 2 to use. Move R 2 up half way (5) and it passes half the voltage it has available or only 25 per cent of the total voltage. Thus to bring the system back to equilibrium and return the meter to "0", R 3 has to be moved up only 25 per cent, making its pointer read 25.

Think through other such problems, and understanding of the mechanism will come quickly. Here's another: Push R 1 up all the way passing total voltage to R 2 (dial reads 10). Push R 2 up half way (dial reads 5). Only half of total voltage reaches meter. To bring meter back to "0" it will be necessary to turn R 3 up half way and its dial will read 50 (product of 10×5).

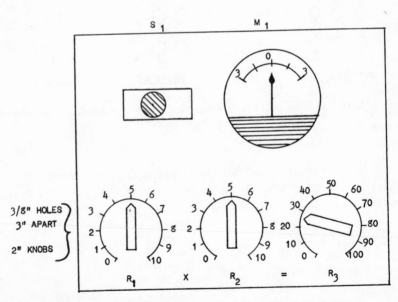

FIG. 8-13.   Front control panel of analog computer

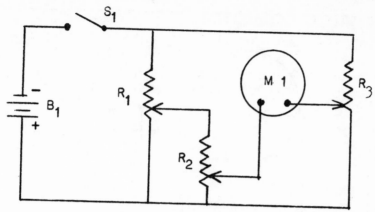

FIG. 8-14.   Analog computer schematic diagram

Computer may be constructed on ¼″ plywood, wooden box, cigar box, cardboard box or poster board. Since materials will cost about eight dollars, a substantial base should be used for durability.

MATERIALS

R 1   10-ohm potentiometer (CTS-IRC Type WPK-10)
R 2   100-ohm potentiometer (WPK-100)
R 3   10-ohm potentiometer (WPK-10). All "pots" must be linear taper.
M 1   Voltmeter 3-0-3 vdc Shurite type 550 (Lafayette MT-181)
S 1   Push button, door-bell type
B 1   Two standard (Size D) flashlight batteries
Battery holder (Lafayette MS 382)
Three pointer knobs, 2″

Hook-up wire, solder, pliers, screwdriver, ⅜″ bit and brace, hack saw, and miscellaneous small items.

PROCEDURE

Parts layout is suggested in FIG. 8-13 although any layout will do. With the ⅜″ bit, drill three holes for potentiometers with at least three inches between holes. The meter hole should be about 2⅛″ in diameter. It may be made with a circle cutter, expansion bit or large bit and enlarged with file. Drill a hole for wires under position planned for push button. Mount battery holder, FIG. 8-15. Use hack saw to cut potentiometer shafts down to ½″ long, and mount "pots" as in FIG. 8-15. Meter is placed into panel from front and held with its clamp bolted down from behind panel. Wire the components as shown in FIG. 8-15 and screw the push button into place after its wires are attached. Solder connections on battery holder and "pots."

Turn all shafts fully counterclockwise and install three knobs all pointing down in same direction. Mark this position "0" for each control. Turn fully clockwise and mark "10" for R 1 and R 2; mark "100" for R 3. Next

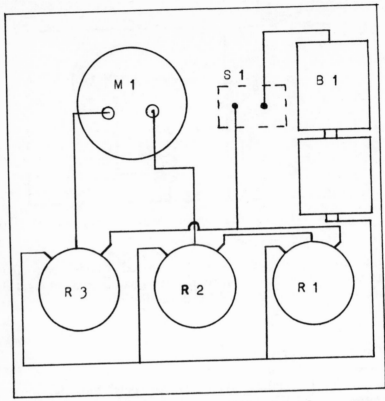

FIG. 8-15.   Analog computer pictorial

mark the half-way point on each dial, then fill in remaining numbers. These markings must be carefully done and you may prefer working them out on paper to be transferred to the panel.

USE

Use the computer as described earlier. Enter factors on R 1 and R 2; turn R 3 until meter reads "0" and read answer off R 3 dial. The push button is included to prevent excessive battery drain which would be considerable if they were in service at all times. As with the slide rule, you can mentally add zeros to all dials. You might have $100 \times 100 = 10,000$. Since two zeros must be added to R 3 when one is added to the first two dials, you may want to avoid confusion by printing a second set of numbers on each dial.[1]

---

[1] Individuals who become seriously interested in computer design should see: Ronald Benrey, "Build an Electronic Computer," *Electronics Illustrated*, January 1960, Vol. 3, No. 1. Article describes theory and construction of transistor flip-flop computer.

CALCULATING POSSIBLE ERROR IN MEASUREMENTS

This information should be of interest to campers of high-school age and may be applied to any project in science involving measurement of any kind: temperature, distance, time, etc. No measurement of any quantity is ever exactly correct. There is always some amount of error due to the design of the instrument, the conditions of use or the observer's method of using it. Some errors can be minimized by using highly refined and costly equipment and using it under controlled conditions by trained observers. Although errors are thus reduced, they are still present.

A classic example of this problem is seen in attempting to measure off six inches with a ruler. For ordinary purposes we assume that six inches is at the line marked "6." But this line also has thickness. Is it at the beginning or end of the line, or in the middle of the line? Where is the middle? Questions of this type and accuracy to this degree are often vitally important in science and industry.

Some of the projects described call for measurements to be made with crude instruments. There are two methods of increasing the accuracy of these measurements.

METHOD 1

The simplest method is to make repeated trials of the same observation and calculate the average. In camp this is easily done. Instead of one person's making many observations, many people can make the same observation. This is also a good reason for everybody to do the same project individually. Make as many observations as you have campers and find the average. According to the laws of probability, the chance that this average is exactly equal to the true value is proportional to the square root of the number of observations. For example, the average of twenty-five observations would be five times more reliable than one observation.

METHOD 2

This method not only gives the average measurement, but also indicates the limits by which that measurement may be in error. For example: The width of a paper is 21.6 cm. plus or minus 0.05 cm. This means that the paper may be as little as 21.55 cm. or as much as 21.65 cm.

PROCEDURE

First make many trials of the same observation. Arrange it so you have a number of trials which will have a whole number square root, such as 4, 9, 16, 25, 36. The mathematical steps for four trials are shown below.

TRIALS

$$A - M = D1$$
$$B - M = D2$$
$$C - M = D3$$
$$\underline{+D - M = D4}$$
$$\overline{N/T} \quad N/\overline{\ \text{Sum}\ }$$
Mean $\qquad$ a.d.

$$N \sqrt{\dfrac{A.D.}{a.d.}}$$

In this example, N would be 4 and the square root of N would be 2.

Key:
N = Number of observations
M = Mean (average) of observations
D = Deviation from mean
a.d. = Average deviation from the mean
A.D. = Average deviation of the mean

The average deviation of the mean (A.D.) indicates the range within which the true value probably lies. The final result is expressed as the mean value (M) ± the A.D.

USE

There are many projects to which the above may be usefully applied, such as calculating the diameter of the moon, taking temperatures, and finding distances with rangefinder.

A special project to illustrate this method might be to have campers take measurements of the width of a piece of paper at different places along the paper using a centimeter ruler. The distance between any two lines should be imagined to be divided into ten units to estimate inter-line distances in decimals. This is a good project for a small interested group on a rainy day.

ORIENTEERING

Orienteering is an activity now enjoying revitalization in many parts of the world.[1] It consists of finding one's way across a woods, field or similar course, and arriving at a predetermined destination. It may or may not involve the use of a compass; but it usually involves compass directions and distance measuring of some kind. FIG. 8-16 is an example of orienteering on paper using a protractor and ruler.

MATERIALS

Compasses may be used if available but they are not vital; mimeographed sheets of directions (or directions on cards located along trail).

PROCEDURE

There are many variations of this activity. In most cases the contestants or "navigators" start from the same place at one-minute intervals. One with fastest time wins. There may or may not be a treasure at the end of the trail. Following are various methods which may be followed:

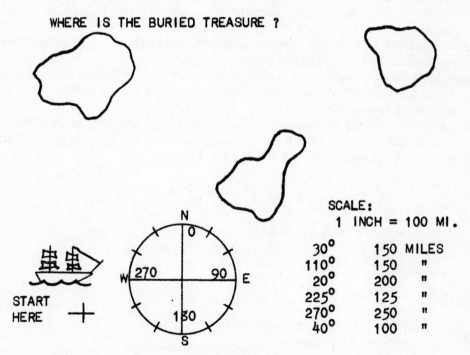

WHERE IS THE BURIED TREASURE ?

SCALE:
1 INCH = 100 MI.

30°	150 MILES
110°	150 "
20°	200 "
225°	125 "
270°	250 "
40°	100 "

FIG. 8-16. Example of orienteering on paper

---

[1] See Gatty, Harold, *Nature Is Your Guide,* in Appendix A.

Method 1: Go N 20 paces; go W 15 paces; Go NW 25 paces, etc.

Method 2: Go N 20 feet; go W 25 feet; go NW 15 feet, etc.

Method 3: Go N 20 feet; turn 30 degrees E and go 25 feet; turn 10 degrees N and go 10 feet; turn 180 degrees and go 50 feet, etc.

Method 4: Go N 20 feet and find note on oak tree; at oak tree turn 30 degrees E, go 25 feet and find note by woodchuck hole. There, turn 10 degrees N, go 10 feet and find note under granite rock, etc.

Method 5: Go N 20 feet and find note on tree. If this is an oak tree, turn 30 degrees E, 25 feet to fern bed; if it is a maple tree, turn 75 degrees E 35 feet to boulder, etc. There need not be a note near boulder, in fact, there need not be a boulder.

USE

The skills developed through this activity have obvious advantages for those who will spend any amount of time hiking or in the woods. Before starting, you may have a discussion of some of the problems of land navigation. Most people have a natural deviation to the right or left if they try to walk in a straight line. This is why lost people often walk in a circle when they think they are going in a straight line. For this reason mountain climbers when traversing rock or snow form a long single file with a guide at the rear to sight along the line and call out if they are beginning to curve to the side. Campers will enjoy finding their individual deviations. Have blindfolded campers attempt to walk in straight lines. Each person should do it a number of times to determine the direction in which he tends to deviate. This is best done on a level, smooth floor where there are no bumps to give clues. A climber with a pack on his side tends to be thrown off direction by its weight.

Campers should also learn to observe and remember natural signs along the trail such as unusual trees, rocks, water, animal homes, plants, etc. (See also GEOLOGY: EARTH'S MAGNETIC FIELD.)

ANIMATED THERMOMETER

This simple project may be built around a discussion of how the thermometer works by the expansion of a liquid (alcohol or mercury) and the two common temperature scales. The centigrade scale, used widely in Europe, is now coming into wider use in this country as most government agencies have adopted it as standard. Thermometers using a silver liquid contain mercury, those containing a red or blue liquid use colored alcohol. The freezing and boiling points of these liquids limit the places where such thermometers may be used.

	Mercury	Alcohol
Boils	675° F.	172° F.
Freezes	− 37° F.	−179° F.

Although the lowest monthly average temperature at Antarctica is only −80° F., temperatures as low as −127° F. have been recorded there. Clearly, a frozen mercury thermometer would be of little use in recording such temperatures. Campers will think of other places these thermometers cannot be used. In such places temperature is indicated by electrical thermometers.

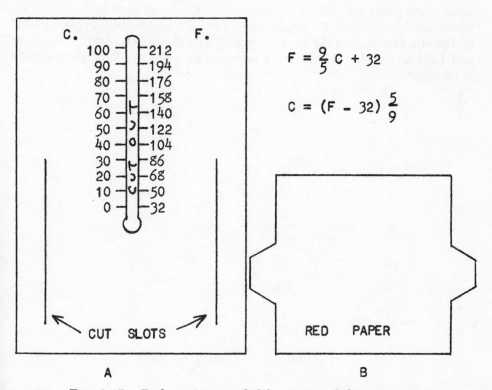

$$F = \frac{9}{5} C + 32$$

$$C = (F - 32) \frac{5}{9}$$

FIG. 8-17.   Both sections needed for animated thermometer

MATERIALS

Red construction paper, white construction paper, scissors, pen or pencil, modeling knife, staples or tape.

PROCEDURE

Prepare the top paper as shown in FIG. 8-17 A. The different scales are shown on opposite sides of the tube. Cut out thermometer section with knife.

Cut second sheet of red paper as shown in FIG. 8-17 B. Insert tabs of B into slots of A and place a third piece of paper (white) under B as backing piece which is stapled or taped to top piece A, allowing B to move freely in the center.

USE

Use as basis for discussion of above topics. You may also mention Kelvin (or Absolute) temperature scale. Zero K. = $-273°$ C. and $-459.7°$ F. Zero degrees Kelvin (or absolute zero) has been calculated as the temperature at which all molecular motion ceases. It is therefore the point of no heat. This is the temperature of space. Although $0°$ K. has never been reached in the laboratory, scientists have come within a fraction of a degree using liquid gases and more complicated magnetic processes. Temperatures of some liquid gases are: liquid helium, $-269°$ C.; liquid hydrogen, $-252°$ C.; liquid nitrogen, $-195°$ C.; liquid air, $-192°$ C.; and liquid oxygen, $-183°$ C. The size of degree is the same on both C and K scales, so $0°$ C. = $273°$ K. and $100°$ C. = $373°$ K. For more on absolute zero, see *Superconductivity* in Chapter 9.

RANGEFINDER

A rangefinder is a device used to measure distances between two points by sighting rather than by laying a measuring rod or tape between the points. Surveyors, navigators, and photographers are among the people who use rangefinders to calculate distances. The instrument works on well-known mathematical laws of right triangles and trigonometry.

MATERIALS

Oaktag, glue or cement, drinking straws, brass fasteners, yardstick or tape.

PROCEDURE

See FIG. 8-18. Cut oaktag base 12 × 9 inches and cement straw "A" along one side. Cut another piece of oaktag about 7 × 1 inches and cement straw "B" along the edge of it. Punch hole for brass fastener near one end as shown. Fasten this straw assembly to the base with a brass fastener and the rangefinder is completed except for calibration. Draw an arc just in front of the straw assembly as it swings across the base and draw a pointer on the front of this assembly.

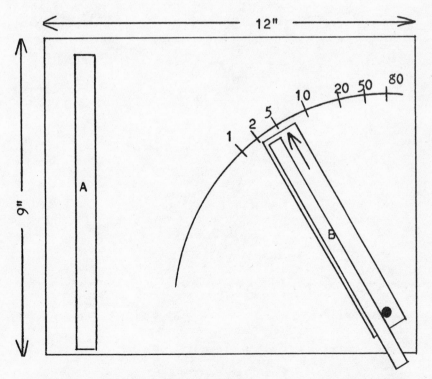

FIG. 8-18.   Rangefinder for measuring distance to a remote point

USE

To calibrate your rangefinder, place it a known distance (five feet) from a tree or post. Sight through straw "A" at the post, moving the entire unit until the object is in view. Once the post has been sighted through straw "A," do not allow the base to move. Now sight the same place on the post through straw "B" by moving the strip of oaktag across the base. When both straws are sighted at exactly the same place on the post five feet away, place a line on the arc along the base and mark it 5. Now move the rangefinder back to ten feet away and repeat for other distances. You should be able to calibrate it from about six inches to fifty feet.

To find the distance to an object with your calibrated rangefinder, sight the object first through straw "A" then, without moving the base, sight it through straw "B." The pointer beside straw "B" will indicate the distance of the object.

As the distance between the two straws is increased, the rangefinder becomes able to measure with greater accuracy and longer distances. Rangefinders using two small telescopes mounted thirty feet apart have been used on ships. You may make a longer rangefinder on a board to explore its accuracy and uses. Compare its range with the small one described here.

THE CLINOMETER AND PLAIN TRANSIT

The *clinometer* and *plain transit* are used to measure vertical and horizontal angles respectively across earth or space. Both functions may be combined into a single instrument usually then called a surveyor's transit. You may think of many uses for these instruments in astronomy and geology.

MATERIALS

Oaktag, drinking straws, string, weight (washer, paper clip), thumbtack, pointer (toothpick, nail, card), stick for stand (¾" × ¾" about 3½' long, slightly pointed end to stick into ground).

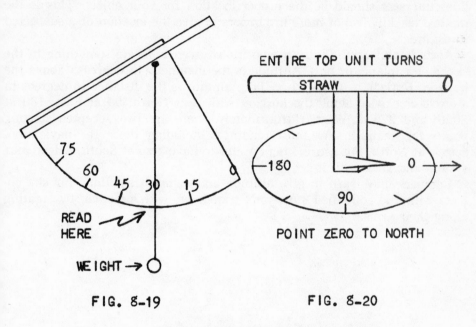

FIG. 8-19.   FIG. 8-20.

FIG. 8-19.   Clinometer for measuring vertical angles

FIG. 8-20.   Plain transit for measuring horizontal angles

PROCEDURE

Construct the instruments as shown in FIGS. 8-19 and 8-20. If you do not have a protractor, degrees and angles may be traced from the page. The straws are cemented in place. Commercial models of these instruments use telescopes with cross hairs instead of straws. The two instruments may be easily combined into a single unit by constructing the clinometer as shown, making the transit as shown but without the straw and tacking the clinometer to the upright of the transit. The clinometer string would have to be kept short so the weight does not touch base of transit.

USES: CLINOMETER

Following are some specific uses of these instruments suggested by other projects in the book. Clinometer: See Chapter 4, FINDING LATITUDE WITH NORTH STAR. The clinometer may be used in a manner similar to the sextant to find north-south position on earth by shooting the North Star (determining its altitude in degrees above the horizon).

PLAIN TRANSIT

See Chapter 5, FIELD GEOLOGY. Instrument may be used to give position of formations on map from a fixed position (tree, road, bench-mark, boulder). Select two permanent positions as those mentioned and sight the object to be located from both positions. Note its position in degrees at both positions and draw lines at the same angles on your map. Where the lines intersect should be the proper location for your object. This is the method used by two or more fire towers to give the location of a suspected forest fire.

Altitude and *azimuth* are the positions given to locate something in the sky, a star, plane, or bird. Altitude is the distance (in degrees) above the horizon. Horizon = 0, zenith = 90. Azimuth is the distance in degrees in a circle clockwise along the horizon with 0 at North, 90 at East, 180 at South and 270 at West. Unfortunately, there are two accepted starting points for azimuth. For most readings, including those for navigation, zero is at North; but astronomers prefer to have zero at South. Select your system and stick with it.

Campers may learn to give altitude and azimuth positions for sky objects with the combined surveyor's transit or, with practice, by sighting along their arms.

RESOURCE MATERIALS FOR MATHEMATICS

Films

About Time. Measurement of time and Einstein's Relativity. Free film. Order through the local Bell Telephone business office. User pays return postage.

Booklets

Yes, No — One, Zero. Free booklet on binary mathematics and digital computers. From Esso-Humble office serving your area, or: Humble Oil Co., 15 West 51 St., New York, N. Y.   10019.

Supplies

J. L. Hammett Co., Kendall Square, Cambridge 42, Mass.
Edmund Scientific Co., 101 East Gloucester Pike, Barrington, N. J.

Sources of Computers

Geniac: Oliver Garfield, 31 Broadway, New Haven, Conn. ($10 to $20)

Brainiac: Berkley Enterprises, Inc., 815 Washington St., Newtonville 60, Mass. ($10 to $20)

Minivac: Scientific Development Corp., 372 Main St., Watertown, Mass. (Under $100)

Analogs: Heath Co., Benton Harbor, Mich. ($200 and up)

Computers are also listed in the catalogs of Edmund, Lafayette Radio, and Radio Shack.

Chapter

9: Electricity and Electronics

SUGGESTED REFERENCE

Steinberg and Ford, *Electricity and Electronics—Basic*. Chicago: American Technical Society, 1961. $4.50. An excellent hard-cover book of practical information and simple experiments. Outstanding in the range of material covered. Also see booklets listed at end of chapter.

THE UNSEEN ATOM is the basic structure of the universe and all it contains. Working with electricity and electronics is the closest practical experience the young person can have with the world of the atom and atomic particles. If the camper realizes that he is actually working with and manipulating atoms, ions and electrons, even though he cannot see them, it will bring him closer to an understanding of the structure and organization of all matter. Such experiences emphasize the existence of fundamental truths lying at the basis of all nature and of a unity tying together all the diversity of the universe. They also provide a practical foundation on which to build the knowledge of chemistry, physics and other sciences.

As will be seen in the following pages, electricity is closely linked with atomic physics. The nature and properties of atomic particles should be made clear to the camper from the beginning, as should the mystery, organization and similarities of the very small atom and the very large solar system and universe.

While nuclear physics releases the energy from within the nucleus of the atom, electricity simply utilizes the electrons around the nucleus and the atom as a whole. It is these atoms, their motions and combinations, that make up the other subjects of this book—weather, plants, animals, planets, stars, films, pictures, rocks and earth. But it is only in electricity that we are able to actually work with the individual atoms and subatomic particles.

Note that INFORMATION OF IMPORTANCE in this chapter is only able to touch the highlights of this subject. The information has been selected to provide explanations of the projects described in the chapter and to answer questions which will be raised by campers, some of whom will have experience in electricity. The information will be best understood after a project has been done. If it is read before the projects are done, constant reference should be made to the appropriate project. For example, INFORMATION explains how capacitors work; the projects show how they are used.

A very good electronics course could be developed from the information as it is organized here. Such a course consisting of information and the simple projects would be invaluable for campers hoping to become radio experimenters or licensed radio hams.

INFORMATION OF IMPORTANCE

Present understanding of electricity is based upon atomic theory and electron theory. The information provided by these theories has not been proven, but it does provide satisfactory explanations for various atomic and electrical phenomena that have been observed. These explanations are outlined on the following pages.

FUNDAMENTAL PARTICLES

An atom consists of a nucleus containing *protons* and *neutrons*. Around the nucleus are shells holding electrons, one electron for each proton. *Basic fact:* There are two kinds of charges, positive $(+)$ and negative $(-)$. Like charges repel each other and unlike charges attract each other. Protons are positive and electrons are negative. In a normal atom, there is one proton for each electron. The charges neutralize each other and the total charge on the atom is neutral or no charge. If an atom loses or gains an electron it is left with a positive or negative charge and is called an *ion*. An electron which escapes from an atom travels with a free negative charge. (See FIG. 9-1.)

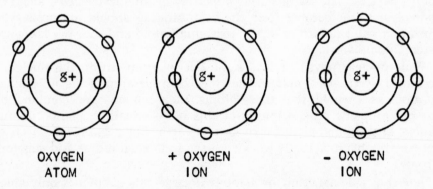

OXYGEN   + OXYGEN   − OXYGEN
ATOM   ION   ION

FIG. 9-1.   Difference between atom and ion

Electricity is a flow of electrons or ions from one place to another through a conducting material. In solid conductor (wire), flow consists of electrons. In gas or liquid, flow consists of positive and negative ions. *Direction of current* is defined as the direction in which *positive charges would* move if present. This would be from positive to negative. Since the actual particles may be negative or positive, the *actual flow of particles* may be opposite to the *defined* direction of current.

NATURE OF ELECTRICITY

For purposes of study, there are two general classes of electrical phenomena. *Static* is electricity at rest. It is an excess of electrons in one place but they are not flowing as a current. They may all jump at once to another body. Static electricity is produced by friction: running comb through hair, or contact between plastic and wool or one's feet on a rug. As two substances are rubbed, electrons are transferred from one to the other. The body with excess electrons is charged negatively and that with a lack of electrons is charged positively. Lightning is a form of static electricity built up in the cumulonimbus cloud as ice and water particles are forced into contact.

Unlike static electricity, *current electricity* is a steady flow of electrons along a wire. It is used in homes, cars, and factories, and may be produced either magnetically by a *generator* or chemically by a *battery*. Moving a magnet in and out of a coil of wire produces a moving magnetic field which will induce the electrons of the wire to move. A generator is simply a large coil of wire with an electromagnet spinning inside to produce a moving magnetic field which drives the electrons through the wire and out into lights, toasters, and other items connected to the generator. The magnet is kept spinning by some source of power such as water, steam, or diesel or gasoline engine. Current electricity is produced in bat-

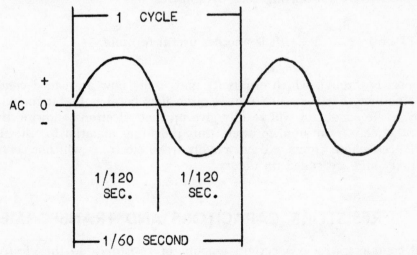

FIG. 9-2.   Waveform of alternating house current as may be seen on oscilloscope

teries as an acid or alkali decomposes a metal plate, leaving behind excess electrons free to do work. The liquid electrolyte is obvious in a wet cell; but in a dry cell it is mixed with powdered graphite to make a moist paste. Other methods of producing electricity include thermocouples and solar cells.

Current electricity may be *alternating current* (AC) or *direct current* (DC). In direct current, the electrons always flow in the same direction. One wire is always positive and the other is always negative. All batteries produce DC. In AC, the positive and negative exchange positions regularly and the particles change direction regularly. Each complete change from beginning of positive to end of negative is called a *cycle*. The number of cycles per second is referred to as a *frequency*. House current has a frequency of sixty cycles per second. A given wire is positive for 1/120 second, then becomes negative for 1/120 second. FIG. 9-2 shows the waveform of AC house current.

UNITS OF ELECTRICITY

Volts (E) measure the difference in electrical potential or excess electrons between two bodies. It is the energy available to push or pull particles through the wire. Since voltage is a measure of *potential* energy, there may be voltage present even though no current is flowing. In formulas, voltage is abbreviated "E." Household voltage is about 110 volts AC.

Amperes (I) measure the amount of electric *current* flowing or the number of electrons passing a given point in a second of time. One "amp" is equal to about 6.28×10^{18} electrons per second. This number may be read 6.28 billion billion or 6.28 with the decimal point moved eighteen places to the right.

Watts (P) measure electrical power, the ability to do work. Watts may be calculated by multiplying volts by amperes:

$$P = EI \text{ or } I = \frac{P}{E}. \quad P = I^2R \text{ is another useful formula.}$$

Materials through which electricity may easily flow are called *conductors*. Conductors will maintain an electron flow because the atoms which compose the conductor will readily give up their electrons allowing them to move freely from atom to atom, thus providing material for the flow. Substances whose atoms will not readily trade electrons will not conduct electricity and are called *insulators*.

RESISTORS, CAPACITORS AND TRANSFORMERS

All conductors have a certain amount of *resistance* to the electrons' flow. In good conductors such as silver, copper and aluminum, this resistance is very low. Iron, tungsten, nichrome and carbon are often used as electrical resistors because of their ability to hold back part of the electron flow. Materials are resistors when their atoms are slow to trade electrons or when the atoms are packed tightly together and become an obstacle course through which the electrons must push their way. Resistance of a wire increases as the length becomes greater and as the diameter becomes less. If the resistance is high enough, electrons will cause friction as they push through and produce heat and/or light. Light bulbs, toasters, heaters and electric stoves use electrical friction to produce heat. Resistors in radio circuits are usually made of carbon or nichrome and may be adjustable, such as a volume control (*potentiometer*) or permanently fixed to provide desired voltages to tubes. Resistance is measured in *ohms:* 1,000 ohms = 1 Kilohm; 1,000,000 = 1 Megohm. Resistance of 1,000 feet of No. 18 wire at room temperature: copper = 6.3 ohms, tungsten = 20.4 ohms, nichrome = 421.9 ohms.

Ohm's Law gives the mathematical relationship between amps, volts and ohms. For DC circuits, Ohm's Law is $E = IR$ (volts = amps $\times$ ohms) or $R = \dfrac{E}{I}$ or $I = \dfrac{E}{R}$. The same law holds for many simple AC circuits not containing coils, transformers or capacitors. Example: A light bulb draws one amp at 110 volts. What is its resistance? $R = \dfrac{110}{1} = 110$ ohms is the resistance of the bulb while it is in the circuit and lighted. The resistance will be less if the lamp is cool because *resistance increases with temperature*, due both to greater distances between atoms in the expanded metal and random sideways motion of electrons.

It has been demonstrated that as temperature approaches absolute zero ($-273°$ C.), atoms are closer together and random motion of electrons is practically zero. The conductor becomes a *superconductor* and once a current is started, it may continue for weeks with no source of power.

A *capacitor* or condenser is a device which is capable of storing an electrical charge. It will "pass" alternating current but will hold back direct current. The capacitor consists of two metal plates separated by an insulator. (See FIG. 9-3.) If a capacitor is connected to a battery as illustrated, two things will happen in one instantaneous surge of current: 1. A surge of electrons will leave the negative battery pole, giving one plate a negative charge which produces a negative *electric field* around that plate. 2. Electrons in the opposite plate are repelled by this electric field out of the plate and into the positive battery pole. Result: One plate has an excess negative charge, the other has an excess positive charge, and each is holding the other in place across the insulator because the positive and the negative have a mutual attraction. If the battery were now removed, the plates would remain charged. Connecting the two plates with a wire will allow the excess electrons to return and join the positive ions, thus discharging the capacitor. A large charge will produce a spark during discharge.

Notice that a current flows in this capacitor system even though the

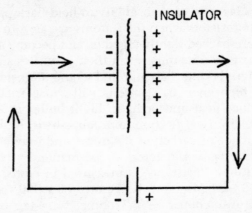

FIG. 9-3.   Construction and operation of capacitor

circuit is broken by the insulator. However, the current flows only during the time of charge and discharge. There can be no continuous flow of *direct current* through a capacitor. If the battery connections are reversed after charging the capacitor, the electrons will flow back and it will be charged in the opposite direction. This is what happens with AC as the positive and negative reverse positions many times a second. Thus there can be a flow of *alternating current* "through" a capacitor. This ability to pass only AC makes it possible to use capacitors to filter AC hum out of DC power supplies and to pass the AC program signal from one tube to another while holding back the high-voltage DC needed to operate the tubes.

Capacitors are rated by their *capacitance,* the ability to store and pass an electrical charge, measured in *microfarads.* The capacitance becomes greater as the size of the plates increases and as the distance between them decreases. Fixed capacitors are constructed of layers of aluminum foil and insulating paper wrapped into a tube. Variable capacitors consist of two sets of metal plates with air as the insulator. As the metal plates are moved together by a knob, the capacitance increases. The tuning device on radios is a variable capacitor.

In considering electric generators, it was said that a moving magnetic field would cause electrons to move along a wire. It is likewise true that a current of electrons moving through a wire will produce a circular magnetic field around the wire. When an *electromagnet* is made by wrapping many turns of wire around a nail, the magnetic field around the wire is being concentrated on the nail causing it to behave as a magnet. Magnetic lines of force have direction. As long as current flows in the same direction (DC), the magnetic lines of force will continue in the same circular direction around the wire. If the current direction is reversed, the magnetic field will be reversed. With alternating house current, the direction is being reversed twice in each cycle or 120 times per second, with the result that the magnetic field reverses direction 120 times per second. This magnetic reversal has the same effect of moving a permanent magnet near a wire. If a simple circuit as shown in FIG. 9-4 is brought near an AC electromag-

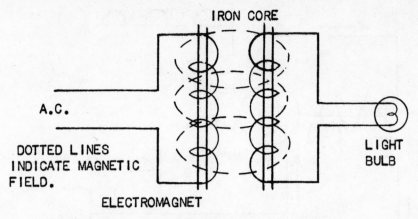

IRON CORE

A.C.

DOTTED LINES
INDICATE MAGNETIC
FIELD.

LIGHT
BULB

ELECTROMAGNET

FIG. 9-4.   Induced current by electromagnetism

net, the alternating magnetic field will induce the electrons in the nearby circuit to flow in a similar alternating manner. This manner of producing electron flow in an independent circuit using only an alternating magnetic field is known as *induction*. It is the principle on which transformers operate and it is the reason that they will only work on AC. FIG. 9-5 shows two transformer diagrams. "A" has more windings on the secondary than the primary, resulting in a higher secondary voltage. This is a *step-up* transformer and is used to provide high voltages for radio circuits. "B" is arranged in the opposite manner resulting in a lower output voltage. This is a *step-down* transformer and is used to provide low voltages for doorbells and electric trains. Motor, clock, doorbell and telephone are all examples of operating electromagnets. Transformers found in radio and television sets and on power lines are examples of induction devices.

TUBES AND TRANSISTORS

Whereas electricity is concerned with the generation and distribution of electric current and uses of the heating and magnetic effects of these currents for appliances, *electronics* is concerned with the individual electron (or ion) and a highly refined control over its movements. It is this

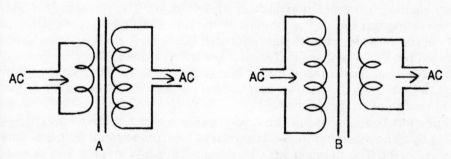

AC

AC

AC

AC

A

B

FIG. 9-5.   A. Step-up transformer.   B. Step-down transformer.

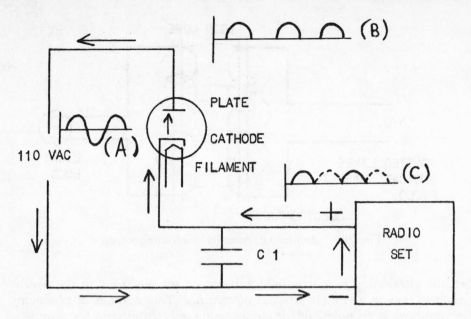

FIG. 9-6.   Use of diode as rectifier

close control of the electron that makes possible the entire field of electronics, radio, television and computers. The basic device for controlling electrons is the *electron vacuum tube* or, as it is more descriptively termed in Europe, the *electron valve*. The tube is a valve much like the valve on a water faucet that will allow more or less water (as compared with electrons) to flow as it is turned.

One of the earliest discoveries leading to the development of the electron tube was made by Thomas Edison. Working with his light bulb, Edison found that the heat of the filament caused the atomic particles to move around so fast that electrons were actually being thrown from the metal into the surrounding vacuum of the bulb. Just as boiling water throws off water molecules as steam, so the hot filament was discharging electrons. This is known as the *Edison Effect* and provides a method of getting free electrons into the space of the vacuum tube where they can be manipulated and controlled.

The simplest electron tube has two elements, giving it the name *diode*. FIG. 9-6 shows a diode with one element, the *plate* (or anode) and the other element a combination *cathode* and *filament*. The filament is a continuous tungsten coil and is the part of the tube that lights. Its function is to heat the cathode, a metal plate coated with caesium oxide or other oxide selected for ability to give off free electrons when heated. The plate (anode) is a piece of uncoated metal and, when given a positive charge, it will attract the electrons in space around the hot cathode, thus producing a flow of current through the vacuum.

The most common use of the diode is as a *rectifier*, a device to change AC to DC. The diode in FIG. 9-6 is shown in a rectifier circuit which is part of a radio set. The filament may be designed for any voltage and is electrically independent of the rest of the circuit. Waveform "A" shows the standard AC house current entering the rectifier with its positive and negative charges alternating sixty times per second. The heated cathode always has electrons available, but they will flow to the plate only during the half cycle when the plate is positive. Current will flow through the tube (and entire circuit) only when the plate is positive. No current will flow during the half cycle that the plate is negative. Waveform "B" illustrates current flowing through plate. When current does flow, it always flows in the same direction, thus forming a direct current, as shown by the arrows indicating direction of electron flow. Capacitor C 1 is added to help fill in the gaps in current flow. C 1 will charge when current is flowing and discharge, adding electrons to the circuit, when current is not flowing. Dotted lines in waveform "C" indicate current added by the capacitor.

The capacitor and tube constitute the *power supply* section of a radio. Since all other tubes must use DC so plates may be charged positive and cathodes negative, the rectifier power supply is a necessary unit in all devices using electron tubes. The unit illustrated is a *half-wave* rectifier. Many rectifier tubes have two plates connected to each side of the AC line so that one is always positive and current flows continuously through the tube, but always in the same direction. These are *full-wave* rectifiers and have less need for the smoothing effect of the capacitor.

A *control grid* may be added to the tube, making it a three-element tube or *triode*. Addition of the grid makes it possible for the tube to increase power of weak signals or *amplify* them. Amplifier tubes are used to increase the strength of weak radio signals and signals from the phono pickup so they may operate a loudspeaker and be easily heard. Amplifier tubes also strengthen weak picture signals until they are strong enough to operate the picture tube of a television set. There are numerous other applications of amplifiers.

Fig. 9-7 shows a triode placed in an amplifier circuit. The grid is a wire screen placed in the path of electron flow. Except in oscillator circuits, it

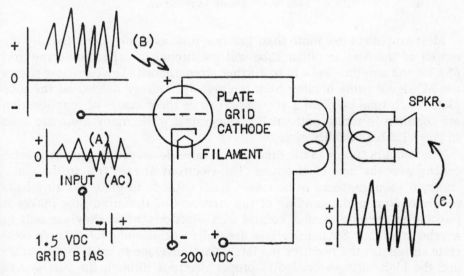

Fig. 9-7.   Triode amplifier

always has a certain amount of negative voltage (*bias*) supplied by a battery or power supply. If the grid is very negative, it will repel many cathode electrons and prevent them from reaching the plate; but if the grid is only slightly negative or nearly neutral, its repelling powers will be weak and the strong positive plate will be able to attract electrons from the cathode thus causing a current to flow through the tube. The amount of negative grid charge is varied by some type of input device such as a microphone or phono pickup producing about one volt of alternating current. The current produced by this device alternates or fluctuates with the changes in frequency of sounds which it picks up. The low power fluctuations in the grid produce high power fluctuations in the powerful stream of electrons flowing to the plate. FIG. 9-8 illustrates this amplification in graphic form. Passing through one side of the transformer, the current sets up a fluctuating magnetic field which induces an alternating current in the secondary of the transformer to operate the loudspeaker and reproduce the original sounds in their much amplified form. Waveforms "A", "B", and "C" illustrate the signal in various sections of the amplifier.

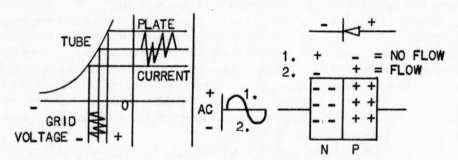

FIG. 9-8.   Waveforms showing use of tube to amplify weak signals

FIG. 9-9.   Diode as rectifier

Most amplifiers use more than just one tube as shown here. Usually the output of the first amplifier tube will go through a capacitor to the grid of a second amplifier tube to be further strengthened. The capacitor passes the AC signal while holding back the high DC voltage needed on the tube plate. Each tube is called a *stage* and two or three stages of amplification are common in radios and small phonographs while many more are used in powerful high-fidelity systems.

The vacuum tube was the first type of valve developed to provide precise control over the flow of electrons. The electrons are set free in the glass-enclosed vacuum, there to be tossed from cathode to plate like tiny balls in space. New understanding of the structure of the atom now makes it possible to exercise similar control over electrons while they are still in a solid material. Such materials are called *semiconductors*. Their solid state eliminates the need for the large glass envelope to contain a vacuum and the high voltages needed to propel electrons through the vast spaces of the vacuum tube; and since only a small piece of semiconductor is needed, the total size of the valve is a small fraction of the size of a vacuum tube. In most uses the semiconductor produces no heat, thus eliminating need for large cabinets and ventilation.

A semiconductor is a very pure crystal material, either germanium (Ge) or Silicon (Si), to which a trace of another element has been added to make the crystal a fair electrical conductor—not as good as most metals and not as poor as most insulators. The added trace element combines chemically with the Ge or Si and releases free negative particles (electrons) or free positive charges (holes) which may flow as current. A crystal with free negative electrons is labeled "N" for its negative charge and one with free positive holes is labeled "P" for its positive charge.

The simplest semiconductor is the *diode* (two sections) composed of an N and P section bonded together. The contact point between N and P is called the *junction*. FIG. 9-9 shows how a diode may be used as a rectifier. During the half AC cycle when P is negative and N is positive, no current flows because the electrical particles are being pulled in opposite directions away from the junction. As this has no excess particles to give, flow must cease. For the other half AC cycle when P is positive and N is negative, particles are being repelled away from the wires toward the junction through which they pass to make a complete circuit, and the current flows. A major application of the diode is as a rectifier, allowing current to flow only when the P is positive and thus eliminating the negative half of the AC cycle from the positive line.

A much more versatile semiconductor is the *transistor,* a triode consisting of three sections bonded together. The sections are arranged either as N-P-N or P-N-P. The center section is called the *base* and is similar to the control grid of a vacuum tube. At one end the *emitter,* similar to the vacuum tube cathode, gives off electrons to the other end, the *collector,*

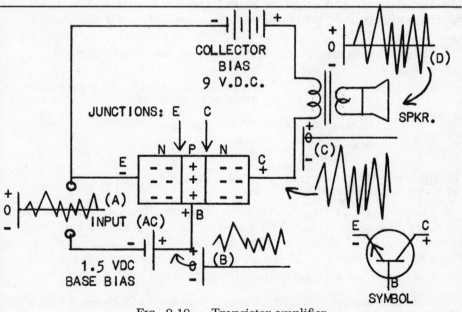

FIG. 9-10.   Transistor amplifier

which collects electrons as does the plate of a tube. Fig. 9-10 shows a transistor arranged as an amplifier. The nine-volt battery provides the reservoir of electrons to flow from E to C.[1] The one-and-one-half volt battery provides a base *bias*. The bias voltage is needed to keep a steady low-level stream of electrons flowing across the transistor at all times. As with the tube, this flow is increased or decreased by the input (microphone or phono) and is reflected by large variations in the output reaching the speaker. A loud signal at the input makes the base more positive, thus attracting more electrons from the emitter.

As soon as electrons are drawn through E junction, more electrons flow from the battery along the wire to take their place. This sets up a chain reaction back through the entire circuit, drawing a large number of electrons. In the transformer, this fluctuating current develops a fluctuating AC current on the secondary by induction, thus operating the loudspeaker and reproducing the much amplified original sound. Waveforms "A", "B", "C" and "D" illustrate the signal at various points in the amplifier. A P-N-P transistor could be used in the same setup with reversed battery connections. Note that unlike the hundreds of volts needed on tube plates, the transistor will operate at low battery voltages. As with tubes, more than one transistor is generally used in an amplifier, the collector of one connected to base of the next, each adding more strength to the signal.

DETAILED SEMICONDUCTOR THEORY

Campers whose hobby is electronics will want more detail on the nature of transistors, especially the "holes." Complete understanding of transistor structure and operation is based upon understanding of atomic structure, electron theory and covalent chemical bonds as used in solid-state physics. The structure of semiconductor material and the operation of holes and electrons are outlined below for reference and advanced discussions. See FIGS. 9-11 to 9-15.

1. Atomic structure of materials used in semiconductors:

USE	ELEMENT	ATOMIC NUMBER	ELECTRONS PER SHELL	VALANCE: ELECTRONS IN OUTER SHELL
Crystal Base	Silicon (Si)	14	2 – 8 – 4	4
	Germanium (Ge)	32	2 – 8 – 18 – 4	4
"N" Impurity	Arsenic (As)	33	2 – 8 – 18 – 5	5
(Donors)	Antimony (Sb)	51	2 – 8 – 18 – 18 – 5	5
"P" Impurity	Aluminum (Al)	13	2 – 8 – 3	3
(Acceptors)	Gallium (Ga)	31	2 – 8 – 18 – 3	3

2. Semiconductor crystal structure, Ge or Si: The basis of a semiconductor is a Ge or Si crystal. The atoms of such crystals are held together by sharing *pairs* of electrons in the outer shells. Such bonds are *covalent bonds.* The covalent symbol for an atom is the element abbreviation surrounded by dots or x's representing the outer shell bonding electrons. Fig.

---

[1] The distance between E and C junctions is very small to facilitate diffusing electrons. This distance averages 0.0012 centimeters.

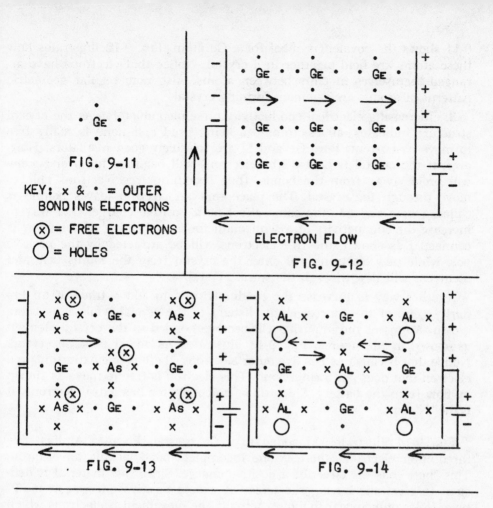

FIG. 9-11

KEY: x & • = OUTER
BONDING ELECTRONS

(x) = FREE ELECTRONS

O = HOLES

ELECTRON FLOW

FIG. 9-12

FIG. 9-13

FIG. 9-14

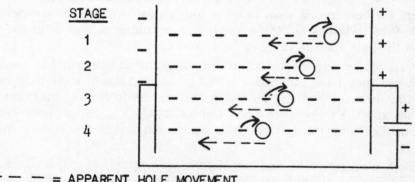

STAGE

1

2

3

4

← − − = APPARENT HOLE MOVEMENT
⟶ = ELECTRON MOVEMENT   FIG. 9-15

FIG. 9-11.   Covalent symbol for germanium atom shows only outer electrons.

FIG. 9-12.   Atomic structure of pure germanium crystal showing how electrons would move if material were a good conductor

FIG. 9-13.   "N" type semiconductor with arsenic impurity

FIG. 9-14.   "P" type semiconductor with aluminum impurity

FIG. 9-15.   Actual electron movement causes apparent hole movement in "P" material.

9-11 shows the covalent symbol for a Ge atom. FIG. 9-12 illustrates how these atoms are held together in a crystal. Notice that electrons have arranged themselves in pairs between atoms. Also note regular geometric patterns of atomic arrangement forming crystal.

3. Increasing electrical conductivity of semiconductors: As the crystal structure indicates, all electrons are being used and none is really free to move as current. Pure Ge and Si are relatively good insulators. However, if the crystal is heated, the electrons will begin to jump and some will break away from the bonds, thus becoming free electrons able to move through the crystal. The place that an electron leaves behind is called a *hole* and has the same effect as a positive charge. One way to increase the conductivity of a semiconductor is by heating. If a battery is connected as shown, the free electrons will be attracted by the positive pole while new electrons will enter the crystal from the minus pole and a current will flow through the warm crystal.

Another way to increase the conductivity is to add a trace of an impurity (one of the four elements listed) to the crystal while it is being grown. Atoms of the impurity will become bonded to the crystal element as shown in the figures. FIG. 9-13 illustrates As added to a Ge crystal. Notice that because As has five outer electrons, there is one extra unpaired electron that does not form a bond. This electron is free to move as shown by flow from the battery. Since this semiconductor has extra electrons, it is the "N" type.

FIG. 9-14 illustrates Al added to a Ge crystal. Because Al has only three outer electrons, there is one incomplete bond lacking an electron. This "hole" has the effect of a positive charge. Since this material is deficient in electrons having the effect of excess positive charges, it is "P" type. Holes only appear to move. Actually the movement is electrons which leave the hole in one atom to move into an existing hole in another atom. FIG. 9-15 indicates electrons moving from minus to plus with the result that the hole appears to move from plus to minus.

Crystals used in diodes and transistors conduct at normal temperatures because they have impurities added as above. However, if they become warm, their conductivity increases (resistance decreases) and they work in unexpected ways. (See CODE OSCILLATOR.) The temperature factor is particularly important in transistor equipment designed to operate in space craft.

Both electron tubes and transistors have many other uses including: *Detector* to detect radio signals and *oscillator* to generate rapidly vibrating, high-frequency signals which we know as radio and television waves traveling as electromagnetic radiation through space. Transistors are particularly well suited to computers and to the on-off flip-flop circuits which make them work well with the binary number system. (See Chapter 8.)

HOBBIES

Below are some popular activities and hobbies connected with electronics which may come up for discussion at camp.

High fidelity is the science of reproducing, by electronic and mechanical means, the exact sounds, frequencies and tones produced by the original sound-making device (violin, voice, piano, drum, etc.). Many phonographs selling for less than one hundred dollars are labeled "Hi-Fi," and they sound good; but they do not conform to the strict standards of true high-fidelity reproduction.

Short-wave listening (SWL) is enjoyed by many people who often try to reach the most distant stations (DX) they can. The same activity may be carried out on the broadcast band with a regular radio. Careful tuning and listening will often bring in stations from distances never before attained.

Amateur radio goes the SWL one better. The radio amateur not only listens but also transmits his own radio messages. In order to operate any radio transmitter, it is first necessary to receive a license from the government. This is to insure that one transmitter will not interfere with the signals of another. The prospective radio amateur must pass a test prepared by the Federal Communications Commission, after which he is given his license and station call letters.

Citizen band operation was arranged by the F.C.C. to permit people to communicate by radio with brief, important messages for business or personal use. No test need be passed to receive a C.B. permit. C.B. is *not* for the use of those who want to experiment with radio without the bother of getting an amateur license.

Other activities include building kits, experimenting, etc. The field of electricity has kept people fascinated for many centuries. Even today we have no proof of what electricity really is. Nobody has yet seen it or any part of it. All that we have done with electricity has been planned and explained only by theory, theory of the atom and theory of the electron. Much of the fascination of electricity must come from its great mystery—from the fact that we can do so much with something that has never been seen. St. Paul was thinking along the same lines when he wrote in Hebrews 11:3: "The world was created by the word of God, so that what is seen was made out of things which do not appear."

PROJECT 108

PAPER-CUP TELEPHONES

One of the simpler projects connected with communications is the construction of paper-cup or tin-can telephones connected by a taut string. Although the sound is always a vibration, the vibrations are caused in many different substances. Sound starts as a vocal-chord vibration, passes into air vibration, to vibration in a paper cup, to string vibration, to vibration in the opposite paper cup, again to air vibration, and finally to eardrum vibration in the head of the listener.

MATERIALS

Paper cups or tin cans (or both), strong string (may try different types), nails, buttons or wood slivers to hold string inside paper cup

PROCEDURE

Provide campers with materials and have them form pairs or groups to work on and use phones. Punch hole in bottom of paper cup, push string into inside from bottom and tie to button or wood sliver inside cup. Place one cup on each end of string.

USE

Walk in opposite directions with cups until string is taut with nothing touching it between the cups. Talk into one cup while other person has ear to opposite cup. What happens if string is touching something in center? Try this with different sized cups, boxes, cans, cones, etc., and compare results. Campers will enjoy using phones between cabins.

DX LISTENING

DX listening is a hobby enjoyed by many people and involves trying to receive very distant radio stations. It is an excellent introduction to radio communication.

MATERIALS

Radio receiver (broadcast or short-wave), long high-wire antenna, paper and pencil to log radio stations

PROCEDURE

String wire antenna as high as possible, using any strong copper wire. The far end of the antenna should be insulated from touching any grounded objects such as trees or buildings. An antenna kit such as Lafayette KT-77 or Allied 83 C 101 may be purchased. *For lightning protection, when not in use, end of antenna inside building should be connected to a water pipe or to a stake driven three to five feet into the ground outside. Never install any antenna without taking this precaution for safety.*

Attach antenna to antenna terminal on radio set. If set has a ferrite stick antenna, your wire may work best connected through a 100 MMFD. (.0001 MFD) capacitor. Reception will be best in the evening. Tune carefully and slowly across the band. On short-wave you should have little trouble hearing the powerful international stations from England, Russia, Switzerland, Holland, and other countries. On broadcast you will begin receiving stations from half way across the country and possibly all the way across. You will also hear Canada and Mexico.

Keep a log of stations heard, giving the date, time, station, location, frequency and type of program. Stations (particularly short-wave) are often glad to hear from DX listeners and will reply to correspondence, usually sending a schedule of programs in English. It will help in logging broadcast stations if you have a copy of "White's Radio Log," found in *Radio-TV Experimenter*.[1] White's lists all AM-FM and television stations in the United States and Canada, giving facts about each. An additional listing includes the more active world short-wave stations.

---

[1] *Radio-TV Experimenter* may be obtained from: Science and Mechanics, 505 Park Ave., New York 22, N. Y. (75¢; $1 by mail.)

TAKE-APART PROJECTS

It is often true that just as much may be learned by taking things apart as by putting them together. This is the time-proven theory behind the following project.

MATERIALS

Any of the following in old or nonfunctioning condition: vacuum tube, light bulb, capacitor, resistor, volume control (potentiometer), dry cell, motor, doorbell, spark plug, switch, fuse—any similar item to be found.

PROCEDURE

Have a few interested campers carefully disassemble the item. If it is glass, the glass bulb must first be broken by placing in a heavy cloth bag and striking with a well-controlled hammer blow. Do not touch the glass but carefully remove the inner section attached to base. The parts should be named and operation discussed as disassembly continues.

USE

When taken apart as completely as desired, all parts may be mounted on oaktag or a board and labeled to make a permanent demonstration for the benefit of other campers. *Caution: Do not include television picture tubes in take-apart projects. Due to a high internal vacuum, these are highly explosive and send glass splinters many yards when broken.* They should be handled only by an expert.

PREPARING FOR AMATEUR RADIO LICENSE

There are over two hundred thousand amateur (ham) radio operators scattered around the world, representing all races, nationalities and conditions of men. All have a common interest in improving their knowledge of radio, experimenting, and possibly adding to the science of electronics. Each has his own private radio station, licensed by his government's radio commission, with which he may conduct experiments and communicate with any other ham. In the United States, the only requirements are U.S. citizenship and passing an F.C.C. exam. There are no limitations due to age or any other factor.

The Federal Communications Commission exam consists of three sections: electronics knowledge, F.C.C. regulations, and Morse code. Three types of licenses and exams are offered for the beginner, and he may take whichever one he believes he can pass. 1. Novice License: about twenty questions and code at five words per minute; 2. Technician License: about fifty questions and code at five wpm; 3. General License: about fifty questions and code at thirteen wpm. Each license offers greater privileges than the easier one.

The American Radio Relay League is the official ham society in this country. It offers many inexpensive booklets to help in obtaining the license. Booklets are listed at the end of the chapter.

Learning the Morse code is often a problem for those planning to take a license exam. Camp provides an ideal setting for this activity where a small group of interested people may work on it together. Obtain a copy of *Learning the Radio-Telegraph Code* (see RESOURCE MATERIALS), build one or more of the transistor code oscillators and provide some code keys (the up-and-down switch). Campers may practice sending messages to each other within a building, between buildings or over greater distances, using mirrors or flashlights. Of course, a buzzer or sounder may be used instead of the code oscillator. Once a person has begun to master the code, he is well on his way to obtaining his ham license and participating in the excitement of radio communication.

The letters of the International Morse code are given here for reference.

A	$\cdot\,-$	J	$\cdot\,-\,-\,-$	S	$\cdot\,\cdot\,\cdot$
B	$-\,\cdot\,\cdot\,\cdot$	K	$-\,\cdot\,-$	T	$-$
C	$-\,\cdot\,-\,\cdot$	L	$\cdot\,-\,\cdot\,\cdot$	U	$\cdot\,\cdot\,-$
D	$-\,\cdot\,\cdot$	M	$-\,-$	V	$\cdot\,\cdot\,\cdot\,-$
E	$\cdot$	N	$-\,\cdot$	W	$\cdot\,-\,-$
F	$\cdot\,\cdot\,-\,\cdot$	O	$-\,-\,-$	X	$-\,\cdot\,\cdot\,-$
G	$-\,-\,\cdot$	P	$\cdot\,-\,-\,\cdot$	Y	$-\,\cdot\,-\,-$
H	$\cdot\,\cdot\,\cdot\,\cdot$	Q	$-\,-\,\cdot\,-$	Z	$-\,-\,\cdot\,\cdot$
I	$\cdot\,\cdot$	R	$\cdot\,-\,\cdot$		

COMPLETION PUZZLES

This is a particularly good activity for those studying for amateur radio licenses.

MATERIALS
Mimeographed sheets of symbols without names, circuits without wires or names, etc.

EXAMPLES
FIG. 9-16 shows various symbols used in radio diagrams. Such a sheet could be provided to campers without the names inserted in the blanks. FIG. 9-17 is a diagram of a full-wave rectifier. This diagram may be given to campers with all wires (dotted lines) omitted. They may then label parts, draw wires and do other things called for. The same thing may be done with oscillators, amplifiers, half-wave rectifiers and other circuits required by the amateur license examination.

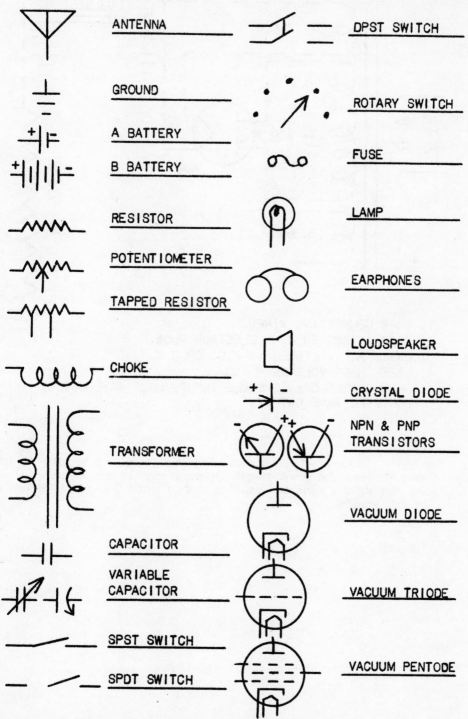

FIG. 9-16.   Schematic symbols used in electronics diagrams. Prepare similar paper without answers to use as puzzle.

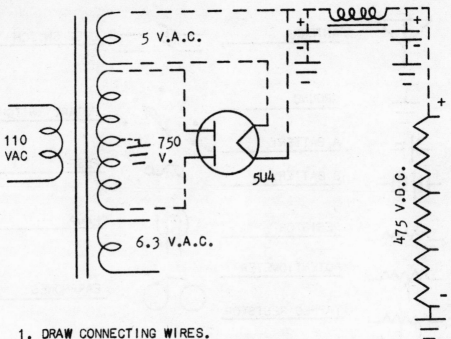

1. DRAW CONNECTING WIRES.
2. DRAW ARROWS SHOWING ELECTRON FLOW.
3. LABEL ALL VOLTAGES AS A.C. OR D.C.
4. LABEL HIGH VOLTAGE + AND -.
5. DRAW CURVES OF: 60 CYCLE INPUT, HALF WAVE OUTPUT
   AND FULL WAVE OUTPUT.

FIG. 9-17. Example of electronics completion puzzle. Schematic of full-wave vacuum tube power supply. Diagrams may be mimeographed showing only various parts and omitting wires (dotted lines) to be drawn in by radio student.

EXPERIMENTS IN BASIC ELECTRICITY

FIGS. 9-19 to 9-44 illustrate a number of simple experiments useful in teaching basic facts about electricity. They are probably better suited to a free-time individual activity than an organized group activity. Many of them may be done using odd parts found scattered among camp property. The electricity board (FIG. 9-18) provides all needed parts permanently and safely mounted in an organized fashion. All the materials listed may be purchased for less than fifteen dollars, or some parts may be purchased each year and placed on the board until it is complete. Explanations of the experiments will be found in INFORMATION OF IMPORTANCE. Many of the experiments using DC may be revised to use dry cells.

MATERIALS

		SOURCE
A.	Doorbell (Trine 172)	Hardware
B.	Bell transformer 16-volt, 15-watt (Trine 25115)	Hardware
C.	Selenium rectifier (IR #J29B1)	Allied 4A837
D.	Push button (Trine 25700)	Hardware
E.	Lamps #1487	Allied 52E654
F.	Knife switch	Allied 34B889
G.	Voltmeter 0-15 VDC Shurite type 550	Lafayette MT-186
H.	Ammeter 0-1 ADC Shurite type 550	Lafayette MT-141
I.	Hookup wire, 25 ft. (Belden 8529)	Allied 47TT216
J.	Twenty Fahnstock clips	Lafayette MS-249
K.	Four lamp sockets Type 505	Allied 52E410
L.	#26 magnet wire, enameled	Lafayette WR-81
M.	Forty wood screws ½ inch #6	Hardware
N.	Nichrome wire heating element	Hardware
O.	Six-inch spikes for magnets and coils	Hardware
P.	Plug and lampcord for transformer	Hardware
	Compass, aluminum foil and miscellaneous materials	
	Wood base	

Caution: The sixteen volts used on this board is generally safe. However, do not touch water pipes or wet ground while using it. You may complete a higher-voltage circuit!

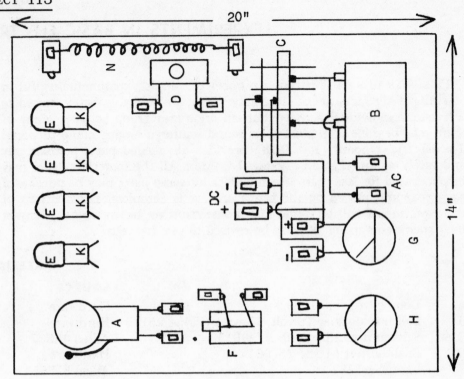

FIG. 9-18

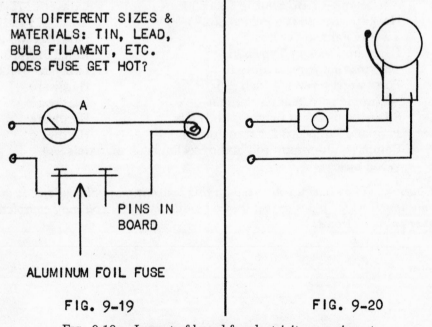

TRY DIFFERENT SIZES &
MATERIALS: TIN, LEAD,
BULB FILAMENT, ETC.
DOES FUSE GET HOT?

PINS IN
BOARD

ALUMINUM FOIL FUSE

FIG. 9-19

FIG. 9-20

FIG. 9-18. Layout of board for electricity experiments
FIG. 9-19. Household: Fuse
FIG. 9-20. Household: Doorbell

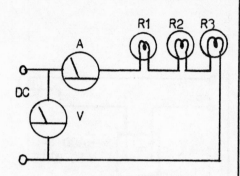

WHAT HAPPENS IF ONE BULB
IS TURNED OFF ?
WHAT HAPPENS IF BULBS ARE
ADDED OR REMOVED FROM
CIRCUIT ?

RESISTANCE = R1 + R2 + R3

FIG. 9-21

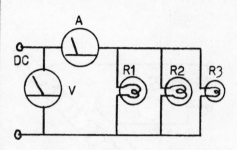

DO SAME TESTS DONE IN
SERIES WIRING & COMPARE
RESULTS.

$$\text{RESISTANCE} = \frac{1}{\frac{1}{R1} + \frac{1}{R2} + \frac{1}{R3}}$$

FIG. 9-22

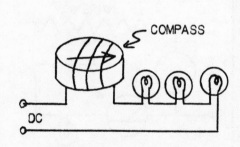

COMPASS NEEDLE DETECTS
MAGNETIC FIELD AROUND
WIRE.

FIG. 9-23

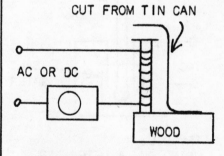

MAGNET MAY BE ONE
DESCRIBED IN FIG. 9-31.

FIG. 9-24

FIG. 9-21.   Household: Series wiring
FIG. 9-22.   Household: Parallel wiring
FIG. 9-23.   Magnetism: Compass galvanometer
FIG. 9-24.   Magnetism: Telegraph

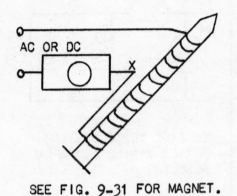

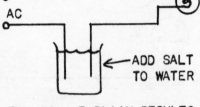

SEE FIG. 9-31 FOR MAGNET.
INSERT RESISTANCES (BULBS)
INTO CIRCUIT AT "X".

FIG. 9-25

TRY DC - EXPLAIN RESULTS.
ADD METERS TO CIRCUIT.
WHAT IS EFFECT IF WIRES
ARE MOVED IN & OUT OF
THE WATER ?

FIG. 9-26

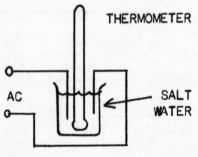

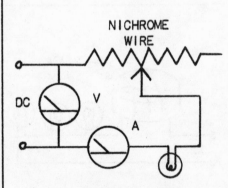

TRY D.C.
USING DC, & METER, IS
THERE ANY RELATION BETWEEN
CURRENT AND TEMPERATURE ?

FIG. 9-27

IS NICHROME THE SAME AS
A LIGHT BULB FILAMENT ?

FIG. 9-28

FIG. 9-25. Magnetism: Electromagnet
FIG. 9-26. Heat and resistance: Salt-water rheostat
FIG. 9-27. Heat and resistance: Heating effects of electron current
FIG. 9-28. Heat and resistance: Nichrome resistance wire

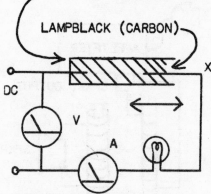

PLASTIC OR CARDBOARD TUBE

LAMPBLACK (CARBON)

DC

V

A

X

MOVE WIRE "X" IN & OUT -
NOTE VOLTAGE, CURRENT &
BULB BRIGHTNESS.

FIG. 9-29

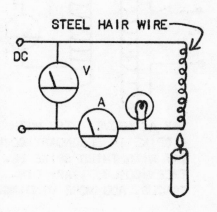

INCREASE IN TEMPERATURE =
INCREASE IN RESISTANCE

STEEL HAIR WIRE

DC

V

A

FIG. 9-30

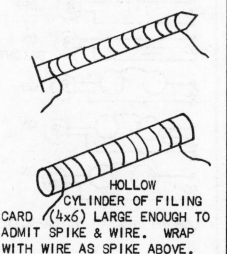

6" SPIKE WRAPPED WITH TAPE,
26 ENAMEL WIRE AND MORE
TAPE.

HOLLOW
CYLINDER OF FILING
CARD (4x6) LARGE ENOUGH TO
ADMIT SPIKE & WIRE. WRAP
WITH WIRE AS SPIKE ABOVE.

FIG. 9-31

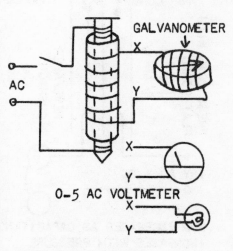

GALVANOMETER

AC

X

Y

X

Y

0-5 AC VOLTMETER

X

Y

ALSO TRY ON D C.

FIG. 9-32

FIG. 9-29.   Heat and resistance: Carbon rheostat
FIG. 9-30.   Heat and resistance: Thermoelectric effect
FIG. 9-31.   Induction: Preparing induction coils for experiments
FIG. 9-32.   Induction: Iron core transformer

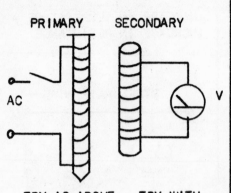

PRIMARY   SECONDARY

AC

V

TRY AS ABOVE. TRY WITH
A SPIKE IN SECONDARY COIL.
TRY WITH THIRD SPIKE BE-
TWEEN COILS. VARY DIS-
TANCES. ADD MORE WINDINGS.

FIG. 9-33

MIC OR PHONO

AMPLIFIER

SPKR. OUTPUT

SPKR.

HOW FAR CAN YOU SEND THE
SOUND?

FIG. 9-34

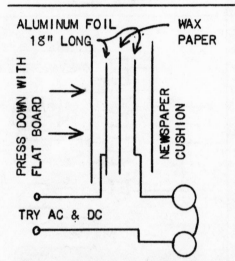

ALUMINUM FOIL   WAX
18" LONG   PAPER

PRESS DOWN WITH
FLAT BOARD

NEWSPAPER
CUSHION

TRY AC & DC

HUM INCREASES AS CAPACITANCE
INCREASES WITH PRESSURE
PERMITTING ALTERNATING
CHARGE TO MOVE ELECTRONS.
FIG. 9-35

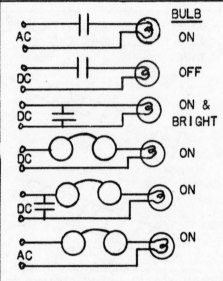

BULB

AC   ON

DC   OFF

DC   ON &
            BRIGHT

DC   ON

DC   ON

AC   ON

USE 50 MFD. 25 V. CAPACITOR

FIG. 9-36

Fig. 9-33.   Induction: Variations in induction
Fig. 9-34.   Induction: Primitive wireless
Fig. 9-35.   Capacitance: Homemade capacitor
Fig. 9-36.   Capacitance: Variations in capacitance.   CAUTION: *Do not
wear earphones on ears as buzzing may be uncomfortably loud.*

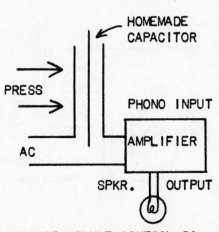

HOMEMADE CAPACITOR

PRESS

AC

PHONO INPUT

AMPLIFIER

SPKR. OUTPUT

ADJUST VOLUME CONTROL SO
PRESSURE TURNS LIGHT ON &
OFF, OUTPUT WILL BE 0 TO
2 VOLTS AC.

FIG. 9-37

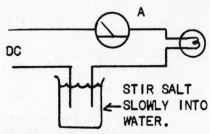

DC

A

STIR SALT
SLOWLY INTO
WATER.

COMPARE WITH SUGAR, VINEGAR;
LEMON, MILK, ETC.

IN DILUTE SOLUTION, IONS
HAVE UNOBSTRUCTED PATHS TO
ELECTRODES. IN CONCENTRATED
SOLUTION, OPPOSITE IONS
ATTRACT EACH OTHER. THOSE
REPELLED FROM ELECTRODES
ADD TO MIX UP & REDUCE
CURRENT FLOW.

FIG. 9-38

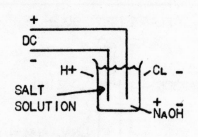

+
DC
-

H+ · · CL -

SALT
SOLUTION

+
NaOH

$$2NaCL + 2H_2O \longrightarrow$$

$$2NaOH + CL_2 + H_2$$

FIG. 9-39

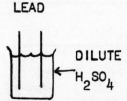

LEAD

DILUTE
H_2SO_4

MARK ONE POST + AND OTHER —
AND CHARGE BATTERY FROM YOUR
DC POWER FOR AT LEAST 15 MIN.

WHAT CAN YOU OPERATE WITH
THE BATTERY? WHAT VOLTAGE
DOES IT PROVIDE?

FIG. 9-40

FIG. 9-37. Capacitance: Principle of automatic door mat used in stores

FIG. 9-38. Exchanging ions and electrons in solution: Comparing
conductivity and concentration of solution

FIG. 9-39. Exchanging ions and electrons in solution: Electrolysis of salt
water

FIG. 9-40. Exchanging ions and electrons in solution: Storage battery

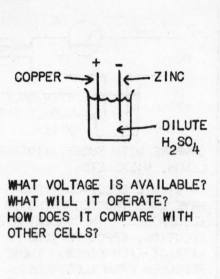

COPPER → + − ← ZINC

DILUTE H₂SO₄

WHAT VOLTAGE IS AVAILABLE?
WHAT WILL IT OPERATE?
HOW DOES IT COMPARE WITH
OTHER CELLS?

FIG. 9-41

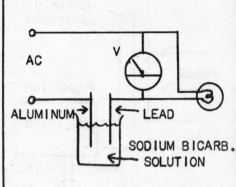

AC

V

ALUMINUM → ← LEAD

SODIUM BICARB. SOLUTION

FIG. 9-42

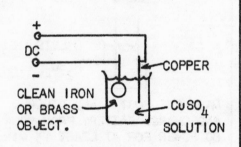

+
DC
−

COPPER

CLEAN IRON
OR BRASS
OBJECT.

CuSO₄
SOLUTION

OBJECT TO BE PLATED MAY
BE CLEANED BY BOILING IT
IN VINEGAR.

FIG. 9-43

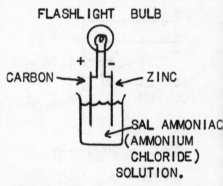

FLASHLIGHT BULB

CARBON → + − ← ZINC

SAL AMMONIAC
(AMMONIUM
CHLORIDE)
SOLUTION.

CARBON ROD & ZINC MAY COME
FROM CENTER AND CASE OF
A DRY BATTERY.

FIG. 9-44

FIG. 9-41.   Exchanging ions and electrons in solution: Voltaic wet cell
FIG. 9-42.   Exchanging ions and electrons in solution: Electrolytic rectifier
FIG. 9-43.   Exchanging ions and electrons in solution: Electroplating
FIG. 9-44.   Exchanging ions and electrons in solution: Wet dry cell using
liquid instead of carbon sal ammoniac paste

BUILDING ELECTRONIC KITS

There are two general groups of kits suitable for use at camp. One group consists of multi-purpose kits which may be quickly assembled and disassembled to make fifteen or more different circuits. Most of these require little previous experience and only a minimum of tools, if any. This is the type of kit that the camp may buy for its permanent use for experiments by interested boys. The second group consists of those kits that actually result in a finished permanent product such as a radio. Construction of these should only be attempted if there is a counselor with some electronics experience. These sets may be bought by campers through the camp or directly from the company.

MATERIALS

Sources of multi-purpose kits: Erec-Tronic Kits from A. C. Gilbert Co., Erector Square, New Haven 6, Conn.; Knight 10-circuit transistor kit, Knight 12-in-1 electronic kit, Knight 100-in-1 electronic kit from Allied Radio, 100 N. Western Ave., Chicago 80, Ill.

A permanent set well suited to campers with strong interest and some experience is the "Space Spanner" broadcast-short-wave receiver kit from Allied. Another permanent set for the serious radio student is the Heathkit GR-91.

TOOLS

Screwdriver, needle-nose pliers with cutter, heavy pliers, solder iron or gun (Wen 199, Weller 8200, Wall 863), rosin-core solder (1 lb., 3/32″ diam.). A multi-meter such as Eico 536 is helpful in checking out the circuit and also makes a good general-purpose tool around camp.

PROCEDURE

With the multi-purpose kits the procedure is not rigid and will be decided by the circumstances. With permanent radio kits there are many parts. Camper should become familiar with these by identifying them and checking them off on the parts list. Keep all parts in small boxes or paper cups. Follow step-by-step directions carefully. If set does not work when completed, camper should check each wire and part against the pictured diagram, drawing a colored line through each part as it is checked. Errors are easily found by this method. As construction progresses, discuss operation of various parts with camper so he will know how his radio works and will be adding to his knowledge of electronics. This is the ultimate purpose for building the kit.

ONE-TRANSISTOR RADIO RECEIVER

This set (FIG. 9-45) can be built for about three dollars, less earphones. It uses a germanium diode as a detector of radio signals, and a P-N-P transistor as an amplifier of the signal.

MATERIALS

C 1	365 MMFD tuning capacitor, miniature (Lafayette MS-445)
C 2	.02 MFD capacitor (any voltage)
R 1	Ferrite loop antenna coil—Hi "Q," 230 MH. (Miller 6300 or Lafayette MS-287 or MS-299)
S 1	Any small switch or break in wire
CR 1	Diode 1N64 or equivalent (colored band on minus end)
TR 1	Transistor 2N107 or equivalent
Antenna	Wire as long and high as possible (See antenna caution in Project 109.)
Ground	Wire to water pipe or other ground
Earphones	Any 2000-ohm DC headphone
Battery	Two flashlight cells (1½-volt), size D
Chassis	Piece of cardboard or perforated circuit board 3″ × 6″ (Lafayette MS-305)

Battery holder for size D, Lafayette MS-382. This may be omitted if wires are soldered to batteries.

Two Fahnstock clips may be used for phone connection (Lafayette MS-249).

PROCEDURE

All parts are placed on one side of board with wires pushed through holes and connections made on opposite side (FIG. 9-46). All connections should be soldered. Take care not to overheat parts while soldering wires. Any part may be damaged by excessive heat.

USE

This set is a modern version of the old crystal set which has been in use since the turn of the century and has always been one of the first projects tried by newcomers to the field of electronics. The crystal has been replaced by the germanium crystal diode and a one-transistor amplifier has been added. The wave forms explain how the radio waves are received. "A" shows the radio wave as received. It is composed of two segments: a high-frequency *carrier wave* which carries the program from transmitter to receiver, and low-frequency sound waves superimposed on carrier by varying its strength (amplitude). Frequency of carrier determines where we tune to receive it. If frequency is 850 kilocycles (850,000 cycles per sec-

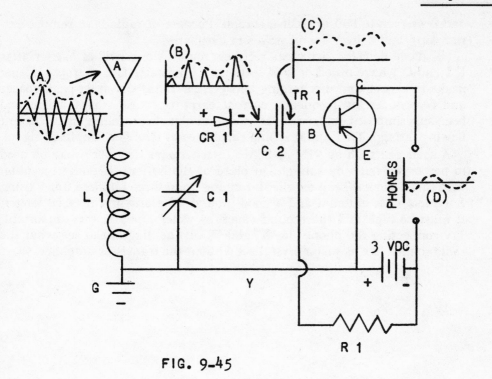

FIG. 9-45

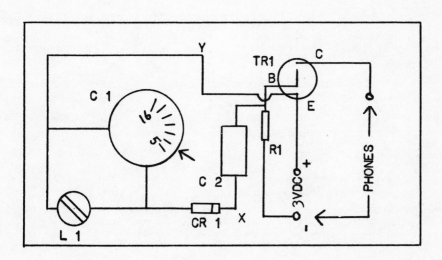

FIG. 9-46

FIG. 9-45. One-transistor radio receiver schematic (Courtesy General Electric Company)

FIG. 9-46. Pictorial showing layout of parts on oaktag base. Parts are mounted on front with wires running behind oaktag.

Electricity and Electronics   301

ond), we turn to 850 to receive station. Purpose of radio is to remove carrier wave and deliver sound waves to earphones.

"B" diode *detector*, acting as rectifier, removes one half of carrier after L 1 and C 1 have tuned desired station. "C" indicates C 2 charging during peaks in carrier and discharging between peaks, fills in inter-peak spaces and reproduces low-frequency current carrying sound waves which had been superimposed on carrier. "D" is a weak signal controlling large current flowing through TR 1 and reaching earphones as stronger, amplified signal.

A solar cell such as S1M or S3M (International Rectifier) may be used to power the radio by sunlight in place of the battery. Evening reception with this radio has been excellent, ranging up to three hundred miles using a ten-foot wire antenna and a good ground. The antenna may be longer. It must be high and the ground (such as water pipe) is very important. Try connecting the phones to "X" and "Y" in the diagram to see what the radio sounds like as just a crystal set without the transistor amplifier.

CODE PRACTICE OSCILLATOR

Since those wishing to become radio hams must pass a test in Morse code, a very practical project is the construction of a code practice oscillator. The oscillator the construction of which is described below was built for less than a dollar. This is exclusive of phones and battery, which may be the same ones used for the radio.

MATERIALS

C 1	.01 MFD capacitor
C 2	.01 MFD capacitor (may be any value from .01 to .1 MFD for desired pitch)
R 1	22,000-ohm resistor, ½-watt
R 2	1,800-ohm resistor, ½-watt
R 3	2,700-ohm resistor, ½-watt
TR 1	2N107 transistor (P-N-P) or equivalent. Phones must be 1,000 or 2,000-ohm set such as Trimm "Acme" type, Allied 39D070.
Battery	Two flashlight cells (1½-volt), size D, or penlight
Battery holder	For size D, see Project 115.
Code key	

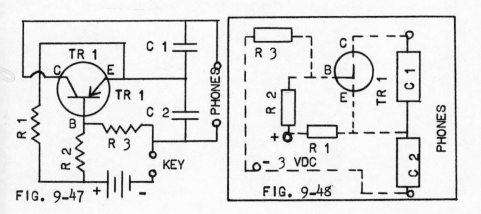

FIG. 9-47. Code practice oscillator schematic (Adapted from General Electric Transistor Manual)

FIG. 9-48. Pictorial showing parts layout on oaktag base. Dotted lines indicate wires behind circuit board.

PROCEDURE

Follow same construction procedure as described for radio. Piece of cardboard or oaktag with parts on one side and wires on reverse side. Solder all connections. See FIGS. 9-47 and 9-48.

USE

Use the oscillator to send code from one person to another for practice. Remember it is much easier to send than to receive. Practice is needed in both.

An interesting experiment may be done with the oscillator. While a tone is being heard on the phones, heat the transistor over a light bulb. The tone will change in pitch as the heat causes the atoms to move more freely in the semiconductor, thus decreasing its resistance. Do not overheat the transistor as permanent damage may result.

GEIGER COUNTER

The Geiger counter can be built for about seven dollars, and features high sensitivity, rugged components, one transistor amplifier, and portability, with long battery life and a simple, almost foolproof, circuit.

C 1	.05 MFD 1,000-volt molded tubular capacitor
C 2	.0005 MFD 600-volt capacitor
R 1	2.2-megohm ½-watt resistor
T 1	Output transformer, 8,000-ohm primary to 3.5 ohm secondary (Stancor A-3329)
V 1	CK 1026 Geiger tube
TR 1	Transistor 2N107 or equivalent
TS 1	Terminal strip, two solder lugs, one mounting lug
Earphones	Any 2,000-ohm DC headphone
Battery	Two flashlight cells (1½ volt). Size D gives longest life.
Battery holder for D cells	Lafayette MS-382 (may omit if large dry cells with screw terminals are used)

Six Fahnstock clips (Lafayette MS-249)

Six wood screws, half-inch No. 6

Chassis, soft wood, about 7″ × 10″

Hookup wire: No. 20 solid copper wire

The breadboard type of construction is recommended as the simplest but if true portability is desired, parts may be mounted in a plastic parts cabinet such as the Lafayette MS-300. With this arrangement the smaller size AA penlight cells should be used with the MS-382 battery holder.

Place parts in position as shown in FIG. 9-49. Drill hole in which transistor is inverted. The Geiger tube is held in place by clamping its positive lead in the Fahnstock clip. The negative terminal is a metallic coating on the outside of the tube. Contact is made with this by wrapping about three turns of bare wire around the tube and attaching to C 1. S 1 is a pushbutton switch formed by clamping a wire in the center clip allowing the other end to hang above the negative clip. Contact is made by pressing wire onto negative clip. A commercial push button may be used, but some are not satisfactory for this circuit. TS 1 is the support for a spark gap which must be completely insulated from the wood base. (See detail FIG.

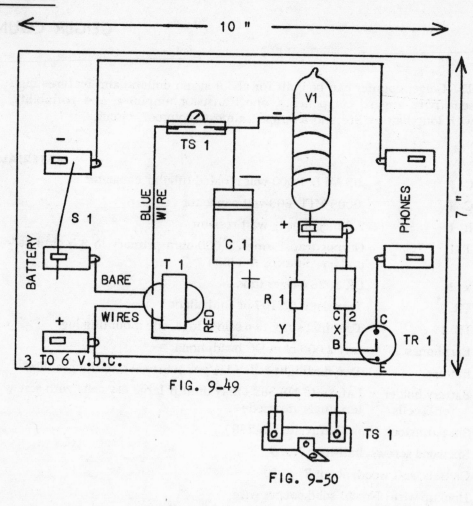

FIG. 9-49

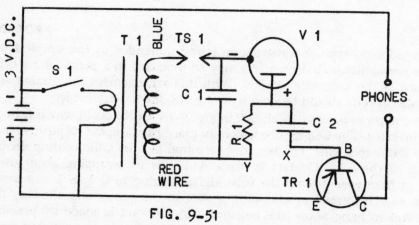

FIG. 9-50

FIG. 9-51

FIG. 9-49. Geiger counter pictorial showing layout of parts
FIG. 9-50. Detail of spark-gap construction using terminal strip
FIG. 9-51. Schematic diagram of Geiger counter

9-50.) The gap between the two wires is little greater than the width of two sheets of paper. This will have to be adjusted experimentally. No wire connected to the negative side of C 1 may touch the board as it is a simple matter for the high voltage to leak off through dampness in the wood. C1 should be a new high-quality capacitor. Screw parts in place and solder all connections except plus and minus on tube. Take care not to heat transistor with soldering gun.

OPERATION

Attach battery and phones as indicated. This circuit uses the small output transformer in reverse to build up a very high voltage of about 800 volts which is stored in C 1. This is done by pushing S 1 repeatedly. Each pulse sends a surge of current into T 1 where it is built up and must jump the isolation gap as a visible spark. Adjust this gap at TS 1 until you see a spark for most pulses. The current is stored in C 1 for use by the Geiger tube. Once C 1 is charged you need push S 1 only a couple of times every few minutes to help build up the charge. *Caution: Connect a wire across C 1 to discharge before working on circuit.* Just as it appears to be, the Geiger tube is simply a glass tube with a wire through the center, another conductor on the glass, and a partial vacuum inside.

A radioactive particle passing through the tube tears electrons from the gas atoms inside, thus forming charged ions and free negative electrons. The freed electrons are attracted by the positively charged center wire and as they travel toward it they tear other electrons from nearby atoms. All these electrons, initiated by a radioactive particle, arrive as an avalanche of current on the positive wire, resulting in a click. The clicks are applied to the base of TR 1 where they are amplified for greater volume in the earphones. Attach the phones at "X" and "Y" to hear the clicks without amplification. The clicks may be heard through a loudspeaker by connecting wires from the phone clips to input of a larger amplifier. Keep phones on clips also.

USE

The Geiger counter is used to measure the presence of radiation from cosmic rays and from earth materials. Cosmic rays originate on the stars and shoot to earth from all directions of space, entering the atmosphere at nearly the speed of light. No lead is thick enough to stop these most powerful rays, and some are known to penetrate as much as two thousand feet of earth and water. Most of them are hydrogen and helium nuclei and they account for the *background count* of the Geiger tube when no other radioactive materials are near by. A background count of about fifty clocks per minute is average for this instrument. Cosmic radiation reaches a peak at an altitude of between twelve and fifteen miles. (See Chapter 4: FILMS.)

You may purchase radioactive minerals (Chapter 5: RESOURCES) or use a radium dial watch to activate the Geiger tube. Most such minerals emit three types of rays: 1. *Alpha particles* which are helium nuclei and may be shielded by a piece of paper or a few inches of air; 2. *Beta particles* which are electrons (or positive electrons called positrons) and may be shielded by a few thicknesses of aluminum foil. Beta particles have no independent existence inside the nucleus. They are created at the instant of emission, which is accompanied by the change of a neutron into a proton, thus changing the atomic number of the atom. 3. *Gamma rays* are electromagnetic waves produced as particles are shot from the nucleus. They are more powerful than X-rays and may penetrate up to five inches of lead.

A good outfit for other experiments in radioactivity is the "Atomic Energy Kit" available from the Lionel Corp., Hagerstown, Maryland, for less than two dollars. Specific button-sized radioactive sources may be ordered for about three dollars each from Cenco Instruments Corp., 1700 West Irving Park Road, Chicago 13, Illinois.

RESOURCE MATERIALS FOR ELECTRICITY AND ELECTRONICS

Magazines

Popular Electronics. Monthly, $4.00 per year. 434 South Wabash Ave., Chicago, Ill. 60605.

Electronics Illustrated. Monthly, $4.00 per year. Fawcett Bldg., Greenwich, Conn.

QST Monthly, $5.00 per year, includes ARRL membership. American Radio Relay League, West Hartford 7, Conn.

Films

The following films are free. The user pays return postage. They may be ordered through the local Bell Telephone business office.

Big Bounce—Echo satellite

Mr. Bell—Biography

Bottle of Magic—Vacuum tube

The Transistor

Telstar

Many other films listed in the catalog available on request.

The following films are available free from the Air Force Film Library Center, 8900 South Broadway, St. Louis, Mo., 63125. User pays return postage. In color, they were produced for the Air Force by Walt Disney in animation.

Basic Electricity. Order No. AF 213-A

Basic Electronics. Order No. AF 213-B

Booklets

How to Become a Radio Amateur. 50¢, American Radio Relay League, West Hartford 7, Conn.

Radio Amateur's License Manual. 50¢, ARRL

Learning the Radio Telegraph Code. 50¢, ARRL

A Course in Radio Fundamentals. $1.00, ARRL

Transistor Manual. $1.00. General Electric Sales Promotion Dept., Charles Bldg., Liverpool, N. Y.

RCA Receiving Tube Manual. $1.00. Radio Corp. of America, Electron Tube Division, Harrison, N. J.

Experimenter's Handbook for Solar Cells. 50¢ International Rectifier Corp., available from electronics suppliers below.

Supplies

Lafayette Radio Corp., 111 Jericho Turnpike, Syosset, L. I., N. Y.

Radio Shack Corp., 730 Commonwealth Ave., Boston, Mass. 02117.

Allied Radio Corp., 100 N. Western Ave., Chicago, Ill. 60680.

Heath Co., Benton Harbor, Michigan.

Arkay International, Inc., 2372 Linden Blvd., Brooklyn, N. Y. 11208. Building electronic kits; inexpensive materials for transistor lab kits.

Appendix

A collection of reference materials in addition to those listed at the close of each chapter. Prices have been included where possible, as an indication of probable cost, but may have changed since publication.

A. Bibliography of selected reference books
B. Publishers of field book series
C. General magazines on science and camping
D. Lists and sources of paperbound science books
E. Suppliers of general science materials

A. BIBLIOGRAPHY OF SELECTED REFERENCE BOOKS

GENERAL BOOKS

BROWN, VINSON, *How to Make a Home Nature Museum*. Boston: Little, Brown & Co., 1954. $3.50. A practical book of techniques and information not readily available. 214 pages. Other books by the same author: *Amateur Naturalist's Handbook; How to Make a Miniature Zoo; How to Understand Animal Talk*.

COMSTOCK, ANNA BOTSFORD, *Handbook of Nature Study*. New York: Comstock Publishing Co., 1939. $6.75. Detailed information on plants and animals, brief treatment of other subjects. 937 pages.

COOPER, ELIZABETH, *Science in Your Own Back Yard*. New York: Harcourt, Brace, 1958. $3. All phases of outdoor science covered with many ideas for counselor and camper. 192 pages.

GATTY, HAROLD, *Nature Is Your Guide*. New York: E. P. Dutton, 1961. $4.95. Explains the art of pathfinding in the wilderness using the signs provided by nature. Practical and interesting guide for anybody who spends time outdoors. 287 pages.

GIRL SCOUTS OF THE U.S.A., *Day Camp Book*. New York: Girl Scouts of the U.S.A. Includes many nature and science projects.

HAMMETT, CATHERINE T. *Your Own Book of Campcraft*. New York: Pocket Books, 1957. 35¢. Profusely illustrated book on techniques of outdoor camping. 197 pages.

HAMMETT, CATHERINE T., and MUSSELMAN, VIRGINIA, *The Camp Program Book*. New York: Association Press, 1959. $5. Covering the over-all field of camping, this book will be equally useful to the experienced administrator and the beginning counselor. 380 pages.

HODGMAN, WEAST and SELBY, editors, *Handbook of Chemistry and Physics*. Cleveland: Chemical Rubber Publishing Co., annual publication. $12. An extensive reference book of scientific tables and data, approximately 3,500 pages.

JOSEPH, BRANDWEIN, MORHOLT, POLLACK and CASTKA, *A Sourcebook for the Physical Sciences*. New York: Harcourt, Brace and Co., 1961. $7.95. An extensive collection of projects and information that should be in the library of every science counselor and teacher. 674 pages.

PRICE, BETTY, *Adventuring in Nature*. New York: National Recreation Association, 1954. $1.25. A well-organized book of many practical ideas for most areas of nature. 95 pages.

UNESCO, 700 *Science Experiments for Everyone*. Garden City, New York: Doubleday, 1958, 1959. $3. Well-illustrated collection of simple science projects. 220 pages.

VINAL, WILLIAM G., *Nature Recreation*. New York: Dover Publications, $1.75. Illustrated guide to nature study, camping, crafts projects, etc. Paperbound, 310 pages.

METEOROLOGY

DONN, WILLIAM L., *Meteorology with Marine Applications*. New York: McGraw-Hill, 1951. A readable coverage of meteorology for the lay reader, mariner or student. 465 pages.

LAIRD, CHARLES and LAIRD, RUTH, *Weathercasting*. Englewood Cliffs, New Jersey: Prentice-Hall, 1955. $3.95. A practical book of forecasting methods and techniques for constructing instruments. 163 pages.

PHOTOGRAPHY

KODAK, *How to Make Good Home Movies*. New York: Random House. Paper, $1, hardcover $1.95. Clear approach to taking good movies.

KODAK, *How to Make Good Pictures*. New York: Random House, 1957. Paper, $1, hardcover $1.95. Excellent guide to taking good pictures. Does not include developing. 192 pages.

MARSHALL, LUCILE R., *Photography for Teen-Agers*. Englewood Cliffs, N. J.: Prentice-Hall, 1957. $3.95. Good treatment of fundamentals plus techniques for stills, movies, developing and printing. 185 pages.

ASTRONOMY

JOHNSON, GAYLORD, and ADLER, IRVING, *Discover the Stars*. New York: Sentinel Books, 1957. $1. Well-illustrated book of information and projects for the beginning astronomer. Good addition to camp library. 146 pages.

MAYALL, WYCOFF and POLGREEN, *The Sky Observer's Guide*. New York: Golden Press, $5.32. Very useful guide to the heavens with numerous charts, lists and tables.

SKILLING, WILLIAM, and RICHARDSON, ROBERT, *A Brief Text in Astronomy*. New York: Holt, Rinehart and Winston, 1959. $8.50. Well-illustrated, concise and detailed introduction to astonomy. Much valuable reference information, star charts for each month. 333 pages.

GEOLOGY

HAMMOND, PHILIP C., *Archaeological Techniques for Amateurs*. Princeton, N. J.: Van Nostrand, 1963. $5.95. This book may be the means of introducing another subject into camp science. An accurate reference to current methods and techniques. Includes state-by-state lists of sites, museums, etc.

HELLER, ROBERT, editor, *Geology and Earth Sciences Sourcebook*. New York: Holt, Rinehart and Winston, Inc., 1962. Paper cover $2.50. A large 400-page book of projects, problems and information.

LAHEE, FREDERIC H., *Field Geology*. New York: McGraw-Hill, revised 1961. $10.75. A book of over 900 pages that has been the basic guide to field geology for the novice with an elementary knowledge of general geology, and for the expert since its first printing in 1916. 926 pages.

WOLFE, C. WROE, *This Earth of Ours—Past and Present*. Watertown, Mass.: Geopublishing Company, 1949. Concise and very readable, practical introduction to the general field of geology. 374 pages.

PLANTS AND ANIMALS

BERMAN, WILLIAM, *How to Dissect*. New York: Sentinel Press, 1961. Paper, $1. Clear diagrams illustrate dissection technique starting with earthworm and going up through the frog. 127 pages.

HEADSTROM, RICHARD, *Adventures with a Hand Lens*. Philadelphia: Lippincott, 1962. $4.25. Well-illustrated descriptions of simple observations with a magnifying glass. 220 pages.

MOORE, CLIFFORD B., *The Book of Wild Pets*. Boston: Charles T. Branford Co. 1937. $6.50. A basic guide to care and feeding that should be in the hands of anybody who has wild animals in his care. 553 pages.

MORHOLT, BRANDWEIN and JOSEPH, *A Sourcebook for the Biological Sciences*. New York: Harcourt, Brace and Co., 1958. $6.75. An inexhaustible collection of projects and information that should be in the library of every science counselor and teacher. 506 pages.

PICARD, ROMANAK and MARION, *Biology Experiment Manual*. Chicago: The Cenco Press, 1962. Paper, $2. A well-illustrated manual of 100 experiments and projects with plants and animals. 84 pages.

WILSON, CARL L., *Botany*. New York: Dryden Press, 1955. $6.90. A basic text in botany with all material nicely clarified through the use of hundreds of photographs and illustrations. 483 pages.

ELECTRONICS

BENDER, ALFRED, *Let's Explore with the Electron*. New York: Sentinel Books, 1960. Paper cover $1. This well-illustrated book of simple projects would make an inspiring addition to the camp library.

HICKEY, HENRY V., and VILLINES, WILLIAM M., *Elements of Electronics*. New York: McGraw-Hill, 1955. Takes a more technical and detailed approach to electronics than the Steinberg and Ford book suggested in Chapter 9. Excellent for the serious experimenter. 487 pages.

MORGAN, ALFRED, *Things a Boy Can Do with Electricity*. New York: Charles Scribner's Sons, 1938. $2.95. A time-tested book, simple instructive experiments. 243 pages.

Radio Amateur's Handbook. West Hartford, Conn.: American Radio Relay League, annual publication. $3.50. A "must" book for every radio ham and experimenter. Approximately 600 pages.

B. PUBLISHERS OF FIELD BOOK SERIES

G. P. Putnam's Sons, 210 Madison Ave., New York, N. Y. 10016. (Putnam's Nature Field Books and Putnam's Beginner's Guides)

Houghton Mifflin Co., 2 Park St., Boston, Mass. 02107. (Peterson Field Guides)

Doubleday & Co., Inc., Garden City, N. Y. (Doubleday Nature Guides)

E. P. Dutton & Co., Inc., 300 Fourth Ave., New York, N. Y. 10010. (Dutton Nature Fieldbooks)

William C. Brown Co., 215 W. Ninth St., Dubuque, Iowa. (Pictured-Key Nature Series)

Paperbound field guides are also published by the following companies listed in APPENDIX D: Golden Press, Pocket Books, New American Library and Dover Publications.

C. GENERAL MAGAZINES ON SCIENCE AND CAMPING

Camping Magazine. Ten issues per year. 114 South Ave., Plainfield, N. J.

International Science and Technology. Monthly, $5 per year for faculty and students. 205 E. 42 St., New York, N. Y.   10017.

National Geographic Magazine. Monthly, $8 per year. National Geographic Society, 16 and M Streets, N.W., Washington, D. C.   20006.

Popular Science Monthly. $3.40 per year. 355 Lexington Ave., New York, N. Y. 10017.

Recreation. Ten issues per year, $5. National Recreation Association, 8 West Eighth St., New York, N. Y.   10011.

School Science and Mathematics. $6 per year. Central Association of Science and Mathematics Teachers, Inc., 450 Ahnaip St., Mensha, Wisc.

Science. Weekly, $8.50 per year. American Association for the Advancement of Science, 1515 Massachusetts Ave., N.W., Washington, D. C.   20005.

Science and Mechanics. Monthly. $4 per year. Davis Publications, 505 Park Avenue, New York, N. Y.   20022.

Science News Letter. Weekly, $5.50 per year. Science Service, 1719 N Street, N.W., Washington, D. C.   20006.

Science Teacher. Eight issues per year, $6; student rate $3. National Science Teachers Association, 1201 Sixteenth Street, N.W., Washington, D. C. 20006.

Science World, Edition 2. 16 issues per year, $2. 900 Sylvan Ave., Englewood Cliffs, N. J. Written for ages 11 to 18.

Scientific American. Monthly, $6 per year. 415 Madison Ave., New York, N. Y. 10017.

D. LISTS AND SOURCES
OF PAPERBOUND SCIENCE BOOKS

Affiliated Publishers, Educational Division, 1 West 39 St., New York, N. Y. 10018. *Educational Paperbacks.* Includes Pocket Books, Golden Press, Washington Square Press, Simon and Schuster, All Saints Press and Cornerstone Library.

American Association for the Advancement of Science, 1515 Washington Ave., N.W., Washington, D. C. 20005. An *Inexpensive Science Library*, 25¢.

Doubleday and Co., Garden City, L. I., N. Y. List of Science Study Series.

Dover Publications, Inc., 180 Varick St., New York, N. Y. 10014. Catalog available.

Fawcett Books, Greenwich, Conn. Free catalog.

National Council, Boy Scouts of America, New Brunswick, N. J. List of Merit Badge Booklets including many science subjects. Books may be ordered through local council office.

National Recreation Association, 8 West Eighth St., New York, N. Y. 10011. *Guide to Books on Recreation*, 25¢. Also lists of selected publications.

New American Library, Education Division, 501 Madison Ave., New York, N. Y. 10022. Catalog of paperbound science books (Signet and Mentor books). Also available, compiled by Hilary Deason, *Guide to Scientific Reading*, 60¢. Prepared under the auspices of A.A.A.S.

Row, Peterson and Co., Elmsford, New York. Request list of prices and titles in Basic Science Education Series.

Sentinel Books, 112 East 19 St., New York, N. Y. 10003. Catalog of Science Books.

Superintendent of Documents, Washington, D. C. 20025. Request following free price lists: Nos. 15, 31, 35, 41, 43, 44, 47, 48, 64, 79, 81, 82, 84. Additional assistance may be obtained from your congressman through his Legislative Reference Service.

University of Michigan Press, Ann Arbor, Mich. List of Ann Arbor Science Paperbacks.

E. SUPPLIERS OF GENERAL SCIENCE MATERIALS

A. C. Gilbert Co., Erector Square, New Haven 6, Conn. Chemistry and science outfits.

Allied Radio Corp., 100 North Western Avenue, Chicago, Ill. 60680.

Central Scientific Company, 1700 Irving Park Road, Chicago, Ill. 60613. Supply division of Cenco Instruments. Contact branch warehouse nearest you; Mountainside, N. J.; Somerville, Mass.; Birmingham, Ala.; Montreal, Que.; Toronto, Ont.; Ottawa, Ont.; Tulsa, Okla.; Los Angeles, Calif.; Santa Clara, Calif.; Houston, Texas.

Edmund Scientific Company, 101 East Gloucester Pike, Barrington, N. J.

General Biological Supply House, Inc., 8200 South Hoyne Ave., Chicago, Ill. 60620.

Lafayette Radio Corp., 111 Jericho Turnpike, Syosset, L. I., N. Y.

Lionel Corp., Hagerstown, Md. Catalog of "Chemcraft" and other science outfits plus books, equipment and small amounts of chemicals.

Macalaster Scientific Corp., 243 Broadway, Cambridge, Mass. Suppliers of PSSC, ESSC and ESI equipment.

Radio Shack Corp., 730 Commonwealth Ave., Boston, Mass. 02117; 1515 So. University Dr., Fort Worth, Texas.

Science Materials Center, 220 East 23 St., New York, N. Y. 10010.

W. N. Welch Scientific Company, 1515 Sedgwick Street, Chicago, Ill. 60610.

Ward's Natural Science Establishment, Inc., Box 1712, Rochester, N. Y. 14603; or, Box 1749, Monterey, Calif.

Index